# HEART OF HAREFIELD

# HEART OF HAREFIELD

## The Story of the Hospital

## Mary P. Shepherd, MS, FRCS

Quiller Press
London

First published 1990 by
Quiller Press Limited
46 Lillie Road
London SW6 1TN

ISBN 1 870948 21 1

Designed by Hugh Tempest-Radford Book Producers
and printed in Great Britain by Southampton Book Company.

'Probably the most appropriate tribute that can be paid to the early years at Harefield is the way in which members of the different departments have co-operated to form a team which, starting from scratch in 1940, has become accepted as one of the major units for thoracic work in the country. The efforts of many have helped to found a tradition which is now the obligation of the younger generation to maintain and enhance.'

Sir Thomas Holmes Sellors
*Harefield Gazette*, March 1965

# Contents

# List of Plates and Figures

COLOUR PLATES

IN THE TEXT

# Preface

It all began for me when I walked into the front hall as the first woman to be appointed a surgical registrar to the Thoracic Unit in October 1963. It wasn't long before I found the atmosphere of Harefield Hospital like none other in my experience as a junior hospital doctor. Several can bear witness to my comment then: 'What a wonderful place to work. It is just the sort of hospital where I could happily spend the rest of my career.'

No history of the Hospital had been written by the time I departed twenty-two years later. It was high time to put on record the substance of the place where I had spent so many happy years and had learnt so much about people and life and death, and about myself. To me Harefield Hospital is unique. I have tried to express why I feel so in this story of its relatively short but interesting and exciting life.

I dedicate this book to the memory of Sir Thomas Holmes Sellors, 'Uncle Tom', the pioneer thoracic surgeon largely responsible for founding the Harefield Hospital of today. He encouraged and taught so many like myself so much, including the art and principles of thoracic and cardiac surgery. He also never stinted

> in a broader service . . . whether in delivering . . . lectures or in presiding over Committees. . . . The knighthood you received . . . was . . . one of many honours . . . in recognition of your attainments. You have been President of the Royal College of Surgeons of England and the British Medical Association, President of . . . leading Societies in your specialty and a lecturer to many academic audiences. In conferring . . . the Gold Medal . . . the Council testifies to the esteem in which your colleagues hold a great surgeon and a medical statesman.

Thus said the citation accompanying the Gold Medal of the British Medical Association, presented to this wise and gentle man in 1979, and one of his greatest treasures.

I hope many will enjoy the story. The work is offered with love, on behalf of all those throughout the world who have ever worked or been a patient there, as a present to Harefield Hospital on its 75th Birthday, 2 June 1990.

Mary P. Shepherd, MS FRCS

xiii

# · Acknowledgements ·

First and foremost, acknowledgement is due to the Hospital administration for, without Hillingdon District Authority's blessing, publication of this book may never have been possible.

Many friends made while at Harefield have helped me paint this picture. I am most grateful to them, and the many others with whom I have only corresponded. Their reminiscences and photographs, some of which are reproduced in the book, have made it so much easier to tell the story, and the narrative is more complete than it otherwise would have been. With their help, too, especially that of Mrs Loraine Neuhoffer and Miss Pam Durand, I hope to have avoided factual errors but trust that those which may surface will be forgiven.

My thanks are also due to erstwhile colleagues at Harefield Hospital for making me an Honorary Consultant after my departure. It has made access to official Minutes of the many and various committees of management over the years very straightforward. It is from these documents, and material produced by the Community Health Council, that the vast majority of quotations have been extracted.

For the copying of old photographs and snapshots I am indebted to the Hospital photographer, Mr Ron Blake, and freelance photographer E. Lindsay Gray who has willingly devoted much time and expertise to this project.

The following have granted me permission to reproduce their work:

Frontispiece  Reproduced by kind permission of the President and Council of the Royal College of Surgeons of England
Plate 8   by kind permission of the Harefield Local History Group (WEA Class 1974 to 1976)
Plate 48   Aerofilms
Plate 54, 61   by kind permission of the *Nursing Times*. Plate 54 is part of a photograph which first appeared in the *Nursing Mirror* in 1959. Plate 61 appeared in the *Nursing Times*, 21 October 1966

## Acknowledgements

Plate 46   The British Tourist Authority
Plates 52, 53, 58, 60   *Gazette* photographs
Plate 59   Photo-Reportage Ltd
Plates 69, 70   by Chris Kelly
Plates 5, 6, 51, 73   by Siobhan Davis
Colour plates 1, 4   by Graham Tatlock
Colour plates 5, 6   by John Callan

To Mr F. Brown of Harefield goes my appreciation of his willing contribution in drawing most of the figures. I recognise how much time and effort went into the plans we devised depicting Harefield Park House and the Hospital at various stages of its life.

Finally in this, my first attempt to write a book, my sincere thanks goes to those who unconsciously have helped. They are authors themselves, those who have taken the trouble to publish books to guide the beginner like me.

# · 1 ·

# A Day at the Hospital

HE must be dead. He was looking down at himself lying in the hospital bed. There was quiet intense activity among the doctors and nurses gathered around. Suddenly he felt a tremendous jolt. That beautiful light which had so attracted him faded. He seemed to float away from the tunnel back down to himself. Then he heard his name and opened his eyes.

## A Patient

The defibrillator had done the trick. The surgical registrar who had called his name gave a sigh of relief. He knew the man well. He had met him first about a month before when he had come to Harefield with angina. In his late forties, he had been nervous and frightened. After his coronary angiogram, when the coronary arteries are outlined with radio-opaque fluid, he had said, 'I've never been on television before . . . and watching it done was new to me.' He hadn't liked it very much 'especially when I was told later that . . . an operation was vital as the damage to an artery was serious enough to cause my death at any time.' Nevertheless, as there were so many others already waiting for similar help, he had to wait a few weeks and 'enjoy my panic in the comfort of home and family'.

He had returned a couple of days before for his scheduled coronary artery bypass grafting operation. All the ' "routine" tests, blood samples galore, X-rays, ultrasound, urine and liquid intake and output, blood pressure,' had been done and he had been seen by the physiotherapists – or 'physioterrorists' as he called them. There had been time too to 'make sure the patient and his family knew exactly what was going to happen and how the patient would look and react in the ITU and afterwards.'

Now he was told that he had had a cardiac arrest and that his operation was to be done that very day. In the meantime he was to be transferred to the Intensive Therapy Unit (ITU) where he would be monitored and closely watched. Having explained the position to his wife as well, the registrar went to see the other patient whose operation would have to be postponed to make way for this more urgent one. He knew it would cause disappointment but when this sort of situation arose, he found the patients amazingly understanding. Meanwhile the senior house officer (SHO) told the Haematology Department of the operating list change so they could get on with cross matching the right blood.

By late morning, drowsy from his premedication and very relieved that nothing else had occurred, the patient found himself being wheeled into the anaesthetic room. He recognised the consultant anaesthetist who had visited him in the ITU. While he was being anaesthetised and the necessary tubes and wires inserted or attached to him, the heart/lung machine was being prepared in the theatre. The operation went smoothly. While the heart/lung machine took over the function of his own heart and lungs, veins taken from his legs were used to bypass the narrowed places in his coronary arteries. When completed, his own heart took over well, its muscle enjoying the increased blood supply now flowing through the vein grafts. Afterwards, still being artificially ventilated via a tube in his trachea, he was settled back in the ITU next to the first patient of the day. Everything was going nicely.

## A Surgical Registrar

Having answered the crash call for the cardiac arrest, the registrar had not had time to have breakfast. Today he would have to make do with something from the vending machine, which he passed on the way to the cardiac theatres. He had not been able to do his usual early ward round either. That would have to wait until after the operating list, which could last most of the day. But he had to check on one or two other patients first. One had chest pain which was caused either by the herniation of his stomach into his chest, a hiatus hernia, or else he had angina. One of the cardiologists had seen him. Wanting to know what he thought, the registrar detoured into the Cardiology Department. Giving a wave to the receptionist in the spacious waiting area, he went towards the corridor to the left and came across the very person he sought.

Brief discussion over, he took the opportunity to slip into the X-ray Department next door and look at the chest film of a woman who had had a lobe of her lung taken out a couple of days before. The drains had been removed and he wanted to check for himself that all was well. X-ray was already busy. The paediatric cardiologist was just starting to investigate an infant with a congenital heart defect in one of the rooms, and the radiologist was doing a barium swallow in a second. This was on another patient the registrar looked after, part of whose oesophagus had been resected. He would have to try and slip out of the theatre between cases this morning to discuss the films. The sooner the lady could start drinking and eating the better, and she would be delighted too!

He also wanted to see the radiologist, before he left for his afternoon session at another hospital, about another patient. One of the few out-patients nowadays with an empyema drainage tube in his chest was coming to the ward to have it changed. One rarely saw such a collection of pus as had been drained some weeks ago. A special X-ray was needed to see how much smaller the space had become. With luck he would soon be able to 'lose' his tube.

In the corridor outside the cardiac theatres he met one of the physiotherapists coming from the Children's Ward. She was able to tell him that the lad who had inhaled a peanut into his bronchus was fine. He had extracted it the evening before through the tubular, rigid bronchoscope, passed through the mouth into the trachea, under a general anaesthetic. If this morning's chest X-ray was OK, his parents could take him home. The 'physio' also wanted him to know that another patient, whose lung had been removed, though generally all right, was finding it difficult to cough up his sputum. Asking her to keep him informed, he teasingly said he would bronchoscope him too if there was no improvement during the course of the day, to suck out the sticky secretions. He knew full well that she would consider a bronchoscopy for secretion retention nothing short of a confession of her failure!

Finally reaching the changing-room with these things buzzing around his mind, he put on his 'greens' while munching his breakfast. He might just have time for a cup of coffee too, before scrubbing up. The consultant was already there he knew, but so, fortunately, was the senior registrar. And so this particular day got under way.

## A Cardiologist

The registrar had appeared just as the cardiologist was thinking that he would try and fit the patient with the hernia in for a coronary angiogram on his list in X-ray the next day. He also had patient for angioplasty. A tiny tube, complete with balloon at its end, is inserted into a narrowed coronary artery and the narrowing stretched up by inflating the balloon with saline. He wanted to get on with it. He must try and fix a time when one of the cardiac surgeons would be available if things didn't go quite right. Things usually went well, but the one time contingency plans aren't laid is when something surely happens! It would have to be a day when he didn't have an afternoon clinic at another hospital as he did today. He liked to be readily available after one of those. Tomorrow perhaps?

He finished dictating his letters and gave the tape to his secretary. He would sign them at lunch time. As he left the department for the wards, the pacemaker clinic was getting under way. That reminded him, the woman who went in and out of heart block needed a pacemaker. The 24-hour electrocardiograph (ECG) tape had given him the information he needed. He might be able to do that tomorrow too. Putting in a pacemaker was so simple and straightforward nowadays, and they certainly improved the quality of life for a lot of older people. Every pacemaker put in had to be checked regularly though, and the clinic was invariably hectic.

Meanwhile the paediatric cardiologist was busy with a sick baby whom she had admitted earlier. Less then a month old, she suspected a transposition of the great arteries, an abnormality which Harefield was renowned for treating. Yes, the main arteries were coming out of the wrong side of the heart. The hole in the septum was only just large enough. The 'switch' operation would have to be soon if the tiny mite was going to make it. She knew Harefield had a 80 per cent success rate with this sort of problem. There were many complex congenital heart defects which could be corrected these days but the next two patients had simple ones – a ventricular septal defect and a straightforward atrial septal defect. Closure of these could safely wait until the youngsters were a little older. The waiting list was quite long enough. She had children – and infants – already waiting for surgery who should be dealt with first. With only one surgeon for the complicated paediatric work it was difficult to fit everything in, especially with the transplants as well.

There was another infant being flown in to Heathrow later that day, too, who might well need to be investigated straight away. This happened fairly frequently. Babies could become very ill very quickly and she liked to be there when they arrived. She would have to do her clinic at the other hospital and get back as quickly as possible. She had her ward round to fit in before that though. The Children's Ward was a pleasure to go into. The hard working Sister and her nurses were much happier with the vastly improved conditions

4

made possible with the help of the 'Give a Child a Chance Appeal' and the Sportsman's Aid Society. Funds were now forthcoming from the Government too since Harefield's recognition as a Supraregional Centre for Neonatal and Infant Cardiac Surgery.

## A Transplant Officer

The Transplant Co-ordinator had been hard at work. She had been trying to find a heart through the UK Transplant Service, the Euro-transplant Service and Regional Transplant Co-ordinators. Now one was available. The sick man was waiting at home not very far away and could be got to the Hospital fairly quickly, but the donor heart would have to be collected by helicopter. A car would take too long. Everything had to be arranged to coincide with other teams collecting other organs. To keep costs down transport had to be carefully timed too. The Co-ordinator hoped the Harefield team would be ready to go whatever time she fixed.

Midmorning a Transplant Officer came into the cardiac theatre suite to say that a transplant was on the horizon. The Theatre Manager knew that, if it did come about, it would continue into the evening. This operating day was not going to be a smoothe one. The day's regular list of three heart patients would have to be confined to only one of the two theatres and so would go on later than planned. That meant reorganising her nurses. There was a general thoracic list going on upstairs too. That should finish on time even though one of the cases was an oesophageal resection. But such rearrangements were not too unusual an occurrence. They were all pretty well used to it.

From theatre the Transplant Officer went back to his ward round. He had finished in the Children's Ward. Most of the children had congenital heart defects amenable to surgical repair or correction. Some were very ill. But the one transplant patient was doing fine. He had recently been given his new heart, when he was barely two weeks old. He was the youngest heart transplant yet.

The doctor then went on to the adult Transplant Ward. There he checked the patients, their observation charts, fluid balance, cardiac biopsy reports and made any alterations to the immuno-suppressive drug dosages needed. He spent more time with the young woman who had had heart and lungs transplanted, listening attentively to her chest and carefully examining her chest X-ray for any signs of rejection. He encouraged her by telling her of the young woman

5

who had had a baby three years after she had been given a new set of heart and lungs.

Transplant Out-patient Department, at the end of the ward, was getting busier and busier. On passing it, he was delighted to see a lass whom he remembered well. She told him she was back at school and she had just finished her exercise test on the cycle ergometer. Part of the history of Harefield now, she had needed a new heart and lungs because her lungs had failed her. Her heart had been good and so it had been given to a boy in need of a new one. They had called the swap the Domino Procedure. He had heard a little while before that the lad was as happy as a lark too, playing his beloved soccer again.

He had just finished talking when the man for the possible transplant arrived. It had all worked out rather well. He was on duty that night and had wanted to be able to see the patient right away and spend as much time as necessary with him and his wife. They would need to know the result of the tissue typing as soon as possible as it was that which would finally determine whether the operation would go ahead.

## A Senior House Officer

The SHO was on a rotational training scheme and this was his six-month section in the cardiothoracic specialty. He had not been at Harefield very long and was just learning the ropes. On duty last night, the cardiac arrest had been the first one he had been called to. But now the excitement was over he realised that he too had missed breakfast and he was hungry. He went over to the Friends Pavilion for a snack, having already tasted their delicious toasted cheese sandwiches! But at lunchtime he would try and have a good substantial hot meal in the main dining-room under the concert hall. He had an ulterior motive. If he timed it right he might see that nurse he had taken a fancy to. He knew she always ate there. It was his evening off. With luck she wouldn't be working late and perhaps he could make a date. When she was on duty she was always so busy that there was never any time to talk.

Going back to the main block, his bleep went as he entered the front door. It was the general office wanting him to sign a death certificate. He had been called to certify a death in the night. That presented no problem. The poor soul had terminal cancer and it was a blessed release. The family had thought so too. Coming out of the office he saw the personnel office. It reminded him that they had asked him to fill in some form or other. He would get that over now because when once back on the ward he knew he would be busy and probably forget.

Several patients were being admitted under his two chiefs that day. It was his responsibility to 'clerk' them. That meant taking a history, doing a general physical examination and ordering the 'routine' tests. He would have to have his wits about him because they were getting quite sticky about tests that were not strictly indicated. But first there were the 'bloods' to take and the forms filled in. He hoped there weren't too many. Sticking needles into people wasn't his favourite job, but it had to be done.

Mid morning his bleep went again. He was wanted in the Out-patient Department. Seeing it was raining, he went down the stairs between F East and West Wards and made a dash from the door across the road to the temporary building just inside the gate, shared with the Medical Records Department. Sister had the clinic well organised. The consultant hadn't arrived yet. A senior registrar and registrar were there but getting a little 'snowed under'. He would be needed until the consultant arrived he was told. He hoped it would only be for half an hour or so. He had more clerking to do before his other 'boss's' ward round. He didn't want to leave too much for later as he wanted to be off duty on time, especially if the date materialised.

## A Thoracic Surgeon

Before going to Out-patients, the consultant whose clinic it was had gone to the Private Ward to see a patient who had given him a tech-nically difficult time in the operating theatre the day before. Finding all well he wasn't long and decided to drop in the General Manager's office and hope to catch him before his management meeting. He was in luck. If truth be known, apart from discussing one or two things, he wanted to have a closer look at the magnificent carpet presented to the hospital in 1987 after a visit from the King of Morocco.

On his way to the front door, he was greeted by the smart, cheery Receptionist. That reminded him. He took some papers from his case which he wanted photocopying. He knew, when she wasn't greeting patients, giving relatives directions or answering the telephone, she would do it for him. He would collect them later in the day. He knew his senior registrar would be getting on with things in the clinic but he wanted to see the newcomers himself. He knew too that one of his 'pet' patients was due for her annual check. Three years before, on New Year's Eve, she had been in a road accident. With a torn bronchus she had been extremely ill. They had managed to repair things but the poor girl had spent her 21st birthday in hospital. Now she was fit and well. It was always a pleasure to see her and it invariably made his day. And it did once again.

There were a lot of administrative matters to deal with, mostly local budget problems and plans and ideas for the future. Having finished the clinic he went in search of some of his colleagues to discuss one or two items on next weeks' Medical Committee agenda. He knew where to find a couple of them. One was in cardiac theatre, but there was no point going there at the moment as they would be in the middle of operating on that patient who had arrested earlier in the day. He had also heard the transplant was on and knew this would bring the other cardiac surgeon. If he went down a bit later, he might be able to see both at the same time. Wishful thinking maybe, but worth a try!

So first he went up to see the other in the thoracic theatres, hoping he wouldn't be in the middle of the oesophagus. He wasn't, and could spare a moment between cases. He had a long list of patients needing examination of bronchus or oesophagus, or both, under anaesthetic. Pressures had been taken off a bit by the arrival of the senior registrar from Out-patients who was getting on with one of the other major cases on the list in the other theatre. The paediatric cardiologist, much involved with administrative matters, had seen the agenda too and wasn't the least bit surprised to be caught by him as she emerged from X-ray.

Glancing at his watch the surgeon realised that he would have time for a quick lunch – sandwiches in the office today. He needed to get on with his ward round if everything was to be fitted in. When he left Harefield he had patients to see at two other hospitals before he could get home. He wanted to miss the rush hour if he could. He drove around enough during the week and could do without that. Maybe he would miss it by being after it. If so, he must let the family know.

## A Ward Sister

Sister had just come on duty when the crash call went out, but had been able to get some sort of brief report from the night staff before they departed. What a start to the day! She could begin to get herself organised because the registrar not involved in the incident had done his early morning round. But first she must reassure the patients in beds nearby that everything was all right so far, and then see how

8

all the other patients were. A number of admissions were due that morning. Thank goodness it would be all neat and tidy before they arrived.

The girls were really marvellous. Despite the upheaval they had quietly got on with their routines for sending patients to theatre, waiting for the signal to give them their premedication, and the major cases were ready too. Most of the everyday things could be left in the Ward Clerk's capable hands she knew. It wasn't the day for ordering medical supplies, but she must check to see that the stores were adequate. Each ward had their own budget and by careful housekeeping she wanted to ensure the best possible total patient care. The Sisters were proud of their wards, determined to run them efficiently and leave no room whatsoever for criticism.

Things had soon got back to normal and her last job before going off duty was to give the report to the Sister and nurses coming on duty for the afternoon shift. This one was particularly important in view of the morning's events. With the Nursing Process, the nurses had to know what had been happening to 'their' patients. She had just finished the report when the consultant walked in. That was good. It always irritated her to be interrupted just then. Now she could go happily for lunch.

The Sisters knew which days the consultants came round but were never sure exactly when. They liked the challenge of having all the right notes, X-rays and test results on the ward. But because of the uncertainty of the time, occasionally they could get caught out – and this they did not like at all! This morning had been a bit of a scramble but the invaluable Ward Clerk had been an enormous help. Everything was ready and she had even called the SHO from his clerking. Ward rounds usually took the form of a discussion in the office of the progress of the appropriate patients, going through the results and X-rays and deciding the next step. Sister enjoyed the rounds if she wasn't too busy. She often found herself the one summarising the clinical state of each patient. Then, when everything had been digested, they all trooped onto the ward. The consultant chatted briefly with each of his charges, told them how they were doing, what was planned and when, and answered any questions forthcoming.

## A Nurse

The nurse whose patient had been so ill this morning liked the system of the Nursing Process in many ways, but this sort of thing was unexpected and came as a bit of a shock. Nurses were allocated to specific patients and 'clerked' them too. Thus they got an idea of the home surroundings and the sort of person the patient was. She also enjoyed deciding with hers what they were going to call each other, and the patients seemed to like it too. Sister had told them of an occasion in the past when this would have had a positively beneficial effect. A very ill man wouldn't respond to either his christian name or surname. When his relatives arrived, his wife called him something entirely different and he had replied at once 'yes my dear'. It transpired he disliked his own names so much he insisted on being called by the nickname!

During the morning she thought about her absent patient. They had chatted and laughed together, especially when the dentist had come to check his teeth for any infection only to find he had a full set of dentures! She also thought back to the time a few weeks ago, when she was on a medical ward. Among patients with asthma, chronic bronchitis, industrial lung disease and, of course, lung cancer, many were cardiology patients. Some were in for assessment for cardiac surgery or transplant and she had learnt quite a bit about ECGs. She wondered if she would have recognised ventricular fibrillation on the trace.

But she must get back to the here and now – and her other patients. They worked together for as long as possible, but it was often only about three days. The patient usually spent part of the time in ITU and frequently only in hospital about a week. Everything happened so quickly there was hardly time to get to know them. She wasn't very keen on this, but the patients generally seemed to do well. It was not unusual for a cardiac patient to be under a shower or in the bath, or going up and down a few stairs on day four, and home by day six after the operation. The lung patients could be in a day or two more and 'an oesophagus' usually rather longer. Often they were less well to start with as they had not been able to eat properly for a while beforehand.

Her mind wandered to that SHO who seemed to be so attentive. She wondered if she would see him in the dining-room at lunch time. It was so hectic on the ward that there was little or no time for social niceties. She had briefly seen him at the episode this morning. She was on first shift and so would be off tonight and hadn't got anything arranged. But for now, if there was time before she took another of her patients to theatre, she had to find her compatriot and sort out which general stores would need ordering tomorrow.

## The End of the Day

An hour or so after his operation the patient was awake and breathing on his own, the tube having been removed from his trachea. He still had various other tubes and wires attached to him though, going either to the assortment of bottles under his bed or to the battery of monitors and plugs behind his head. A nurse was always beside him, which he found very reassuring. Later on he admitted that he had 'lost a couple of days . . . and judging from what my folks told me, it was not a bad thing to do as I wasn't looking my best.'

It had been a tiring day for the registrar. The transplant had delayed the list but he had managed to remember everything and fit most things in. He phoned home at a time when he thought he wouldn't be too late. But the ward round had taken him longer than expected. The patient about whom the 'physio' had spoken was quite a bit better, but there were one or two who were not quite so well. The oesophageal resection patient was loving her drinks though! Being later than planned, the registrar missed his daughter's school concert. He would have to make it up to her somehow.

The Transplant Officer was very pleased with how smoothe his day had been. The tissue typing result had been excellent and the timing good. The recipient was in theatre and ready just when the donor heart arrived by helicopter not quite three hours after being removed. The operation had gone well and the patient was regaining consciousness in one of the transplant rooms in the ITU. He had just told the patient's wife the good news. She was staying at the hospital. He might just have a reasonable night, always supposing another heart didn't come along.

Sister was content with her day. She had managed to hand over to the junior Sister before the ward round. She had been only a little bit late off duty. There had been time to get to London and find that present she wanted. The buses to and from Uxbridge had run on time and she was in her cosy little house in Harefield village in plenty of time to prepare for friends who were coming to dinner.

The nurse found the afternoon dragging a bit. She had been late for lunch in the dining-room and hadn't seen him. Now she was at a loose end with nothing to take her mind off wondering how things had gone in theatre. One of her friends suggested they see that Oscar winning film that was showing in Ruislip and have a meal out. If they went soon they could browse round the shops too. She accepted with alacrity even though she was on early shift the next day.

11

For the consultants, who can never foretell what each will bring, the day ended reasonably well. None had been delayed at the other hospitals and none of their long-range radio pages had brought more work. The baby that arrived did not need investigating urgently, there had been no road accidents and no more transplants. But most did not get home until after the rush hour – just in time for a preprandial pick-me-up before the evening meal.

For the resident SHO things hadn't gone very well at all. He hadn't reckoned on two of the admissions being so complicated. Taking up far more time than he had thought they would, he had missed his rendezvous in the dining-room and realised the date would not be on. Then he was landed with even more admissions. One of his fellow SHOs had gone off sick. He had to cover the night for him too.

## · 2 ·

# The Very Beginning

AT the end of his day, the weary medical resident wends his way to an old house in the Hospital grounds. Unlike some he walks the short distance, having left his car in the sizeable car park on the north side of the house. But he has to watch that he doesn't trip over either of the speed control ramps – or 'sleeping policemen' as some call them – across either limb of the circular drive. The Mansion and its two flanking buildings are almost 300 years old and Grade II Listed of Historical and Architectural Interest. It is too dark to see the two smaller ones. Each has a tower on its roof surmounted by an eagle with wings outstretched and an ancient painting on its wall. One is a sundial and the other a clock.

*The Mansion*

He fumbles for his key. The front door has to be kept locked because there have been too many intruders in recent years. On entering the spacious hall he would have been greeted at one time by 'Judy', a dog of uncertain ancestry whose antics amused them all. Now he has to decide whether to go straight up the main staircase to his room or poke his head into the sitting room on the left, resplendent with its bay window. Perhaps some of his dozen or so fellow juniors are watching television. Maybe one or other of them would join him at the bar in the back room on that side of the house. He had eaten in the Hospital dining-room – there were no meals to be had from the Mansion's spacious kitchen – but he had kept an evening snack in one of the large refrigerators there. Perhaps he needs to do some washing in the laundry room, which used to be the butler's pantry, or he might only pause for a nightcap before retiring. Residents now have little time to themselves. The Mansion does not seem like a home any longer, just a place of lodging.

When time for bed comes, and his bleep hasn't called him back

13

to the hospital, he ascends one of the staircases as there is no lift. Perhaps he has been allocated the 'Eagle room' at the back of the billiard-room on the other side of the house. In that case he probably uses the more convenient 'back stairs'. The House is centrally heated and his room will be warm. There will be no fire burning in the splendid fireplace, with its mantelpiece flanked at each end by another eagle with outstretched wings.

As he walks around the billiard table he may notice marks on the high wood panelled walls showing where many portraits have hung in the past. But he probably will not meet Harefield's ghost. 'The White Lady' has appeared from time to time over the years in the other doorway at the back of the billiard-room, leading to the bathrooms and tiny stairway up to the top floor. She has been seen too in the window over the front door, and in the archway which used to lead into the courtyard by the side of the house. As recently as this century she manifested disappearing through the wall of the kitchen garden at a point which, on closer examination, revealed there had once been a gate. Who is she? No one knows. Could she be someone who had died there under curious circumstances? Or could it be Penelope Anne Cooke preparing for one of her clandestine, happy meetings with Robert Brudenell? His family did not approve of the match for the heir to the earldom of Cardigan.

## Belhamonds

It was on 4 February 1704 that an ancient house called Rythes (or Ryes), standing in 170 acres of land and owned by John Stanyon, was bought by John Cooke as part of a marriage settlement for his son. Twenty-nine-year old George was to become Sir George Cooke, lawyer, Knight of the Inner Temple, Chief Prothonotary of the Court of Common Pleas and Lord of the Manor of Hayes.

Between 1710 and 1718 George replaced the old house. A new square one appeared at the east end of two oblong lakes. It had three floors, some thirty rooms, many windows, a cellar, tall chimneys and a cast lead roof. Rooms at the back looked onto the lakes and over the valley to the west. The room over the front entrance extended the whole width of the house and was provided with centrally placed fireplaces with grand mantelpieces. Another, overlooking the rose garden, was also spacious and provided with ornate fireplaces, but none compared with that in the 'Eagle room'. Most rooms on the first two floors had elaborate carved wooden ceiling cornices below which were hanging rods with pictures, prints or tapestries. On the north

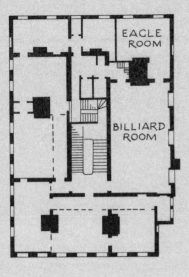

FIRST FLOOR

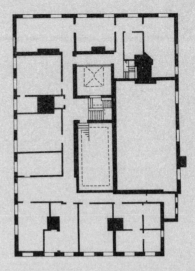

TOP FLOOR

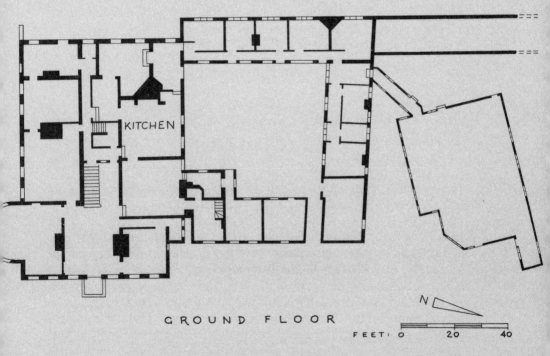

GROUND FLOOR

Fig. 1 The 'new' house later known as The Mansion

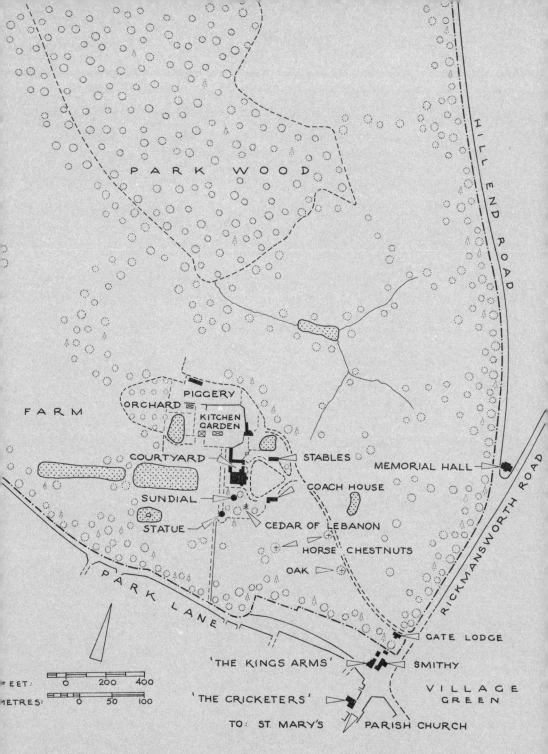

Fig. 2  Nineteenth-century Belhamonds – Harefield Park

side of the House the billiard-room, warmed by a black iron stove at the 'Eagle room' end, was soon resplendent with family portraits. These included paintings of Sir George himself (1726), George his only son (1734), his daughter and her husband, all by John Vanderbank; of his parents by Hargrave; and of his wife and her father by Gossebowe.

The servants' hall, kitchen and butler's pantry lay on the north side of the House. These looked out into a walled courtyard which had rooms contained within the walls. Behind lay an enclosed kitchen garden. The south wall of the House, with its plaque marking the previous existence of Rythes, looked on a rose garden laid out near an ancient cedar of Lebanon. Water came from a well in the centre of the courtyard and a second immediately beyond the southwest corner of the House. The rainwater heads of the cast iron drainpipes were embossed with the Cooke Coat of Arms and the date 1710. By 1733 a stable block flanked the House to the north and a coach house to the south. By 1748 these had been decorated with sundial and clock respectively. A curved drive led to the entrance of the property on the Rickmansworth Road.

The estate, named Belhamonds from a tenement, stable and three acres of ground which George had bought in 1713, covered 400 acres. It had all the appurtenances of a country gentleman – a gracious luxurious residence with shuttered windows outlined by creeper which turned a brilliant red every autumn, surrounded by lakes, lawns, ancient trees, woods and parkland, and with horses, coaches, a kitchen garden, fruit trees and tenant farms.

## The Cookes

Belhamonds was inherited by 32-year-old son George in 1740. Five years before he had been made Chief Prothonotary like his father. He also became MP for Middlesex, a Freeman of the City of London and a member of the Society of Grocers. He commissioned Michael Rysbrack to carve a white marble statue in memory of the builder of his home. He died in 1768 at the age of 59. Son George John, also 32 years old, became MP for Middlesex, but now called 'of Belhamonds'. Before he died suddenly in his chambers at the early age of 49, his portrait by Zoffany had joined the others in the billiard-room. Subsequently so did that of his widow's second husband.

In 1786, 20-year-old George, eldest of seven, became head of the household. He was to become General Sir George Cooke, KCB, command a division of the Guards at the Battle of Waterloo and lose an arm in the process. His sister Penelope Anne, 'very pretty . . . a sweet woman possessing a temper both mild and engaging', became Countess Cardigan and mother of James Thomas the 7th Earl. It took the intercession of uncle Henry, nicknamed 'Kangaroo' Cooke because he was very long in the leg, to help James Thomas achieve his ambition of an army career. Major General Sir Henry Frederick Cooke, KCH, had 'considerable backstairs influence', being Aide-de-Camp to 'the Grand old Duke of York', Commander in Chief of the British Army. The headstrong 7th Earl was to be a controversial figure in the 'Charge of the Light Brigade' of 1854, and also give his name to a knitted woollen jacket, the cardigan.

Over his 50 year tenure General George acquired more land and, as the estate had become rich in game, established Sporting Rights. But he also had to deal with the Fencing Law and the trebling of the already high Window Tax, levied on each window above a minimum of seven. Belhamonds had many and several were bricked up. Then the Grand Junction Canal was constructed beside the River Colne at the property boundary. Linking up with others further north, it became part of the Grand Union Canal in 1810. When unmarried George died in 1837 aged 71, Harefield Park, as Belhamonds had become known, covered nearly 1000 acres. It extended to Springwell and Hill End in the north and down to the banks of the Canal at Jack's Lock. It included the Fisheries and the copper mills where, it is said, the ball on top of St Paul's Cathedral in London was made.

Henry inherited but survived his brother for only one month. By the terms of his Will, when his widow remarried in 1840 the beneficiary became his nephew William Frederick Vernon, second son of sister Maria. But for the next 22 years Harefield Park was leased.

## Thomas Wakley

Between 1845 and 1856, Thomas Wakley, perhaps one of the most forceful men of the nineteenth century, took up the lease. He believed that the law of the land must be respected but if that law was not the will of the people, then the law must be changed. He fought for medical, political, and social reform, holding positions which enabled him to attack on all three fronts.

Medically qualified at the United Hospitals of St Thomas' and Guy's and a founding editor of *The Lancet*, Wakley made it quite clear through its pages that he was waging war on vested interests within the medical profession. Being somewhat radical in his views, as MP

## STATUE OF SIR GEORGE COOKE by RYSBRACK
### 'On the Pedestal . . . are the following Inscriptions'

*Pietatis private privatum Testimonium M. S.*
*GEORGII COOKE MILITIS*
*Curiae communum Placitorum*
*Principalis per viginti duos annos Prothonotarii*
*Natu fuit minimus*
*E duodicim Liberis (filus septum et quinque Filiae)*
*Johannis Cooke de Cranbroke in Com: Cantii Armig.*
*Equidem etiam, curiae Protonarii*
*Quod officium a Patre acceptam*
*Pro summo amore*
*In suum itidem Filium transferri curavit*
*Uxorem duxit Annam filiam natu minimam*
*Edwardi Jennings de Duddlestone in Com. Salopiae Armig.*
*Diminae Reginae Anne a Consilio*
*Prolemque ex illa reliquit Annam et Georgium*
*Annosque Domini MDCCXL sue vero aetatis LXV.*
*Paralasi paulatim dissolutus est.*

———————————

Hence ever honoured rise
amidst the silence of this grave.
The loved remembrance and the form revered
of a kind father and a faithful Friend.
Stranger to civil or religious rage.
Born to no pride, inheriting no strife.
The Goods of Fortune.
(not meanly nor ambitiously pursued)
Blest with the sense to value,
with the art to enjoy,
and the virtue to impart.
Diffusing
Happiness and plenty to his children,
Ease to the oppressed and relief to the Poor.
He maintained his integrity
Thro' various circumstances of Fortune
and dying in an age of general Corruption,
Had the satisfaction to leave his own Family
Free and Independent.

Fig. 3.

for Finsbury he was respected rather than liked by his parliamentary colleagues. He was instrumental in laying down the basis for the Medical Act of 1858 which ultimately led to the creation of the General Medical Council. He also played his part in the successful campaign to bring home six Dorsetshire farm labourers and trade unionists who had been transported to Australia for 'having administered "illegal oaths" for "seditious" purposes', – the Tolpuddle Martyrs.

Wakley was Coroner for West Middlesex as well, holding the view that all coroners should be medically qualified. In 1846 he conducted an inquest which had great social and political impact. In the Riding School at Hounslow Barracks, Private White was flogged with the cat-o'-nine-tails for a relatively minor breach of army discipline. Fifteen days later he was dead. The army was arranging his burial at Heston, when the vicar intervened insisting on informing the coroner. The case rekindled public outrage which had been simmering for five years. In the self same Riding School arena a soldier had been flogged on the order of James Thomas, 7th Earl Cardigan, a mere half hour after the Easter Sunday Service had been held there. But on this occasion the man had died and there was an inquest. The jury, guided by Wakley who was not afraid to act upon his convictions, denounced this form of punishment so vehemently that its practice was discontinued at once, though not prohibited by Act of Parliament until 1881.

Leaving his arduous work and family cares behind in London's Bedford Square whenever he could, Wakley would retreat to Harefield Park. There he relaxed with friends, had good conversation over a glass of port and indulged himself in one of his favourite pastimes, game shooting. But even there, being a man of principle with a strong sense of justice, Wakley prosecuted a man caught poaching. However, with his sense of fairness and compassion, he ensured that the gaoled man's family was supported until his release.

Wakley's public duties took their toll and his health began to fail in 1851. In 1852 he did not contest his parliamentary seat, and died from pulmonary tuberculosis ten years later at the age of 67. It was also in 1862 that William Frederick Vernon, cousin of the 7th Earl Cardigan and now 52 years old, took up his inheritance. But before moving to Harefield Park, the House was restored and refurbished. The upheaval did not evict the ghost nor solve the mystery of the underground passage which was supposed to lead from the cellar to the bank of the Canal. The entrance has been sought, even by excited children, but has never been found. Perhaps time has confused it with the tunnel known to have connected the nearby house at Breakspears with Moorhall Preceptory in the days of religious persecution.

## The Vernons

William Vernon, his wife, and his younger brother and family, took up residence. A bay window now graced the ground floor room looking out onto the rose garden, and white china with blue Harefield Park pattern, and silver, their table. William had a marked sense of history and became greatly interested in the locality. After much reading and research, his 'Notes on the Parish of Harefield' was privately printed in 1872, and the careful weather records of Mr Batchelor, the gardener, appeared regularly in the local paper. The Vernons soon became well known in the village, and by 1870 a beerhouse at Hill End was named 'The Vernon Arms'! Under the terms of Uncle Henry's will, when William died without children in 1889, Lt-Col. George Augustus Vernon of the Coldstream Guards, who had been living there with him, succeeded to the estate. 'Physically infirm . . ., his presence was sufficiently removed from the general . . . life of the parish to make his occasional appearances partake . . . of the nature of chronological landmarks. To have seen the Colonel was an interesting item of news for many a parishioner to convey to his neighbour.' Nevertheless involvement in the life of the village continued, the flower show being held in the grounds of the Park in 1893 and 1896, no doubt to Mr Batchelor's delight.

The centre of Harefield village was the crossroads by the green, a popular place for public events where the village policemen, of which there were about fifteen, were not allowed to go when on duty! It was there Mrs Stedall would hold suffragette meetings, and its duck pond where the horses of the village would be driven with their carts to wash the wheels. Opposite, and next to the King's Arms, one of fourteen public houses, was the village smithy. The blacksmith not only shoed horses and made weathercocks but was also a wheelwright. Much of the iron he used was supplied by Mr Stedall. The Stedall family, known locally as 'kind people', lived in Harefield Grove, a 'plain nineteenth century house standing in beautiful grounds', lying a little way along the Rickmansworth Road. Previously it had been owned by Mr J. Barnes, a Manchester merchant who built the village Memorial Hall in memory of his only son.

On the left of the narrow, gravelled and dusty High Street was 'The Cricketers', with its sign standing practically in the middle of the road. Another of the public houses, it was a popular meeting place.

Next door was the post office, exactly a mile from the steps of which, via the crossroads and down Park Lane, lay the Fisheries. On the way along Park Lane one would pass the 'Red House by the Strolleys', Harefield Park farm on the right and Bottom Park could be seen down the hill to the south west. Southwards down the main street towards the church, the Rev. Albert A. Harland, vicar of Harefield between 1871 and 1921, lived in the vicarage with his family of twenty-one children. 'Lying so beautifully secluded in the dip of the hill amongst green meadows, below the village', was St Mary's Parish Church.

## Debts

'The old cast lead which had been on this roof since 1718 was taken off and replaced with new 8 lb lead to the order of Lt-Col. G. A. Vernon. New lantern lights were also fixed. July 1896. Beeson & Sons, Rickmansworth.' So says a plaque on the roof of the House at Harefield Park. Why should he go through all this upheaval in the twilight of his life? Was another skylight needed because so many windows had been blocked up? Were there debts to be paid? The answer probably is that his son and heir was a lover of cards and a considerable gambler. The amount of original cast lead was more than that needed to re-roof the house. Lead was a very valuable commodity and, even with labour costs, sale of the excess lead produced a profit. When his father died in 1896 at the age of 85, son Bertie (pronounced Bartie) Wentworth Vernon, High Sheriff of Northamptonshire in 1892, and Justice of the Peace, had to find more funds.

Most of the Vernon's Harefield property passed into the hands of one J. G. Hossack and many in the village who lived in 'Vernon houses' were faced with either finding the money to buy or having a new landlord. Harefield Park was leased once again, this time to an Australian family. In 1896 Charles Arthur Moresby Billyard-Leake and his wife, Letitia Sara, took '33 acres at Hill End and the 47 acre Upper Park'. They moved in at once with son Edward and daughters, Letitia and 2-year-old Mary Deyncourt. But Mary was only to enjoy her new home for two years. She died in 1898 and was buried in the family plot in St Mary's Parish Churchyard.

The family soon found that Harefield Park was largely self supporting. The kitchen garden was prolific. Peaches came from the espalier trees along its walls, and apples from the orchard. There were gooseberry bushes and filbert nut trees. There was quince and mulberry and a vinery. For other crops, ground was tilled by faithful workhorses that lived in the stables; one of the farms provided chickens

19

and eggs, and pork came from the piggery. In 1909 the Billyard-Leakes bought the House and 136 acres of surrounding land for £18,500. Rumour in the village had it that 'it was her that had the money'. By 1913 they had acquired quite a bit more of the erstwhile Vernon land including the old corn mill, Black Jack's Mill and the 'Red House by the Strolleys'. To his relief, Mr Batchelor was allowed to continue his care of the gardens and noting of the weather. To maintain the Park's stock of game and protect it from poachers, a keeper lived in a cottage in the grounds down Park Lane.

## The Billyard-Leakes

It wasn't long before the local gentry were once again being entertained at Harefield Park. Unlike George Augustus, the Billyard-Leakes were gregarious people. Their winter skating parties on the lakes quickly became popular events which lingered long in the memories of the village folk. Charles was also a cricket fanatic. He saw to it that one of the first changes to be made on the estate was the laying out of a cricket pitch beyond the rose garden, within reasonable reach of the house. He needed only the slightest excuse to get a team together and arrange a match. Anyone who happened to be around, even workmen contracted to do some job or other, had to down tools and were 'pressganged' into playing for the Billyard-Leake team! The pitch was an excellent one. The Harefield Cricket Club and the local Asbestos Company Cricket Club were invited to – and did – make use of it.

But this pleasant life did not last long. The first world war was on the horizon and the authorities were trying to arrange the care of war wounded. They determined that casualties returning to Britain would receive initial treatment in British hospitals. To make room for more arrivals from the front, when the first stage of recovery was complete the wounded were to be transferred to 'convalescent depots'. In the main these were large country houses lent by their owners.

Nations of the Commonwealth were rallying round the 'mother country'. Each one sending troops looked to make their own arrangements. Australia was seeking places for men of the Australian Imperial Force (AIF) 'to recuperate after sickness or injury, for officers, warrant officers, non-commissioned officers and rank and file' and to 'collect invalids for return to Australia'. Charles Billyard-Leake was an expatriate from New South Wales. Now 54 years of age, he decided to make his contribution to the war effort. Accordingly he offered the house and 250 acres of Harefield Park to the Ministry of Defence in Melbourne 'for the period of the war and six months after'. This offer was accepted in December 1914.

The wheels started to turn quickly. Within the month the Australian Ministry of Defence had approved staff for the Harefield Park Depot: 'one Captain of the AAMC [Australian Army Medical Corps.], one sergeant, one corporal, four men as wardsmen and orderlies, one Matron and five nursing sisters.' The first to sally forth were the nurses, little knowing what lay in store.

## The Next Australians

January 1915 brought a telegram to Ethel Gray in Melbourne. An Australian Queen Alexandra Nurse of thirty-eight summers, she had volunteered for war service abroad. Specifically selected for the job, she was asked to proceed to England, there to set up and take charge of the Australian Convalescent Depot at Harefield Park.

Leaving home on 16 February, she embarked on the RMS Osterley in Adelaide, South Australia, the next day with four more chosen Sisters. The fifth joined them in Perth, Western Australia. All were determined to make the most of their first venture abroad and enjoy the trip. During the coaling stop in Colombo, Ceylon (as Sri Lanka was known in those days), they had their first taste of 'eastern life'. Sailing through the Red Sea and Suez Canal, barbed wire entanglements could be seen covering the shores and calls of 'cooee' came from many little camps. As time was pressing, they could not visit Cairo, but two of their comrades stationed there came to see them on board. The passage through the Mediterranean was broken by a call at Naples which, in the early morning light, impressed them greatly. They spent the day at the 'old ruined city of Pompeii'.

Most passengers disembarked at Plymouth but the nurses stayed on board to sail up the English Channel. Despite the danger from submarines, they docked safely at Tilbury at 4 pm on 26 March being met by an official of the Australian High Commission. At 11 pm, greeted at St Pancras Railway Station in London by the Australian High Commissioner's son and the Chief Medical Officer, Dr Norris, they were taken to the Ivanhoe Hotel as guests of the Commonwealth Government. Four of the Sisters were posted temporarily to Netley Hospital. The fifth had been unwell since arrival and, as she ended up in the QA Military Hospital in London, the small planned complement was already reduced by one.

On 30 March 1915, Miss Gray, with Dr Norris and an architect, visited Harefield Park to find out what would need to be done. They discovered 'in fine rain and a little wintry snow . . . a large stone building in some acres of ground, with a fine lawn in front and two lakes at the back on which were floating two white swans. On one side of the house was another fine lawn and rose garden, in the midst of which stood a quaint old sundial.'

## The Task

Shown round by the housekeeper, who was happy to remain and take charge of the kitchen, it was as if they were paying a call at a country estate, except that it was bereft of its owners. The Billyard-Leakes had moved into nearby Black Jack's Mill to make way for the changes. Still containing much of its furnishing and the sumptuous carpets muffling every footstep, the atmosphere was one of a gracious home still, and certainly not a hospital!

The visitors assessed the formidable task. The furniture would have to be removed and stored; the spacious rooms upstairs, including the billiard-room, provided with hospital beds, bedside lockers, a few armchairs and dressing trolleys; the drapes and curtains replaced with more suitable ones; the carpets removed and the wood floors stained a 'uniform dark colour'; and additional equipment, such as vegetable boilers, installed in the kitchen.

The large room with the bay window on the ground floor would make an adequate operating theatre if provided with sterilisers for instruments and dry dressings. The only service not adequate there was the disposal of waste water, but Miss Gray thought that this could be 'overcome by carrying the water across the hall to the nearest sewer'. The top floor rooms were not so readily accessible and so were reserved for staff. The courtyard wall rooms would provide offices, a staff recreation room and a dispensary. An old lumber room, when cleared of its branches, could be turned into a dispensary store and small reading room.

But additional space would be essential. If 150 were to be accommodated, hutted wards would have to be built, as the House could only reasonably house a quarter that number. They determined that the best place for these would be on the beautiful front lawn. A mess hall to seat 120, with a pantry and hot and cold running water, would have to go up in the courtyard. They acknowledged gratefully that most of the produce of the estate would be available to them. Whether it would be sufficient for Harefield Park's new role only time would tell.

After her visit, Miss Gray spent much time in London scouring

Pl. 1  *Top:* Sir Thomas Holmes Sellors, DM, MCh, FRCS, FRCP. *Bottom:* The head of the last family to own Harefield Park, Australian Charles Arthur Moresby Billyard-Leake, *c.* 1918.

Pl. 2  The south aspect of Harefield Park House across the rose garden, with outside shades on the windows of the bay, c. 1905.

Pl. 3  Harefield Park House in the distance at the east end of two oblong lakes, *c.* 1905.

Pl. 4 An ancient cedar of Lebanon beside the rose garden, *c.* 1916. Huts of the 'Australian Hospital' in the 'top fields' lie beyond. The hospital's 'telephonette' wires cross beside it.

Pl. 5   The west and south walls of the stables, 1989. The eagle sits atop a reconstructed tower on the roof but the sundial still tells the time. (Partly masked by the tree.) Extended on the north side, the Building and Maintenance Department is to be found here.

Pl. 6   The north wall of the coach house, 1989. Little changed outwardly – an eagle still adorns the roof and the original painted clock remains visible. The building houses the Domestic Department.

Pl. 7　One end of the mantel in the 'Eagle room', 1988.

Pl. 8　Memorial Plaque commemorating the centenary of Thomas Wakley's death. Unveiled in 1962, it lies just inside the hospital gates on Hill End Road by E Ward.

Pl. 9   The Memorial Hall, *c.* 1900. The mid nineteenth-century building, facing the junction of Rickmansworth Road and Hill End Road opposite the hospital entrance, was a working man's hall, school, wartime first-aid post and hospital waiting-room. It was demolished after about 100 years to make way for private housing.

Pl. 10   The centre of Harefield village. Opposite the 'smithy', convalescent Australians relax on the village green at the crossroads, *c.* 1917. The houses in the distance lie on the Northwood Road, at the corner of which was the duck pond.

Pl. 11  The Cricketers Inn with its sign standing in the middle of Harefield High Street.
A popular meeting place, it disappeared in 1936.

Pl. 12 View from Harefield Park House to the east, over the first three wards of the 'Australian Hospital' on the front lawn. The open parkland on the other side of the drive will be the site of the future sanatorium.

Pl. 13 Rysbrack's statue in memory of the creator of Harefield Park, Sir George Cooke, at the south end of the terrace behind the house, is the backdrop for Matron Gray and Lt-Col. Hayward, seated with nurses and patients. Inscriptions on the base of the statue are quoted in Fig. 3.

Pl. 14 Looking over No. 1 Australian Auxiliary Hospital almost due south towards Park Lane. 'An example of casual improvisation', it occupied the 'top fields'.

Pl. 15 The 'Long Ramp', a covered way and the main thoroughfare of the 'Australian Hospital'. Starting a little way inside the entrance, next to an old oak tree which still stands, it ran almost due west over the 'top fields'.

warehouses, wholesale establishments and shops to obtain furniture, furnishings, equipment and utensils. She had about six weeks to get everything ready. The first commanding officer and five orderlies, sailing on the troopship 'Runic', were due in the middle of May.

## Making a Hospital

It was not until 11 May that Miss Gray was ready to return and stay at Harefield Park. New acquisitions had been stacked all over the place. The three huts on the front lawn and the mess hall in the courtyard were nearly complete, and two more huts were going up at the back of the House. She settled herself in a top floor room where she could look down on the rose garden. For her office she chose one on the ground floor at the back overlooking the lakes. The window there formed the upper half of 'french' doors opening onto the terrace. They would conveniently enable her to come and go without having to go through the kitchen or hall.

The next day the four other Sisters arrived and they set to work. Unable to get help from able bodied local men as they were all at the front, and those that were there were fully occupied with the huts, they manhandled the unneeded furniture into one room themselves. With the help of two local women to clean and scrub floors, they removed carpets, stained, waxed and polished floors, distributed bedsteads and mattresses and all the other furniture and equipment into the selected rooms on the first two floors. They sorted the contents of 31 bales and cases full of blankets, pillows, jackets and other linen sent from Australia and stamped them with the 'hospital mark for the outside laundry'.

In a gale of activity they ran up and down stairs putting up and making up beds, storing spare linen, checking there were enough pairs of pyjamas and dressing gowns, and dealing with the thousand and one other things that needed doing to make a hospital. To prepare the huts, clad in coats, hats, long grey serge skirts and sometimes carrying umbrellas, they picked their way through the mud and debris of the quagmire which had been the front lawn. By Sunday 16 May, 80 beds were ready. Despite all the problems and hindrances the five women had achieved the conversion in just three days! Then they prepared top floor rooms for the contingent of staff arriving on 19 May. Exactly two weeks later, on 2 June 1915, the first eight patients arrived.

## · 3 ·

# The First Hospital

WHAT the authorities had not anticipated was the ferocity of the battle engagements. Many Australians fought at the terrible Gallipoli landing and Harefield Park was the only Australian Depot available. Orders to prepare as quickly as possible to accommodate 500 arrived on the self same day as the first patients, and two weeks later, on 17 June, that number was doubled. As there was no time for planning, huts began to go up wherever it seemed convenient. Most were put on the 'top fields' where the cricket pitch had been.

## Early Months

By 22 June, Harefield Park had 170 patients. Two weeks later there were 362, many of whom had been badly injured and in need of constant attention. It was a blessing that the new commanding officer had brought with him several nursing Sisters, though sadly eight were only temporary being en route for France. The Asbestos Works, who had offered to convert the bay window room into an operating theatre, fortunately had completed the job as, on Friday 9 July, the first operation was carried out.

During July more wards, the pay office, a pack store, post office, Red Cross store, guard house, and a mortuary and chapel beyond the courtyard, appeared. It was a great relief when the field kitchen and mess hall were ready. Cooking for four hundred in the House kitchen was proving very difficult! Produce from the estate did not now meet the need. At first, supplements through the Army Service Corps in Hounslow were adequate, but soon additional supplies had to be bought in the open market.

By September 1915, men were arriving directly from the front and on one occasion 49 beds had to be found at a moment's notice. Every patient had to be issued with 'a suit, flannel shirt, underpants, socks, slippers, pyjamas, two towels, washer, two plates, knife, fork, two

24

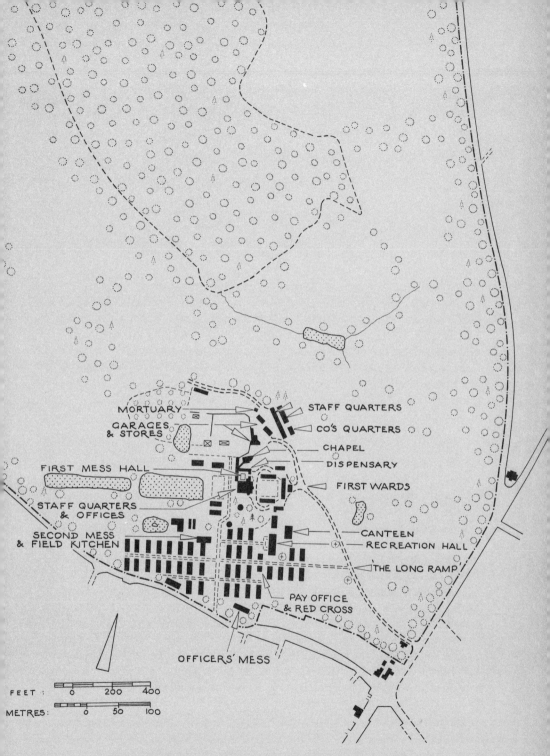

MORTUARY

GARAGES & STORES

STAFF QUARTERS

CO'S QUARTERS

CHAPEL

DISPENSARY

FIRST MESS HALL

FIRST WARDS

STAFF QUARTERS & OFFICES

SECOND MESS & FIELD KITCHEN

CANTEEN

RECREATION HALL

THE LONG RAMP

PAY OFFICE & RED CROSS

OFFICERS' MESS

FEET : 0    200    400

METRES : 0    50    100

Fig. 4   1918: No. 1 Australian Auxiliary Hospital

spoons, mug and bowl, for which he is responsible'. There seemed no respite from the incredible pressures on the very limited staff. But help was gradually gathering. Wives and daughters of local Harefield residents, as well as Australians in Britain anxious to play their part, came forward as volunteers.

The place was a hive of activity and building still in full swing, when word was received at noon on 16 August 1915, that King George V and Queen Mary would visit that afternoon. And come they did, staying nearly two hours. They spoke to every man confined to bed. Many were survivors of Gallipoli and the King asked about the battle. The Queen was very taken by one – and his little dog who had been with him for three days in the trenches. She visited the kitchens, both old and new, and promised playing cards and reading stands for the bedbound. These, with autographed photographs of them both, arrived soon afterwards.

Right from the beginning there was a stream of interested official and unofficial visitors. The Hospital's Visitors Book soon came to read 'like pages from Debrett'. Everyone wanted to see, and be seen to be helping, the enterprise at Harefield. Because the place was so busy, the visits were not always convenient. But no matter what, all were welcomed even if as many as fifteen or twenty arrived in a day. On one epic day there were 70. The importance of these visitors was fully recognised.

As the offer of Harefield Park had been made directly to Australia, British authorities 'were shy of having anything to do with it, seeing that they had not been consulted in any way'. The War Office was not at all enamoured of the project, considering 'Harefield . . . unsuited as the site of a major hospital [but] by irregular accretions, functional and structural, it grew to a large and unwieldy unit, disadvantageously situated, expensive, awkward to work, difficult to command, an example of casual improvisation.'

## Hospital Life

The Hospital's main thoroughfare was the 'Long Ramp'. The covered open board walk started under a big oak tree – which still stands on the left, a little way inside the original entrance. Running straight across the 'top fields' beside the House, it was joined to other covered ways which gave the whole conglomerate a degree of cohesion, as well as shelter in the winter months. At the height of activity there were some 50 huts of varying size and shape in use, at least 36 of which were wards.

The 'Long Ramp' was busy most days with men arriving or departing. It was a bustling, colourful place. There were patients in blue, some with white bandages and maybe a broad brimmed hat with side upturned; men on crutches or with eye patches; medical officers in their khaki uniforms with red lapel flashes; a nurse in long grey skirt, white apron, short red cape with brown trim and trailing white cap, or neat bonnet if she was going out; or a volunteer not in uniform at all. Some may have been men on their way to collect their 4*d* a week pocket money to spend in the canteen; to post a card or letter they had written in the writing-room; to a lecture or film or concert in the recreation hall; to have a game of billiards or develop their latest film in the dark room; or just going for a walk in the village. On Wednesdays and at weekends between 2 and 5.30 pm visitors with their passes swelled the throng. Men, women and children were 'looking up old friends and making new', several of which ended in marriage.

The 'Australian Hospital' also remained a Clearing Depot throughout. Pressures 'for onward movement' were enormous and often the availability of ambulance and overseas transport were determining factors. Which patients were to go on leave, to another convalescent home, back to the front or be invalided home, was decided by a Medical Board. Occasionally 300 were transferred in a single day but more often the number averaged about 500 a week. Evacuation work was carried out by 'eleven NCO's and men of the Australian Medical Transport Corps, seven ambulances, two touring cars, one motor lorry and one motorcycle'. Should numbers be high, special trains fitted out with bunk beds were used from Denham Station.

That a patient could be removed prematurely, having started on a plan of treatment frequently difficult and important, caused the medical staff much exasperation and dissatisfaction. The commanding officer wrote to the Director of Medical Services in 1918: 'Considering . . . working under the disadvantage of having to send cases on . . . for further treatment – that we could not hold cases long enough and that . . . even nerve cases had to be sent on much too soon – the results . . . were . . . wonderful. In weeks with us [men] did [better] than . . . in months previous to their coming to us.'

## The Wounded

Despite their awful experiences, 'the great majority [of men] are most plucky and brave and never grumble'. Many told of 'their mate dying in their arms or shot down beside them'. They came having lost an arm or a leg, or 'with only one eye, others with arms, elbows and feet broken, and many with stiff joints'. One 'who was in much pain – shot near the spine affecting the nerves – said "I will be all right tomorrow Matron, I am only tired with the journey".' Another, blind and with 'only one good leg' replied to one of the Sisters who asked him to sit down, 'No thank you, Sister, I have one good leg and I am quite all right.' They showed amazing fortitude.

'The large proportion of patients require further surgical aid to correct deformity, restore function and prevent grave disabilities. The surgical requirements are of a type that will tax the capacity and resources of the most experienced surgeon.' So said the senior surgeon to the High Commissioner in 1915, to emphasise the urgent need for more staff and facilities. X-ray equipment, pathology and physiotherapy departments and a well equipped 'clean' operating theatre for orthopaedic and nerve surgery, were particularly requested. 'Their importance cannot be sufficiently emphasised.' The pleas were heard. An artificial limb workshop opened just before Christmas and an eye ward in January 1916. By May over 1500 men had been admitted directly from the front. Of necessity, the hospital had developed into a specialist centre for radiography and electrotherapeutic services – massage and physiotherapy. By October Harefield Park, retaining an average of 960 patients, had been reclassified 'First Australian Auxiliary Hospital', a general hospital with 'convalescent and auxiliary sides'.

The next two years saw the evolution of other types of specialty treatment – of eye, ear, nose and throat conditions. By 1916 staff numbers had increased dramatically. There were five majors, 12 captains and three lieutenants, including six Australian surgeons in the RAMC (Royal Army Medical Corps) lent by the War Office. There were 26 non-commissioned officers and 94 privates. The nursing ranks comprised 20 Sisters, 36 staff nurses, 120 Australian VADs seconded from the British hospital service, and there were six masseuses. A long way from home, 'senior surgeons, physicians and specialists from the highest ranks of their profession in Australia' were now providing a wide range of rapidly developing techniques for fellow Australians 'suffering various types of breakdown resulting from the war, including severe forms of physical disablement'.

But patients who were up and about and able, had a set pattern of activity to follow. Reveille sounded at 6 am followed ten minutes later by Rouse. Fall In was heard at 6.15 and, after half an hour of physical jerks, breakfast followed at 7 am. The morning was taken up by Sick Parade and/or lectures. After a noon time dinner, a route march or some other exercise was obligatory, lasting until 4 pm. After tea, the day was free until First Post sounded at 9.30 pm. Last Post was half an hour later, Lights Out at 10.30 followed by Bed Inspection at 11 pm.

## Help

To remind folk that there was a war on – if they needed reminding – there was an occasional air raid. Gunfire and bombs were often heard, but on 14 October 1915 a Zeppelin was seen. These, added to their battlefront experiences, made relaxation essential for the men. It was in this regard that the volunteers played such a valuable part. They had both the time and the inclination.

A canteen opened on New Years Eve 1915 and proved a most successful venture. Run under the management of the Director of Recreation and Study, the light refreshments and goods sold well. Mrs Billyard-Leake was the first and only Chairman of the Canteen Committee, and daughter Letitia was a member. Mrs Stedall and her two daughters were also on the Committee. Coming from Breakspears, the Tarleton daughters were often in the canteen too, as were some of the twenty-one strong Harland family.

The Australian Red Cross was much involved. Opening a store in December 1916, run by Australian Red Cross VAD Vera Addison, it quickly became a popular place. There the men could find goods sent from Australia. In 1917 Mr Coxen, another Red Cross member, followed a succession of YMCA representatives as Director of Recreation and Study. He and his wife moved into quarters next to the canteen. Mrs Coxen, based in the sewing-room, ran the Sewing Guild and held classes for patients, many of whom became expert with the needle.

Wives who had come with their officer husbands also lent a hand. One commanding officer's wife helped in the Red Cross Store and that of a Chaplain was librarian of the Red Cross library. Mrs Geddes-Scott, married to a captain in the RAAMC, assisted in the canteen, helped organise concerts, played accompaniments like Mrs Coxen, and was always ready to entertain the men with her accomplished whistling.

Local residents gave unstintingly of their time. Many helped in the canteen or in the splint making room, gave lessons in French to patients and staff alike, or taught handicrafts. Some provided transport and others entertained both staff and patients in their homes. The Stedall family held an 'open house' at Harefield Grove every single week of the war. Living a little further away in Uxbridge was one who promoted bowls, cricket and rifle shooting, extending hospitality to all. M. L. Emery came from Pinner every day. 'Bandy', resplendent with goatee beard and moustache, was a familiar figure in the canteen. The middle-aged photographer took pictures for Christmas cards, postcards or calendars for the men to send home. Or he just provided film and cameras.

The Canteen Fund financed improvements of the amenities. Pianos were purchased, outings and films sponsored, and the recreation hall repainted. The stage had been christened in November 1915 by Sir Henry Irving with his rendering of 'Waterloo'. 'Concerts and dramatic entertainments are given daily by visiting parties, and a cinema show twice weekly.' These were sometimes arranged in conjunction with the YMCA, The Soldiers Entertainment Fund and a similar Fund of the Daily Mail. In June 1916 Edward Billyard-Leake, relating his experiences on HMS *Warspite* at the Battle of Jutland, was well received. Others who came included singer Peter Dawson and the Company of Clara Butt, the famous contralto. Dances were held, too, sometimes to the playing of the Hospital band.

## Leisure and Off Duty

Nicknames abounded. Sister Lucas was called 'dinkum Sister' and three of the patients were called 'Shark', 'Pirate' and 'Fairy' by their mates. Those in the three convalescent wards nearest the exit would say that those at the west end 'lived in the slums' and those suffering from shell shock were good naturedly known as 'the Shellies'. Revelling in the name of 'Butterbox' was an old, rather unreliable khaki coloured car with wire wheels. Used for all manner of errands, including the collection of beer, it gave up the ghost in 1917.

The Hospital had its mascots too. A rabbit might be perched on someone's shoulder – or a cockatoo. Brought from the trenches of Gallipoli, it had the unfortunate habit of suddenly 'imitating the screech of a Turkish shell'! In October 1916, before setting out for France, men of the Third Division AIF presented a wallaby (a small kangaroo) to one of the volunteer workers, the daughter of General Sir William Birdwood, General Officer Commanding the ANZACs. However, one was never quite sure where the creature would pop up. It was frequently seen in the village. On its last expedition it went too far afield. Having reached the hills on the other side of West Hyde, a farmer, not knowing what it was, shot it. The men were so upset they had to be prevented from seeking out and lynching the offender!

The first Hospital magazine, *Harefield Boomerang*, did not catch on. The second, *Harefield Park Boomerang*, was born in December 1916. Starting through the enterprise of two privates, it was given an enormous boost when Theodora Roscoe appeared on the scene in June 1917. An Australian volunteer, she became 'a very capable and energetic editor – the mainstay of the paper'. Printed with the help of a London firm in White Friars Street, it went from a fortnightly journal of 12 pages to a monthly one of 16. Its circulation rose from 250 in April 1917 to 1200 at the beginning of 1918. 'WA from WA' was a great help. Before the war Pte. Anderson had been a journalist with the *Sunday Times* in Perth. In her spare time Theodora Roscoe wrote her own History of Harefield and taught French to anyone who wanted to learn. Her daughters helped in the canteen.

From November 1916, Harefield Park had its own Sports Union 'for the purpose of providing sports and amusements for patients and staff'. Rugby matches were played in winter, some by British and some by Australian rules. In summer there was cricket. Needless to say the Australians won many of the matches! 'Tennis is being played by all sections of the staff, and many good players have put in an appearance on the courts. . . . Some of the Sisters and VADs have given some admirable exhibitions.' Rickmansworth Baths was the place for swimmers to go. Also, many of the men had belonged to rowing clubs at home. Facilities were found through the Master of Eton at Windsor and, at almost any time, the Hospital could produce a fairly formidable rowing eight.

The more disabled or less energetic were not forgotten and they did not have to go very far afield. They could walk by a stream or in bluebell woods, and there was plenty of space to play a friendly game of cricket without leaving the Hospital. In winter they could skate on the lake, often taking 'chairs along for support as they tried out their "ice legs" ' or else, fascinated by that strange white stuff, challenge the nurses to a snowball fight.

## The Central Characters

Matron Gray was an amazing woman, dedicated and full of energy. She automatically gained the respect and loyalty of all her colleagues who gave willing help and support. Her example spurred everyone to superhuman effort. Going without sleep on many occasions, she kept on top of the very rapid expansion of the work, was always charming when greeting visitors, answered numerous official letters, and kept a detailed personal diary into the bargain.

At some time every day she would emerge from her office via the window. Clad in sou'wester and boots when it was raining, she would walk along the cross ramp immediately behind the House. Crossing 'the little bridge over' the embankment at the edge of the terrace, she arrived at the 'Long Ramp' by the field kitchen. Her rounds could take as long as two or three hours because not a building was missed. But she also knew how to relax. Her philosophy was just to put work aside and take a little time off. She loved nothing better than to contemplate the lovely sunset over the lakes, drink in the beauty of an early morning walk in frost or snow, walk in Old Park Wood, visit places and friends, or just spend an hour or so in the rejuvenating atmosphere of Harefield Grove.

In recognition of her efforts Miss Gray was awarded the Royal Red Cross, First Class, in the Birthday Honours of June 1916. In December she handed over to Matron Gould. Considered to have completed her task at Harefield Park, Miss Gray was posted to France.*

In five years the 'Australian Hospital' had six commanding officers. The first was a Captain and the last a Lt-Col. Initially tenure was short, but from November 1915 to December 1918 there were only two. This stability did much to smooth the development and running of the hospital. Lt-Col. W. T. Hayward came in 1915, working with Miss Gray. He was 'a fine man [who] understands hospitals and their workings'. The Visitors Book, to be found in the ANZAC Chapel in St Mary's Church, was his idea. Following him was Lt-Col. C. Yeatman, likewise a man of great compassion, with a deep pride and affection for his countrymen and the Hospital, patients and staff alike. For his service, he was later awarded the OBE. It was largely these three, influencing those under them, who established the atmosphere of hope and fun that pervaded the Hospital despite its busy-ness and all its problems.

Charles Billyard-Leake, known locally as Bill, did not appear on the scene very often. Nevertheless he was extremely interested in what went on. In 1916, when the House was bursting at the seams, as were the four huts behind the stables, he eased the accommodation problem a little by offering for rent the 'Red House by the Strolleys'

* Miss Gray stayed in Wimereux until March 1919. There she steered a tented hospital, lying in the teeth of cold sea winds, into hutted No. 2 Australian General Hospital of 1500 beds. She was invested CBE at Buckingham Palace in 1919 and returned to Australia in January 1920. After being demobbed she converted another old house, this time in Melbourne, into a hospital and was its first Matron. Today, like Harefield, the Epworth Hospital provides facilities for open heart surgery. Ethel Gray died in July 1962 at the grand age of 86 years.

in Park Lane opposite the Officers Mess. He also kept a very close eye on the business and financial side of the venture. In the early days he was not too happy with 'the conduct of business affairs at Harefield' but, as time went on, the authorities were 'better able to satisfy his views and desires at a much smaller expenditure of money than previously was the case'. In the end 'the Commonwealth Government . . . probably spent £50,000 or more on [Harefield]' whereas initially 'it was anticipated that it would be but a small depot, and an expenditure of £1500 would be sufficient'.

## *Special Times*

Australians in uniform became a frequent sight in the village. Gathered in front of the 'Cricketers' they might be waiting for transport to take them to the railway station. A visit to the theatre in London or somewhere in the countryside such as Croxley Mills, or as far afield as Stratford on Avon, might have been arranged. But they could have been there just visiting one of the pubs, or village friends. The locals, especially in the blackout, did not always appreciate 'the walking wounded Aussies'. They had the friendly habit of just opening a front door and walking in. In consequence many were kept locked. But some cottages held 'open house'. At least one lady was happy to do washing for them and, despite food rationing, a meal was always to be had in 'the little room alongside the saddler's shop'.

The men loved the village children. Often giving them a penny, it could be more if they fetched a few bottles of beer! Nor was it unheard of for a youngster to be smuggled into the Hospital under an Army greatcoat. A couple of days before Christmas every child was invited to a party. There were over 300 at the first one in 1915. Under a decorated tree lit by candles, Father Christmas gave each of the excited little guests a gift bought by the men. To end, everyone sat around singing Christmas carols.

Unlike Australia at Christmas, the weather was cold and often snow was on the ground. Everyone did their utmost to make it a happy time for everyone else. At some time during the festivities there was a concert party of monologues, songs, piano solos and sketches by the staff and patients. On Christmas Eve the Australian Red Cross gave a carol concert and presented each patient with a gift from Australia. Christmas Day saw judging of the most original ward decorations and the best decorated one. The traditional Christmas turkey dinner was served to the men by the Sisters with the help of willing volunteers. The meal inevitably ended with the commanding

The First Hospital

officer reading messages from the King and the Australian State Premiers.

There were many brave people at the 'Australian Hospital'. Familiar names often appeared in the lists of honours and promotions. At the first medal ceremony held on the front lawn on 3 September 1915, five men were decorated for gallantry at Gallipoli by the Australian High Commissioner. He conferred the Distinguished Conduct Medal (DCM) on five and the Military Medal (MM) on ten others in November 1916. The Duke of Connaught awarded another with the DCM and four more with the MM on 24 April 1917 and in 1918, the ex-premier of New South Wales presented MMs for courage at Passchendale.

Names of the staff also appeared. In 1917 three Sisters were awarded the Royal Red Cross, Second Class, and two were mentioned in dispatches. Staff Nurse P. E. Corkhill, 'for distinguished service in the field' was awarded the MM in August 1918. 'For courage and devotion on the occasion of an enemy air raid. She continued to attend to the wounded without any regard to her own safety, though enemy aircraft were overhead. Her example was of the greatest value in allaying the alarm of the patients.'

## Sad Times

At the beginning of the war, Mr F. A. Newdegate, MP, (later Sir Francis Newdegate, Governor of Tasmania and of Western Australia, and Hon-Col. 11th Battalion Commonwealth Military Forces) offered the part of St Mary's Parish Churchyard he owned 'for the burial of Australians who might die in Harefield Park Hospital'. He also undertook to bear the expense of the funerals, apart from the coffins. These were supplied by the AIF and made by the village carpenter. He, with the help of the local undertaker, took them as required to the Hospital on a three wheeled truck. Because all able bodied men under the age of 45 years had been called up, there was no official grave digger. This hard and sad job was done by local volunteers. On getting the news they set to work in the evenings or at night when their days work was done.

'When the first death at the Hospital occurred the [Harefield Junior] School's Union Jack was borrowed to cover the coffin at the burial, and throughout the war it was borrowed whenever the sad need for it arose.' The cortège with flag draped coffin would wend its way through the village and down Church Hill to St Mary's Church to the strains of the 'Dead March' from the Hospital band. Many local

33

residents and children joined the procession. The villagers once asked for a change of music because hearing it so often made them feel so miserable. The Hospital Chaplain conducted the graveside services with full Military Honours. After the Firing Party salute and bugle sounding Last Post and Reveille, the procession returned to the tune of 'The Girl I Left Behind Me'.

Unless a headstone was provided by relatives or comrades, the graves were marked by a simple wooden cross 'supplied by Headquarters'. From 1917 a Headstone Fund, set up at the hospital, provided them 'in uniform pattern in scroll form on a flat pedestal'.

Of all denominations, 112 were laid to rest between February 1916 and January 1920. Though most were servicemen, three were civilians and three on the Hospital staff. Two of these were orderlies. Pte Moffat was just 19 when he died of meningitis in 1916. Pte Johnston died a few months later. Sunday, 23 June 1918, must have been an awful day. Not only did two men die, but 'a gloom has been cast over the Hospital at the end of one so good and useful – a veritable "hospital heroine" '. Staff Nurse Ruby Dickinson of Sydney, New South Wales, had been working on Ward 40 the day before. 'One of the best nurses, a "bonzer", to use an Australian adjective' died of 'acute pneumonia'. October and November were also awful months, many succumbing to the influenza epidemic of that year.

The last to go was the Hospital itself. In January 1919, 72 patients were admitted and 691 discharged. The end, smoothed by the efforts of the Australian Red Cross, followed that of Cpl Knell on 15 January 1920. Subsequently two more Australians, one in 1956 and one in 1970, have joined their comrades.

## ANZAC Day

On ANZAC Day, 25 April 1918, the third anniversary of the landing at Gallipoli, a Commanding Officer's parade of Staff and walking patients was held, . . . attended by some 337 personnel. After inspection by the Commanding Officer, the whole marched through Harefield Village to the Parish Churchyard, headed by the Unit Band. Near the graves . . . the troops were drawn up in formation of a hollow square under the Australian flag. The . . . Chaplains . . . conducted the Memorial Service. Many prominent residents of Harefield attended . . . , together with friends of the Hospital, and the nursing staff. The decoration of the graves with flowers was arranged by the wife of the Commanding Officer . . . and many ladies helped and contributed to the cost of flowers, or gave them from out of their own gardens.

*The First Hospital*

Mrs Yeatman and son John had lived just across the road from the Hospital with Mr Jeffreys, the Headmaster who had lent the Union Jack, and his family.

> After the Armistice it was thought that the children of Australia would treasure the Flag because of the use to which it had been put. So I gave it to Lt-Col. Yeatman, . . . and he handed it to the education authorities of South Australia, who placed it in Adelaide High School. A few months after that the Children's Patriotic League sent us . . . a new Union Jack and the Australian flag. . . . We decided to make an annual pilgrimage to the cemetery on ANZAC Day and hoist the flag . . . , and place flowers on each of the graves.

The children paid their first tribute on 25 April 1921. That year, too, the Imperial War Graves Commission arranged for an Australian Military Cemetery to be laid out in the churchyard. The graves were re-sited and a flagstaff and Memorial Gateway designed. The central obelisk was presented by Sir Francis Newdegate and Charles Billyard-Leake and inscribed 'To the glory of God who giveth the Victory and in memory of Brave Australian Soldiers who after taking part in the Great War now rest in Harefield Churchyard.'

But other Australians are also there. Close by the Military Cemetery there is a family plot marked by the stone figure of a child. It is here that the Billyard-Leakes buried Mary in 1898, and where others of the family now rest. Letitia Sara was living in Bisham Abbey in Berkshire when she died only three years after the events of the war, aged 64 years. Two years later in 1925, her daughter-in-law, wife of Capt. Edward Billyard-Leake RN, died at the age of 30. Finally, at the age of 73 Charles Billyard-Leake returned from Kyrenia, Cyprus, in 1932 to rejoin his wife and keep an eye on things once again.

# · 4 ·

# Sanatorium Years

AFTER all it had gone through during the war, the Billyard-Leakes could not bring themselves to move back to Harefield Park. Their lovely home would never be the same. Putting all their Harefield properties up for sale they departed their several ways. Middlesex County Council (MCC), intent on developing a tuberculosis service, decided to buy Harefield Park.

## Tuberculosis in Middlesex

In 1900 'there was no disease so prevalent and fatal as consumption. It causes one tenth of all deaths which occur in . . . [Britain] every year and there is scarcely a family which has not felt its ravages.' Tuberculosis was looked upon with great fear by the man in the street. He knew, breadwinner or child alike, that contracting the disease meant incarceration in a sanatorium for two years or more, if he came out at all. State benefits then were inadequate and a family could face very hard times.

Medical care was provided either by Voluntary Hospitals or by County Councils, who tried hard to form some sort of structured service. The wealthier councils, of which Middlesex was one, progressed more readily and competed with one another in the standards of care achieved. Tuberculosis services were run by County Tuberculosis Officers (TO). Their function was almost entirely administrative. They read the patients' chest X-rays and decided if sanatorium treatment was needed. Knowing where beds were in their county, and how many, they directed the patient and advised the sanatorium accordingly. Sanatorium Medical Officers (SMO) had no say in who was admitted, but were responsible for treatment. This system of admission prevailed for many years.

Reputedly the first purpose-built institution for 'open air' treatment for tuberculosis was in Northwood, Middlesex, only a few miles from

Pl. 16  Harefield Park House from the west. A covered way, crossing the 'Long Ramp', runs the length of the terrace behind the house. The swans are no longer there.

Pl. 17  King George V and Queen Mary with Matron Gray touring the Hospital on 16 August 1915.

Pl. 18 Inside a hutted Australian ward at Christmas.

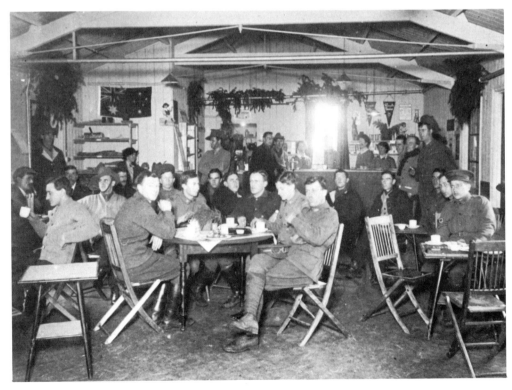

Pl. 19 The canteen. Run by volunteers, it was opened on 31 December 1915.

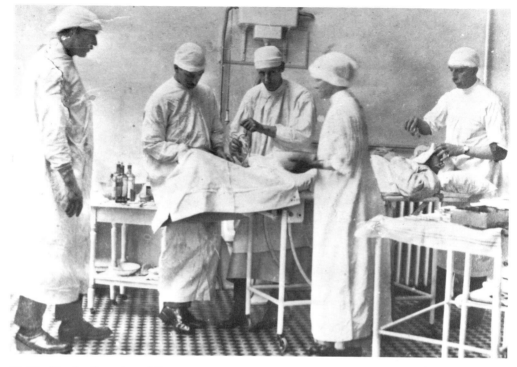

Pl. 20 The 'well equipped "clean" operating theatre' of 1916, with Lt-Col. Yeatman (centre) at work.

Pl. 21 The field kitchen, which relieved the House kitchen in July 1915.

Pl. 22 Patients gathered for 'onward movement'. No. 1 Australian Auxiliary Hospital 'remained a clearing depot' throughout the war.

Pl. 23 Mascots. The cockatoo would 'imitate the sound of a Turkish shell'.

Pl. 24  Mascots. The wallaby that went too far afield.

Pl. 25  Australians at Harefield Park were even good at one-legged cricket.

Pl. 26   The first funeral in February 1916. The cortège of Private Wake passing the vicarage on its way down Harefield High Street to St Mary's Churchyard.

Pl. 27   Every coffin was draped with the Union Jack borrowed from Harefield Junior School which now resides in Adelaide High School, South Australia.

Pl. 28  The first ANZAC cemetery, *c.* 1917.

Pl. 29  The post-war ANZAC Military Cemetery, *c.* 1921, laid out by the Imperial War Graves Commission.

Pl. 30   Mourners at an Australian funeral at St Mary's Parish Church were swelled by local residents.

Pl. 31  The Australian Military Cemetery in 1989.

Pl. 32    Close by the present Military Cemetery is the resting place of the Billyard-Leake family, the first to be buried being Mary Deyncourt, aged four years.

Pl. 33    The first entries in the Visitors' Book are those of Lt-Col. Hayward and Ethel Gray. Presented to Charles Billyard-Leake in 1915, it now resides in the Memorial Chapel in St Mary's Church, Harefield.

Pl. 34  Middlesex County Tuberculosis Sanatorium, *c*. 1927. Viewed from the west, reconstructed 'Australian Hospital' huts make up the Children's Pavilion and Special School.

Pl. 35  Some staff of the temporary Middlesex County Tuberculosis Sanatorium, *c*. 1924. The first Medical Superintendent, Dr J. R. MacGregor, has Matron Ferguson on his left.

Pl. 36 'Knobbie' and 'Confidence' pulling the plough.

Pl. 37 Some of Mr Brady's farm staff by the piggeries, north of the kitchen garden.

Pl. 38   Nurses' Home opened in 1932 by the Chairman of Middlesex County's Public Health Committee, Mrs F. M. Baker, JP. Matron's old bungalow, subsequently the 'Cottage Laboratory', lies beyond on the left.

Pl. 39   Harefield County Sanatorium, c. 1935. View to the south west. The Mansion, coach house, Nurses' Home and Matron's bungalow lie beyond the rising west wing of the new main block.

Harefield. Through an 'anonymous donation in excess of £100,000', the Mount Vernon Hospital for Consumption, a Voluntary Hospital on Hampstead Heath, opened the country branch in 1904. The 'open air' method stipulated that patients

> should have continuous exposure to fresh air and free access to sunlight, an abundant supply of well chosen food, regulated rest, graduated exercise on paths of various gradients whatever the weather (only waterproof capes provided – hats or coats being prohibited), carefully selected and controlled work, scrupulous obedience to all hygienic requirements especially dental (because in a large majority this was deplorable), and constant medical supervision.

To its chagrin, MCC did not have its own sanatorium, let alone one providing 'open air' treatment. Even by 1912, they were still having to borrow beds at close-by Clare Hall Hospital in South Mimms. But they had got as far as buying a site in Essex with the intent of building one. Then, thwarted by the Great War, all their plans had to be put in abeyance.

By 1920 Middlesex Council was 'champing at the bit'. The need for County tuberculosis beds had become extremely urgent. However, their Public Health Committee (PHC) was a very aware and progressive body. For various reasons, including financial ones, they advised against proceeding in Essex. Instead, Harefield Park complete with farm and kitchen garden, was for sale for £20,000. Atop the highest point in Middlesex at 290 feet above sea level, it had plenty of space, was potentially self supporting, and had numerous buildings which could be re-used. The PHC considered a temporary sanatorium could be provided quickly and economically there, and give the Council time to consider their next move. Accordingly, the Essex site was sold and the Council bought the Harefield property.

## The Temporary Sanatorium

The deserted 'Australian Hospital' was entirely unsuitable as it stood. The buildings were all crammed together, there were muddy paths and quagmires all over the place, and the House showed considerable wear. If the temporary sanatorium was going to provide the 'open air' treatment, and keep the sexes and age groups of patients apart, radical re-arrangement was necessary.

The plan of the PHC was to pull most of the huts down carefully so that many could be re-used. Putting them together again in appropriate combinations would provide the buildings needed. But the mortuary beyond the kitchen garden was to stay the mortuary and the corrugated iron Chapel beside the courtyard was to remain so, but also accommodate the sewing and linen room. One of the four huts behind the stables was reserved for a Pathology Laboratory. The rest were to be staff houses, as was the Officer's Mess on Park Lane and the Gate Lodge with its wooden extension.

The 'new' institution looked very different. The 'top fields' were empty. Six single-storey wards, or pavilions, were spread out in the virgin 'open rolling parkland' on the other side of the drive. Each had a straight central portion with end sections set at an angle, forming a sort of curve. The gently pitched roof was covered with roofing felt. One end section was plumbed to provide a kitchen next to Sister's office, and the other end was the sanitary annexe. The walls of over-lapping horizontal boards were painted cream and the brown linoleum on the floors matched the doors and window frames. Inside the 'curve', which faced south, a wide verandah was attached – as if to reach out and attract as much sun as possible in Britain's temperate clime.

The Pavilions presented a pleasing aspect for patients who might have to spend many months there. But they certainly kept the men away from the women and the children from the adults. The men's Pavilions, E and F, were at least half a mile from the entrance. A consulting room lay between them and beside the larger F Pavilion, nearer Hill End Road, was their recreation hall. Further south, about half way to the women's C and D Pavilions and recreation hall, were the dining-hall and kitchen. Beyond these, to the south side of the larger D Pavilion, was the even larger B Pavilion reserved for acutely or seriously ill patients. Outside one end was a tiny X-ray Department.

Nearest to the entrance lay A Pavilion for children. The east end, furthest from the gate, was for boys and the west end for girls. A covered way led to a schoolroom. As education could be rudely interrupted by tuberculosis, County Councils devoted much effort to providing Special Schools in sanatoria, and Harefield was no exception.

In the space of a year the MCC obtained for itself 250 tuberculosis beds for men, women and children. In these spartan conditions, with all the buildings now connected only by gravel paths, there is no doubt that the standard structured and ordered treatment of fresh air, rest, good food and graded exercise would exist in full measure! Satisfied, Middlesex TOs selected 11 women to be admitted to C Pavilion on 21 October 1921.

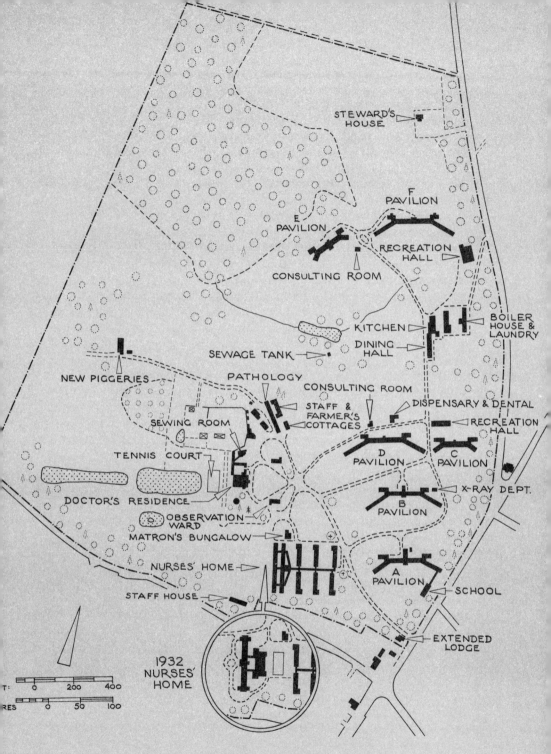

STEWARD'S HOUSE

F PAVILION

E PAVILION

RECREATION HALL

CONSULTING ROOM

KITCHEN

BOILER HOUSE & LAUNDRY

SEWAGE TANK

DINING HALL

NEW PIGGERIES

PATHOLOGY

CONSULTING ROOM

DISPENSARY & DENTAL

STAFF & FARMER'S COTTAGES

RECREATION HALL

SEWING ROOM

TENNIS COURT

D PAVILION

C PAVILION

DOCTOR'S RESIDENCE

X-RAY DEPT.

OBSERVATION WARD

B PAVILION

MATRON'S BUNGALOW

NURSES' HOME

A PAVILION

STAFF HOUSE

SCHOOL

EXTENDED LODGE

1932 NURSES' HOME

T:  0   200   400

RES  0   50   100

Fig. 5   1925: MCC temporary sanatorium

## The Staff

The Mansion, as the House had become known, had been restored almost to its former luxury. The Medical Superintendent's comfortable quarters included a separate dining-room, drawing-room, bedrooms and a 'smoke room' on the middle floor, and a couple more on the top floor. Rooms for three SMOs were created by dividing the enormous front room over the entrance, so that each had its own fireplace, and window complete with window seat. Separation of these from the landing by a wood and canvas partition completed the 'Doctor's Corridor'. Their dining- and sitting-rooms were on the ground floor behind the bay window room, which had been turned into an elegant committee and luncheon room.

Dr John Roy MacGregor, his wife and family settled in on 1 February 1921. The first duty of this quiet, somewhat diffident man was to arrange for the Sanatorium to be suitably staffed, furnished and equipped. In the first few months he was single handed. Matron came in September and the Steward arrived only a week before the patients. One early Mansion resident was Miss Dean, the dispenser. 'Plump and homely', but thought a little 'prickley' by a few, she had only a short walk to work along the path on the northern side of D Pavilion to a small building shared with the Dental Department.

But Mr G. F. Catenach had a longer walk in the other direction. The Sanatorium Steward's wooden house, where he lived with his wife and family, had been put up along Hill End Road beyond the men's Pavilions. From there he wended his way to his office in the Mansion. In the room just inside on the right, it was his job to keep meticulous records of every transaction which took place in running the institution. This ranged from noting the penny postage on letters going out to checking the weight of boxes of fish from Grimsby coming in and whether they had all been beheaded as ordered! Chief Clerk John Henry Marks, an extremely able lay administrator, arrived less than a year later. As activity increased Steward's Clerk G. A. Gurney was appointed.

Others of the 110 staff included a head cook, a laundress and a seamstress, an engineer and a stoker, a lodge keeper, and a driver for the 'White Lady', as the ambulance was known. As deputy driver, and responsible for the Sanatorium's internal switchboard, Frederick William Frost moved into the gatehouse with his family. Other families lived in the old Australian Officers Mess on Park Lane and the huts behind the stables. One of these was Harold R. Winwright, an electrician's mate in the original workforce, who remained for

42 years. His son Richard was born in 'The Bungalow', Harefield Sanatorium. Mr Brady, one of their neighbours, was responsible for the farms and gardens and 'devoted all his time to his work'.

## The Nurses

Between the coach house and gate was the Nurses' Home. It comprised six cubicled huts joined by a corridor at one end of which was an 'H' shaped portion housing dining and recreational rooms. The fifty or so nurses included 11 Sisters, 17 staff nurses and 23 probationers. On the Mansion side of the Home was a wooden bungalow providing separate accommodation for Matron Anne Ferguson. She had sole charge not only of the nurses, but also the domestic staff including the kitchen, laundry, scullery, dining-room and house maids. Those that were resident also lived in the cubicled huts.

Recruiting nurses for the Sanatorium was difficult. Parents did not want their daughters to nurse patients with tuberculosis and the pay was poor. For a 112-hour fortnight a probationer earned about £18 a year, no more than a laundry maid. A Sister might get as much as £120 a year. In confronting the problem, a training course for the Tuberculosis Nursing Certificate was soon established. It had been instituted by the Nursing Committee of the Sanatorium Superintendent's Society, founded in 1920. It was later to become the British Tuberculosis Association (BTA) Certificate.

S. Clarice Woodward, 'Nippy' to her friends because she was 'so small and sprightly', followed Miss Ferguson in 1926. In her navy uniform of silk rep she became a familiar figure as she helped steer the staff through the next period of upheaval. 'In 1929 the County Council decided to replace the existing wooden buildings by permanent structures, and, as a first step, accommodation for nursing and domestic staff was erected.' Before this could be started, the family living in the old Australian Officers' Mess by Park Lane was rehoused in a brand new home near the Steward's house.

For the Nurses' Home the MCC proposed a three-storey building in the shape of an 'H', like the huts it was going to replace. In the end it consisted of only one limb of the 'H', a single-storey central portion of the other, and a grassed garden in between. Outside there was a tennis court. The opening ceremony of the very modern building was carried out, with considerable publicity, by the Chairman of the PHC, Mrs F. M. Baker, JP, 'a most powerful and influential woman'. Appropriately, and in her best dress, Helen, one of Dr MacGregor's daughters, presented the traditional bouquet of flowers. Compared with 'the freezingly cold huts', the accommodation was luxurious and the nurses' lot improved dramatically. Matron moved in too, having been provided with a flat at the Mansion end.

The new Nurses' Home was an enormous boost to morale. Even though it did help recruitment for a while, Miss Woodward knew she could not depend on it, and the publicity surrounding the opening, for long. Difficulties in getting enough nurses persisted and it was certainly fortunate that she had a nucleus of senior nurses devoted to the Sanatorium. All avenues were considered. She knew that, being a tuberculosis sanatorium, a general nurse training course could never be started. But she did succeed in obtaining approval from the General Nursing Council (GNC) for a preliminary training school. Every little helped.

## The Sanatorium Regime

Every sanatorium had to have its observation ward 'entirely separated from the Sanatorium so as to obviate any contact between patients in whom the presence of tuberculosis is still in doubt and established cases of this disease'. The coach house was used for this purpose. These patients had to wait with apprehension for some time while being sorted out, until they found out if they were to be sent home, transferred elsewhere or have to spend months in one of the Pavilions. Meanwhile they could not mix with anyone else.

The Medical Superintendent was all powerful. Having been admitted to one of the Pavilions, the patient had to live by strict Rules. The sexes were rigidly segregated, special care being taken when allocating the 'official walks'. These were of differing length and difficulty marked out by blue, red, green, and yellow arrows in the grounds and woods, including Old Park Wood. If allowed out of bed from 2–4 pm, patients could dress but had to stay on the ward and if up from 2–6 pm they were allowed into the grounds. Excited to have reached this stage, they would 'walk around the gardens and help where they could' on the farm. Then, having progressed to being up from 11 am–6 pm, the village was also within bounds. But this only applied to two from each Pavilion deemed 'sputum negative' because the pathologists could find no tubercle bacilli in their sputum. For a limited period each day, they could go and shop for fellow patients. Everyone had to be in their Pavilions by 10 pm. For serious infringement of the Rules, a patient could be immediately discharged by the Medical Superintendent.

41

Careful attention had to be paid at all times to the use of a sputum pot when expectorating. The blue-enamel 'mickey pots', frequently pretty full, were collected each day by a porter trundling a handcart with two iron bound wheels along the bumpy gravel paths to each Pavilion. An unpleasant but necessary task, the pots were taken to a shed near the boiler house behind the dining hall and kitchen. There, in a steam filled room, the sputum porter emptied them into a copper boiler full of boiling water. No other way was known then to get rid of the infected material. It readily can be understood how members of staff contracted tuberculosis, not least these porters!

The patients themselves were often young, only in their 'teens or twenties, and usually frightened at first. They could be restless and troublesome and very difficult to deal with. After a while they 'found they had time on their hands to read and to think, things they probably never had time for before. They became much more philosophical, especially when they began to feel better in themselves.' And there were always those for whom Rules were made to be broken. E and F Pavilions were fairly remote. The men found they could, and did, sneak out of the side exit up there and drop into The Plough for a little more sustenance in the form of a quick pint – but not when Dr MacGregor was due of course!

## Sanatorium Life

The atmosphere of the sanatorium was unhurried and friendly. Sandy haired Dr MacGregor was anything but frightening. It was his custom to do his ward rounds accompanied by his dog, Peter. Whistling all the way, he let everyone know he was coming and everyone knew which Pavilion he had reached, because Peter would be waiting patiently outside. Sometimes he would be there quite a long time. Sister Graham clearly recalls assisting Dr MacGregor to induce the first artificial pneumothorax in a patient in C Pavilion. Harefield Sanatorium was reputedly one of the first places in Britain where this procedure was used to treat tuberculosis. Deliberate introduction of air into the chest to collapse the lung was gradually used more and more in carefully selected patients.

Increasing numbers became 'sputum negative' and went home. But they had to return fairly regularly for refills of air. To be sure they did come back, a system of fare refund was instituted, adding to Mr Catenach's tasks. Activity in the peaceful place began to increase. Harefield Sanatorium gained a reputation in the eyes of the public: 'It was wonderful to get into Harefield'; 'Harefield was a most important hospital, most forward in the treatment of TB'; 'If you went to Harefield, you would come out.'

There were several rather more pleasant activities to brighten the lives of the patients. An Entertainments Committee arranged whist drives, Saturday entertainments and film shows. Sometimes the patients put on a play themselves. For the monthly outing to some place of interest, a coach would arrive each week at the Pavilion whose turn it was, and collect those selected to go. Then there was Christmas to look forward to when everyone lent a hand in decorating the Pavilions. Christmas dinner in the dining-hall was sure to be delicious.

Sundays were a highlight of the week. First the 'local vicar used to come early Sunday morning and have a service for the patients who could attend . . . [in] . . . a . . . church . . . by the stables.' Then between 2 and 4 pm was visiting time. To come on any other day, a visitor had to get a special pass. Everyone waited eagerly for the first of the coaches, bringing the allotted two visitors per patient, to park on the Rickmansworth Road. Public transport was not good and to own a car was rare. Coming from Chiswick, Edmonton, Harrow, Kilburn and Willesden, the coaches filled the road and became a familiar village Sunday sight. Patients confined to bed would invariably greet those who had braved the distance and the elements on the verandah, even if there was snow on the ground – and on the counterpanes!

## Young Patients

Life for the children was especially difficult. They had been taken away from family and friends and everything familiar to them. Now they had to abide by the Sanatorium Rules. In 1929, specifically to look after the children of A Pavilion, came SMO Kenneth R. Stokes.

Those youngsters who were not confined to bed wore their own clothes, which were sometimes rather ragged and dirty as their parents were often very poor. It did not help either when some disappeared after being sent to the washerwoman.

Other happenings would also break the tedium. Each day they could look forward to a visit from the swans who lived 'on the ponds'. They would 'walk in line . . . to the wards and visit the patients. They were so elegant.' On Guy Fawkes night every 5 November, 'the men patients made a great display for the children. They used to dress up and parade the wards to cheer them. The garden men made a huge bonfire in front of the children's ward.' As soon as it was dark they would 'see it burn and watch the fireworks. It was a great event . . . as in those days fireworks were not cheap. The patients used to collect money for weeks before to buy them.' Then, at Christmas the teachers gave the children a party and Dr MacGregor would dress up as Father Christmas and give them presents.

The Special School started in 1922 with the arrival of headmistress Miriam Wallbank – on April Fool's Day. The Middlesex Education Committee Medical Officer was a member of the Council's Sanatorium Committee, the body responsible for the School. Meeting regularly in the committee room at Harefield with the Superintendent or his deputy and the headmistress, its duty was to see that accommodation was appropriate, staffing and equipment were adequate, and that high standards of teaching were maintained. A member visited the School every week.

The schoolroom was heated by stoves which needed constant stoking with firewood. Occasionally, when no fuel was available or the chimney blocked, it became damp and cold. Nevertheless classes were held there every weekday until precisely 3.55 pm. But the specified rest periods had to be observed. The children soon learnt the ropes and what the sound of the handbell, rung at the beginning and end of each period, meant. The numbers of pupils varied considerably, as did the age range. Over the years there were outbreaks of scarlet fever, chicken pox or measles, some truants and one or two absconders! Running a Special School was not an easy task.

## The Children

The children of resident families were able to live happy and contented lives. But like their A Pavilion counterparts, they had to attend school. For some this meant Harefield Junior School where they learnt about the close ties with Australia from Mr Jeffreys. But whichever school they went to, as they made their way up Park Lane the goats had to be stroked through the fence.

It was after school that the children could all get together – including the MacGregors, despite the eagle eye of their nanny. But they too had their strict rules to obey. Under no circumstances whatsoever could they venture near the patients, adult or child. The Pavilions, the coach house and the 'official walks' were 'out of bounds'. But they were allowed to see the Guy Fawkes bonfire and fireworks outside A Pavilion, and at Christmas Miss Walbank 'used to remember our little group and we mostly received little dolls with hand-made clothes. . . . She was a very kind person and we liked her very much.' Miss Dean too. She always had something for them tucked in the pocket of her white coat – a chocolate bar or a coin.

There were plenty of things to do and places they could go, if they were tolerated. There was tennis to play, tennis parties to go to, held on the courts behind the Mansion, and cricket matches to watch. They could have a quiet sit in the rose garden, watch the ducks and ducklings on the lakes (called moats then) or slide or skate on them when they froze; they could roam freely through the kitchen garden and orchard and pester for fruit from the trees or honey from the beehives; in the woods, parts of which were 'dark and sinister', they could gather primroses or bluebells or violets to take home in the spring, or pick hazelnuts or chestnuts in the autumn; and, exploring Old Park Wood, they could search for the rare protected plant, Cardamine Bulbifera or 'coral root', which grows there.

They could also visit the feathered occupants of the poultry farm, the pigs in the piggeries, or cadge a ride on a hay cart. They loved the four carthorses, especially Confidence and Knobbie whom they were sometimes allowed to ride. A great treat was to go to the village smithy with one of them. There they would watch the blacksmith, known as 'The Major', put on a new shoe. But wherever they went, they made sure they kept clear of the old billy goat 'well known for getting out . . . and . . . butting anyone he met.'

## A Village Within a Village

The Sanatorium was more than self sufficient. The kitchen garden was thriving and the fruit trees continued to bear. There were geese, turkeys and 3000 laying hens, pigs and a few goats. Home-grown salads and vegetables, eggs, chicken, pork and pork products, and even goats milk were provided, and sent to several other MCC hospitals and convalescent homes too. To supply all at Christmas, it took four weeks to pluck and store the turkeys raised for the occasion.

A horse-drawn cart, led by the 'pony boy', would be seen at various times delivering laundry or collecting rubbish and swill from the Pavilions. But every morning without fail it would appear from the farm laden with all manner of produce. Calling at the staff kitchen and main kitchen, and sometimes at the Mansion and Matron's bungalow, the orders were delivered and signed for in the 'vegetable book'. To be found on Matron's account would be seasonal fruit such as grapes, strawberries or peaches as a treat for the patients.

The Sanatorium became a close knit community. As many had lived there almost from the beginning, everyone knew everyone else. It did not matter who or what they were, there was always a moment to stop and pass the time of day. From time-to-time there would be a get together at some sort of function. The Christmas dance in the dining-hall was the highlight of the year for the whole family, including the children, because they were usually fancy dress affairs.

Christmas was also when Miss Dean, who often chatted to any of the gardeners she happened to meet, never forgot them. She gave every one 'half-a-crown' and, if she didn't see them at the time, she always remembered. Another of the characters was Gladys Train, holding sway in the sewing room. For eighteen years she provided the Sanatorium with everything from damask table cloths and uniforms to tea bags of butter muslin and hot water bottle covers of grey flannel. If pillows were needed, she would get the feathers from the poultry farm.

Dr Stokes was 'a keen rugby forward. As a medical student he played for Bart's Hospital and the London Welsh.' Dr MacGregor had been a Scottish international player too. They tried to organise a rugby football team. This didn't succeed but Dr Stokes had much greater success with another of his favourite sporting ploys, cricket. Through his efforts a cricket pitch was laid out on 'the top fields' once more, this time with its own pavilion. There were too few staff at the Sanatorium to get a team together, but he was invariably able to inveigle and 'pressgang' others to play for the Sanatorium, even the village postman.

During the summer, weekly cricket was popular. Mrs Frost was noted for her cricket teas at home matches. Mr Frost, a teetotaller, always drove the van taking the team to away ones. These might be at the Chalfonts Epileptic Colony or the Electricity Works in Uxbridge. He always reckoned to be late back full of fizzy lemonade because of the numerous stops on the homeward journey!

## Harefield Village

To have a tuberculosis sanatorium in their midst had given rise to 'considerable fear and resentment on the part of the local population'. The sight of patients in their beds out on the verandahs in all weathers made them shudder. They dreaded being accosted through the fence by one of the children asking for something from one of the village shops. Children on the 'outside' were adjured 'don't go near, they have consumption'. How different from the 'Australian Hospital' days, and the time afterwards when the 'Long Ramp' was being dismantled. That had produced a bonanza for the curious village children. Five years worth of dropped coins of all sizes were to be found underneath the once busy thoroughfare.

A number of Sanatorium folk made efforts to maintain and foster links with Harefield village. At some time during the Christmas period Mrs MacGregor gave a cocktail party in the Mansion for members of the Sanatorium Committee, Matron and local dignitaries such as the Coxes, who had followed the Stedall's at Harefield Grove.

Dr Stokes would frequent the local pubs of Harefield and Uxbridge, to have a pint and a chat. 'His voice was powerful but musical with just enough Welshness . . . to give it a pleasant lilt.' A 'short, stout and rubicund' man 'with a nice twinkle in his eye', he enjoyed people, and they enjoyed him. 'He had many staunch friends, not chosen because they were intelligent or interesting or useful, but because he found in ordinary good folk a wealth of interest and affection.' His 'willingness to help all good causes, his kindly nature and generosity, his good humour and genial personality endeared him to a host of friends. . . . Although he did not take an active part in public life, he took a lively interest in local affairs.'

It was rare for local people, apart from one, to venture into the Sanatorium precincts. But Primrose Field arrived every day with her horse and cart, to deliver churns of milk from Field's Farm along Hill End Road. But no longer did volunteer helpers come and go. Matron had to directly 'ask a local individual for help in the provision of comforts' for the patients. No longer were convalescent patients to be found waiting outside the 'Cricketers' for the old van with its wooden benches to take them to the station for a shilling, or watch the lamplighter on his familiar round. The Sanatorium became isolated, a forbidden place.

## · 5 ·

# New Plans for Harefield

'IN the first instance it was intended that the institution should only be used temporarily, but the many advantages of having the County Sanatorium so conveniently placed, largely within the border of the County itself, decided the [Middlesex] County Council to retain Harefield as a permanent County Institution.'

## Plans

The MCC was aware that surgery was coming on the scene in the treatment of tuberculosis. There had been competition among the London Counties to establish special centres. Middlesex had chosen to provide one for thoracic surgery at Hillingdon Hospital. Even so, for Harefield Sanatorium, they decided 'to replace the . . . remaining wooden buildings by an entirely new permanent structure, planned on most modern lines' but with 'the important position [of] surgery . . . fully recognised in . . . planning.' Though 'financial conditions throughout the country delayed the scheme of rebuilding until 1933,' the PHC used the time to research the project thoroughly and even go to Switzerland to see the latest sanatoria in Davos.

Finally the plans were ready. The main building was to be 'aeroplane in shape situated on an axial line running from North to South'. Three-hundred-and-seventy-eight patients would be accommodated in two three-storey curved wings, men in one and women in the other. Each wing, 'whilst providing complete separation of the sexes, allows of very adequate supervision by the nursing staff . . . [and] . . . the open, unobstructed balconies . . . obtain the full benefit of a southerly exposure'. The wards would be divided into 'groups for one, two or four patients', have 'centrally placed sanitary annexes, . . . Recreation and Quiet Rooms . . . at the ends . . . , [and] suitably placed Duty Rooms for observation, Consulting Clinics and Ward Kitchens.' Between the wings, 'the Administrative

48

centre . . . contains the Operating Theatre Suite, Treatment Rooms, X-ray Department, Committee Room, Dispensary, Laboratory and General Offices for the Medical Superintendent, Matron and Clerk and Steward.'

In a separate building, 'to the North . . . on the central axial line, the Main Dining Room, Central Kitchen, Steward's Store, Cold Storage, etc.' were to be found. Above was to be the concert hall with a 'recessed Chapel at one end [which] can be used in conjunction with the Hall for Religious Services'. Further north was to be 'the Boiler House block, with . . . Laundry, Main Switch Room, Mortuary, Garages, etc.' The Sanatorium had 'its own water supply and will generate a large part of its electric power on site'. All services, including 'Heating, Steam, . . . Telephones, Fire Alarms [and] Wireless . . . are distributed throughout the Sanatorium . . . by means of . . . underground subways which . . . completely link up the . . . buildings.' Observation Ward lay separately, still further to the north. The new buildings were to be connected with paved roads this time and there would be a new entrance in Hill End Road, just around the corner from the Rickmansworth Road.

But the work of the Sanatorium was not to stop. To prepare the main building site, the patients of B and D Pavilions moved into the vacated nurses' huts and the X-ray and Dental Departments into Matron's old bungalow. Those in C and A Pavilions had to accept being fenced off. Not only did patients have to be protected from the building works but also the workmen had to be protected from them!

## New Buildings for Old

Work started in 1935 and, as the central brick and reinforced concrete block appeared, so did the new A Ward cheek by jowl with the old. The children had to put up with the noise and dust of building going on all around them. Only when they had moved into their new quarters could their fence come down and 'the small school, connected to it by an open covered way' be started.

Having provided the nurses with their new Home only a few years before, and nothing needing to be done for the doctors, attention was paid to new houses for other staff. A Steward's House appeared near the new entrance. It was such a vast improvement, the Catenachs could hardly wait to move. The vacated wooden one, beside that built when the Nurses' Home went up, was replaced with four terraced houses. Two new neighbours proved to be the Chief Engineer of the new Sanatorium and the Clerk of Works.

Conditions for other residents greatly improved too. Another building site appeared in part of the poultry farm. Having their front doors on Park Lane, five houses went up, one standing on its own and the others semi-detached. Now, instead of the old wooden ones behind the stables, there were proper brick homes to go to at the end of the day. Instead of struggling to keep second-hand buildings in habitable order, there were new ones to care for. For the farm workers, it was now a bit further to go to work but worth every step! But the Frosts had to wait a bit. Only when the new wards were ready could both C Pavilion and the fence around it come down. Then the new entrance was provided with its gatelodge. The old entrance was turned into a purely pedestrian back gate and the lodge there pulled down.

At last Harefield County Sanatorium was finished, the astute Council having seen to it that the main block had been paid for entirely by the ratepayers. Patients and staff alike moved into their new quarters and the place was tidied up. The remaining old Pavilions, the nurses' huts used as 'slip wards' during the building, and the old mortuary, were demolished. But the vacated homes behind the stables and the old Australian Chapel were saved. There were plans for these. To complete the project, gardens were 'laid out in a simple manner with large areas of grass lawn, bordered with flowering trees and shrubs'.

On 8 October 1937 the Duke of Gloucester officially opened the 'showpiece' sanatorium of Great Britain. Little did anyone know then that it would be the last hospital to be built in Britain before the second world war.

## Patients' New Surroundings

The ward facilities were little short of palacial for those days. There were bathrooms, showers and a drying room for the patients to use; they didn't have to go outside to see the doctor; and if they needed some treatment or other, now done in the central block, they might have the experience of going in a lift. But the new Sanatorium did not remove the Rules. In fact they could be more readily enforced. It was not nearly so easy to sneak out unobserved. Anyway, The Plough was much further away! There was no more whistling either, and Dr MacGregor now had to leave Peter behind.

Patients confined to bed were tucked away in cubicles and much more isolated from their fellows when inside. But they still spent most of their time on the verandahs and still looked out on green grass and

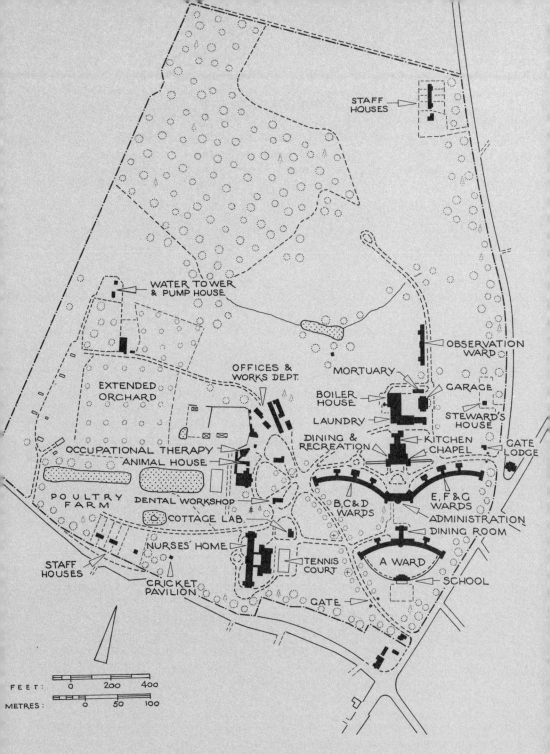

Fig. 6   1938: Harefield County Sanatorium

trees. There was one great boon – wireless. Listening through headphones, the hours could fly by. Using the closed circuit system and one of the channels, an enterprising group of volunteers started Harefield Radio, and patients heard items of local interest. They would not only be told what films were to be shown and when, but also learn of other patients with skills that were available for them to use. There might be a clock or watch mender or someone who could help with family money matters. The wireless changed life for the children too. Now they could listen to Children's Hour, and School was much more interesting with the British Broadcasting Corporation's (BBC) School's broadcasts. It certainly made Mrs Doris Whiting's job easier. She was the new headmistress and, for the next 25 years, was one of the characters around the place. She was quite convinced that 'the indigenous Harefield population were descendents of highwaymen and footpads who operated along the Oxford Road. . . . They could easily escape across the lower marshland up to the village'.

Another boon for the patients was occupational therapy, a new concept. It was for this Department that the old Australian Chapel by the Mansion had been reserved. Mr Sparrow came in October 1938. Within three months he had printing, leatherwork and book-binding workshops ready to use. For those in bed there were baskets to weave and lamps to make. Those who were up and about could still wander about the grounds and help on the farm. But in the spring there were now beautiful pink and white cherry trees to admire as they went. Now too, if they were on their way to the concert hall or Chapel, there were stairs to climb.

If nothing was going on in the hall, the Chapel was a peaceful place. And it had its own stained glass window to contemplate which commemorated the centenary of Florence Nightingale departing with her band of nurses for the Crimea. Regular Sunday services continued with the added enjoyment of hymns being accompanied on the organ. But the hall was frequently busy. Suitably equipped, 'talking pictures' were shown there. Alternatively, on the stage at one end, there might be a rehearsal going on for some entertainment or play.

## New Working Conditions

When the new Sanatorium buildings were complete and officially opened, Miss Woodward bowed out to a new matron. Beatrice Ann Shaw was to hold the nursing helm for 22 years. This 'smart, shortish, slightly plump' woman, 'very pleasant to meet but a disciplinarian with a sharp tongue', soon settled in. Establishing her command over the domestic staff, she acquired a maid for herself who remained with her a long time.

A strong believer in the importance of any and every nurse being trained in the care of tuberculosis, Miss Shaw quickly arranged for student nurses in general training at other hospitals to be seconded to Harefield for a few weeks. Not only did they receive first class training in tuberculosis nursing, but it was Miss Shaw's first contribution to help the Sanatorium's nurse staffing shortage. As Miss Woodward before her, she had the ability to collect together senior nurses and gain their respect. They continued to arrive, come to love Harefield and stay for many years.

The new building meant the end of the leisurely, almost country life that the SMOs had been living. Now it would be different. Whether Dr MacGregor and Dr Stokes liked it or not, various other non-resident specialists, appointed for the comprehensive expert care of all aspects of tuberculosis, would be visiting on a sessional basis. Among them were tuberculosis physician Lionel E. Houghton, general surgeon David Levi, and orthopaedic surgeon Vincent C. Snell.

Instead of the SMOs having to take and develop X-rays themselves, there was now a proper X-ray Department, and staffed into the bargain. Radiologist Dr L. G. Blair and Superintendent Radiographer Mr A. W. Holder had been appointed to run the 'equipment of a type which embodies the latest features . . . for chest radiography, and ample accommodation . . . for the installation of electrical or other forms of treatment which may in the future be found to be advantageous'.

Dr Heathcote, who had held sway over Pathology since 1935, moved the Laboratory from the hut to a new one in the centre block. 'Equipped in a thoroughly practical manner [which] should be fully adequate to meet the demands of the Institution', it soon proved not so. Now with the help of a technician, methods of culturing the tubercle bacillus were being explored. The old hut behind the stables was conveniently placed to be retained as a 'media preparation room'. The medium was blood based and the piggery had a Slaughterhouse Licence, since 1930 at least. An animal house was also needed and space was found in one of the Mansion's courtyard wall rooms.

Another great improvement was that porters no longer had to take the collected sputum pots to the shed. Very concerned about cross infection, the authorities had provided special 'sputum disinfectors . . . so distributed throughout the Sanatorium as to obviate the disadvantages attached to the conveyance of sputum mugs over long distances'.

But the change with greatest implication was the provision of facilities for the latest treatment for pulmonary tuberculosis – surgery. The MCC's thoracic surgeon at Hillingdon Hospital was Libero Fatti. It was on 6 January 1939 that he, and the anaesthetist who worked with him, Dr P. F. Nagle, first used Harefield Sanatorium's 'Operating Theatre unit, with its modern equipment'.

## Threat of War

The second world war was looming. The authorities estimated that 100,000 tons of bombs would be dropped on London in the first 14 days. As 'nearly a quarter of a million casualties might be anticipated . . . in the first week of a new war', arrangements had to be made outside the metropolis for hospital care of London's civilians and air raid casualties. In 1938 Sir Charles Wilson, MC, MD, FRCP, chaired a committee to consider ways and means. A policy of 'dispersal of hospital staffs from the centre to the periphery' was adopted and, because it was conceivable that all the bridges across the River Thames could be destroyed, the problem was addressed in terms of providing facilities north and south of the river.

The Ministry of Health 'had no idea . . . how many hospital beds there were in the country and, given the tangle of voluntary and local government hospitals, . . . had no means of finding out . . . accurately. . . . Estimating that 1–3 million . . . would be needed immediately after the outbreak of war, they strove to provide 300,000' by building 'huts of standard type'. To staff these, a Civil Nursing Reserve was set up and medical personnel enrolled.

London was divided into ten 'triangular zones with apices on the larger London leading hospitals'. These would be evacuated to be available for immediate treatment of casualties. Each Sector was to be run from a peripheral 'base hospital' several miles outside London. Mr Claude H. S. Frankau, CBE, DSO, FRCS, (later Sir Claude) was Director of the London and Home Counties section of the Emergency Medical Service (EMS). In Sector VI, which also contained London's St Mary's Hospital, lay the recently opened Harefield Sanatorium in extensive grounds west of London. Even though in a restricted area because of the proximity of Bomber Command Headquarters near High Wycombe, Fighter Command at Stanmore, and several airfields such as Northolt, a main base for Spitfires and Hurricanes, it presented an attractive site for a base hospital. If huts were added

53

and part of St Mary's evacuated there, Harefield could provide 464 casualty beds and a wide range of expertise.

When the MCC was told that Harefield Sanatorium was to become an EMS base hospital, Mrs Baker was determined that *her* Hospital would not be spoiled. As the wheels started to turn to transform the place once again, she strongly opposed the Ministry plan to put up huts near the kitchens and boiler house. She insisted they be placed where the old Sanatorium's male Pavilions had been, and all necessary services be conveyed up to them.

A National Thoracic Service had been set up too, a task given to Mr Tudor Edwards, MCh, FRCS, surgeon at the London Hospital. He had just started the first Thoracic Surgical Unit at St Mary Abbot's Hospital. More such units were needed to be 'ready to take and treat any civilian in need of thoracic surgery'. Harefield base hospital had modern surgical facilities for pulmonary tuberculosis and was an obvious choice for one of two 'north of the river'.

## Transition

Thirteen prefabricated huts of corrugated iron started to go up where Mrs Baker had decreed. The asbestos-lined buildings had pitched roofs. Each of the ward huts, accommodating 24 beds, was heated by three coke boilers, one in the middle and one at each end. Twelve huts were joined at one end by an open 'covered way', and had reinforced brick and concrete air raid shelters outside the other. The thirteenth lay behind, parallel to Hill End Road. Also in preparation for St Mary's arrival, most of the Sanatorium patients were sent home. Those who had to remain were put on the top floors of the main block.

While all this was going on, large deliveries of everything necessary for general hospital emergency care was arriving, including 11 lbs of gentian violet and half a hundredweight of tannic acid! Miss Dean was very relieved when Mr T. Mapstone appeared on the scene in 1939 to take over responsibility. The Dispensary was soon swamped. Stores had to be tucked away all over the place, including some of the unused rooms in the courtyard walls by the Mansion. For the overflow, marquees were put up where the old nurses' huts had been, but they had a short life being blown down in a gale a few weeks later!

The number of staff rose sharply. The coach house and as many Mansion rooms as possible, apart from the Medical Superintendent's quarters, had been prepared for the additional residents. As for the

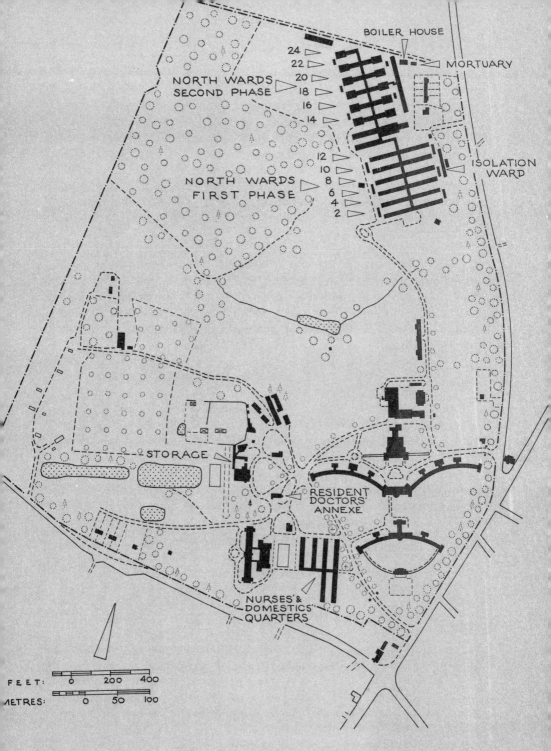

BOILER HOUSE

MORTUARY

ISOLATION WARD

NORTH WARDS SECOND PHASE

24
22
20
18
16
14

NORTH WARDS FIRST PHASE

12
10
8
6
4
2

STORAGE

RESIDENT DOCTORS' ANNEXE

NURSES' & DOMESTICS' QUARTERS

FEET:    0    200    400

METRES:    0    50    100

Fig. 7   1942: EMS Hospital

forty or so medical students of St Mary's Medical School, the billiard-room was turned into a dormitory for twenty. The rest, with the help of the Cox family, were put up at Harefield Grove.

For the influx of nurses, more huts appeared where the ill fated marquees had been. These were spartan. Each was divided into two-bedded cubicles with only a curtain across the entrance for privacy. Heated by gas, they were still very cold. As the authorities put it later: 'Accommodation for . . . nurses was not always adequate. . . . Problems arose out of the blackout, crowded dormitories and dining-rooms, lack of facilities for recreation. . . . [A] word of praise is due to all . . . who transferred . . . to other hospitals . . . adapting . . . to . . . different conditions of work and living, and fitting into new surroundings.'

On 2 September 1939, the day before war was declared, the transfer of St Mary's commenced. Wards on the first two floors of the main block were quickly filled with medical, surgical and a few gynaecological patients. No sooner had they settled in than there was an outbreak of meningococcal meningitis. 'It had a 70–90 per cent mortality', but fortunately the drug sulphanilimide had just come on the scene and not one patient died.

Then news of the National Thoracic Unit arrived. The operating theatre and wards either side of it were needed. Rapid changes in local arrangements were necessary. The St Mary's Unit had to move into the 'north side' huts almost before they were up, and more were now essential. During the course of 1940 a further sixteen appeared beyond the first. These were a different shape, made of concrete with flat roofs and had air-raid shelters between the ends of each two wards. Fourteen were joined by the extended covered way, another went up between them and the staff houses, and the last along the boundary just west of the end hut on the corridor.

## War-time Arrangements

Two young thoracic surgeons had been allocated to Harefield. Thomas Holmes Sellors, employed by the London County Council, came from the East End Sanatorium at Claybury and Vernon C. Thompson, Tudor Edwards' senior registrar, from the London Hospital. With them came anaesthetists with thoracic skills, A. I. Parry Brown, also from the London Hospital, and a South African, Gerry Hoschild. Lionel Houghton associated himself closely with the Unit and, when Wapping Hospital was turned into a casualty Clearing Station, along came Dr John C. Roberts.

The main block provided sanatorium beds in four wards, B and E on the ground floor being reserved for female and male military personnel. F and C Wards were for male and female chest injuries and any non-tuberculous patient in need of thoracic surgery. Children were to be nursed in C Ward's Staff Sick Bay.

All patients except for these, civilian or military, routine or emergency, adult or child, were cared for by St Mary's 'Academic Unit' in the charge of Professor George Pickering (later Sir George). The 'north side', complete with wards, operating theatre, physiotherapy, occupational therapy and outpatient departments, and offices, functioned more or less independently of the rest of the Hospital. But the canteen up there was where all the ancillary and secretarial staff had their meals. The X-ray Department on the first floor of the main building was quite unsuitable in size or site to cope with the vast amount of work expected from the 'north wards'. As soon as the second set of huts were up, a 'north' X-ray Department was established and more help came in the form of three extra radiographers.

Now clinicians of every kind were visiting Harefield on a sessional basis. Many were St Mary's own, including physician Dr E. Idris Jones and surgeon V. Zachary Cope. Some, such as Mr Levi, Mr Snell and radiologist Dr Blair, were Sanatorium staff. A colourful figure was Sir Thomas Dunhill, a pioneer of thyroid gland surgery for which he fashioned the forceps known by his name today. This Australian had reached the rank of Brigadier in the First World War and, much to everyone's delight, would occasionally turn up at Harefield in uniform.

Teaching was 'a bit scrappy at first'. However, Professor Pickering soon organised clinical firms, each with two registrars. He and Dr Idris Jones took charge of general medicine and Mr Levi and Mr Cope, general surgery. The aid of Dr Roberts was enlisted for teaching neurology and tuberculosis in children.

It was certainly useful to have the Sector head regularly on the premises after 1941. Zachary Cope and assistant Mary Scott, 'two people of outstanding ability', took over charge of Sector VI from Sir Charles Wilson. Sir Charles had, for many years, been Dean of St Mary's Medical School and was to become, as Lord Moran, Winston Churchill's medical adviser. He would be seen 'with hat on the back of his head having got off the train and bus, walking slowly home with his greatcoat practically dragging on the ground. . . . He lived nearby and was treated as a VIP at Harefield.'

*Getting Organised*

During the months of the 'phoney war' the Hospital was quiet. The lull was invaluable. Everyone was able to learn about the blackout and how to contend with cars without lights, though there weren't too many going through the village then. They could get used to carrying their tin hat, and gasmask in its cardboard box, literally everywhere they went. Even a nurse making her way in the blackout from the huts to the Nurses' Home to have a bath had to remember. There was time for the teams of male firefighters and runners to be taken through their paces. Mr Holder became expert with a stirrup pump! And the children loved to wave to the female firewatcher at her post on the roof of their Ward. There was time too to fill 30,000 sandbags and pile them around A Ward and the main block. The villagers who helped 'began to feel they were making a contribution again'.

Meanwhile Mr Catenach and Mr Marks had much to do in the office. Steward's Clerk Mr Gurney, Leonard Pearmund the Deputy Steward, and two excellent secretaries, Olive Wintle and Mrs Hand, were towers of strength. Between them they kept track of staff who were called up and were responsible for trying to find replacements. Then there were the Ration Books. They had to be collected and distributed, and provisioning arranged accordingly – a complicated business with patients and staff constantly coming and going. Hard working Mr Brady lost several of his staff to the war but obtained three or four Land Girls to help him extend and increase the productivity of the farm. This was invaluable, but careful track had to be kept of the larger amounts of produce, especially that sent out to the convalescent homes.

Careful note had to be kept too of the precious petrol allocation, stored in a specially excavated 'dugout for inflammable materials' near the boiler house. Petrol was strictly doled out and the amount, to whom and for what purpose, noted. The advent of clothing coupons no doubt cramped Miss Train's style a bit in her sewing room over the laundry. No longer was there a length of cashmere for a dress! Much of her greatly increased work was to be mending and making do. Mr Sparrow too. His Occupational Therapy Department was not in great demand, and so he turned it into an emergency repair shop – including shoes.

Registering admissions became very complicated, apart from tuberculosis patients. Details of these continued to be entered in large leather-bound ledgers in an office just inside the main building.

Every other patient had to be carefully classified, also in ledgers, in an office on the 'north side'. Group A1 were 'civilians with war injuries incurred in the course of Civil Defence duties', and A2, 'Members of the Fighting Services whether injured or sick.' Group B, those 'entitled to treatment as EMS patients, but subject to contribution according to ability to pay', was subdivided into another five categories. 'EMS Forms 105 and MPC [Ministry of Pensions Casualty]' had to be completed for casualties and every EMS hospital had to keep their own civilian casualty record as well.

## Adapting for War

With an office behind the stage of the concert hall and three rooms on the ground floor of the main block to the right of the entrance, Mr Mapstone kept the Pharmacy stocked with most drugs and supplies the Hospital needed. But for certain special X-rays a particular type of radio-opaque liquid, produced only by a French firm, was preferred. Mr Mapstone was equal to the challenge. With great aplomb he managed to get hold of most of the stock in Britain, to avoid running out after the fall of France.

An Almoner's Department was started in 1940. It co-ordinated the Chairman's Fund, set up in 1939 to provide small amounts for 'necessitous patients', and the distribution of 'hospital pay' to servicemen. Also helping with anyone with severe handicap, were charities such as the Red Cross, the National Association for the Prevention of Tuberculosis, The Promotion of Occupational Industries among the Physically Handicapped, and the Invalid Childrens' Aid Association. 'Among efforts . . . to rehabilitate permanently disabled patients have been the loan of a typewriter to a man who had had an amputation of leg, and a course of education arranged, through the Central Council for the Care of Cripples, for a girl aged 19 suffering from diplegia, whose schooling has been neglected.' The activity of the Special School continued with Drs Stokes, Houghton and Roberts very much involved. There were fewer pupils, but education was extended to children and teenagers in the EMS 'north wards'. As they could not mix with the children with tuberculosis in the schoolroom, Mrs Whiting and her teachers went up to them.

Physiotherapy once again played a very important part in wartime rehabilitation. The 'north side' Department, headed by St Mary's Miss Roper until succeeded by Jocelyn Reed in 1942, had five full time masseuses. Treatments were given on the patients' own ward at first. It was a frequent sight to see one or other of them pedalling hard on a bicycle as they made their way to see patients in the 'north' or the main block. Patients then graduated to the 'north' gymnasium and Occupational Therapy Department in the furthest two huts. Advanced classes were also held, as many servicemen would go back to their units after only a short leave. The physiotherapists made good use of the 'north' Occupational Therapy Department, devising an effective way to encourage exercise. It was a popular place because the men could 'make skirt lengths for wives and sweethearts in those coupon troubled days'. By setting up looms appropriately, the legs of orthopaedic patients and the arms of those who had had chest surgery were put through their paces!

Then, in the middle of it all and on the very day she left school, Helen MacGregor had a game of tennis with her father. Afterwards he had some chest pain. In the early afternoon of the next day, 26 July 1940, the 52-year-old Medical Superintendent collapsed and died of a heart attack. Dr MacGregor was buried in the Parish churchyard, joining the many others who had known and loved the Hospital at Harefield Park. This major upset couldn't have happened at a busier time. Who was going to replace him? It would have to be someone who could maintain some sort of order. The MCC chose Harefield's Deputy Superintendent, Kenneth R. Stokes.

## · 6 ·

# War and Peace

OVER the previous eleven years the 39-year-old Medical Director had shown himself to be an able administrator and one who cared greatly for the well being of staff and patients alike. Having settled himself comfortably in the Superintendent's quarters, Dr Stokes took stock. Harefield was now very different from the leisurely sanatorium. But it was still a sanatorium even though it had acquired both a general teaching hospital, ensconced some half mile away from the main block, and a cinderella thoracic unit of unknown potential. There were many more staff too, and the Mansion was full of people. If such an unwieldy place was to become a co-ordinated, smooth running whole, he had a formidable task ahead. Not an easy one in itself, let alone with the added requirements and constraints of war.

## Spectrum of Patients

Initially most of the 'north side' patients were those who lived in London but needed hospital treatment away from the risk of air raids and bombs. The first admission on 24 October 1939 was a transfer from Ealing Hospital, a 6-year-old lad for removal of his tonsils. Nothing much happened after the evacuation of Dunkirk in the middle of 1940, as Harefield was 'north of the river'. Nevertheless all staff holidays were cancelled and the Hospital was ready to receive the few who arrived in the early hours of one morning.

Harefield had its first large influx of patients in the middle of one night in November 1940 – to the Sanatorium. Men of the British Expeditionary Force came from France. They had either contracted tuberculosis, or pre-existing disease had rapidly progressed. There was not enough room on E Ward, and 'north ward' beds had to be used. Unfortunately little could be done in many instances and the mortality was high. A somewhat depressing start, but it did highlight the need for tuberculosis beds to be available for military personnel.

60

During the 'blitz' in 1941, beds quickly filled with casualties. St Mary's Hospital in London gave immediate treatment but as many as possible were sent to Harefield as soon as possible. Each morning a fleet of Green Line buses, 'which could be converted into ambulances in a few hours', arrived. With netting over their windows, they too became a familiar sight in the village. If it was a large convoy, the local residents formed themselves into stretcher parties. If the going got tough, the Red Cross was there providing rest and sustenance at a First Aid Post in the Memorial Hall opposite the Hospital gates. Every patient, many of whom had burns as well as all types of fractures and wounds, was seen on arrival by Mr Levi and Dr Blair. They ordered the first investigations, such as blood tests and X-rays, and these were done before the patients were taken to their allocated ward.

As time went on not only air raid casualties arrived. Even without a military wing staffed by the RAMC, Harefield became one of the hospitals to which soldiers, airmen and torpedoed sailors would come directly from France or North Africa. Sometimes they had received their wounds only a day or so before, having been flown in to Northolt. But others were brought by sea to Southampton and may have been several weeks on their journey home. These men were often very ill, with infected wounds and pressure sores.

Other patients included internees, Polish servicemen, and Free French forces who had a base and convalescent hospital at nearby Gerrards Cross which 'provided some interesting work both general and thoracic'. The Hospital became quite a League of Nations. The different languages caused some difficulties to say the least, but usually an interpreter could be found. Towards the end of the war, many patients were the wounded from the 'small boats', the 'E' boats, and German prisoners-of-war. One of the junior Thoracic Unit staff had been in Britain since the age of five but was German born. When heard talking to German prisoners in fluent German, it created quite a stir!

At its peak, Harefield EMS Hospital had 1200 beds. As the war progressed convalescent servicemen became a familiar sight in the High Street once again, but this time most were British.

## The Greatest Foe

In the absence of antibiotics, the biggest battle that Harefield had to wage was against infection, the scourge of delayed treatment. Survival had greatly improved with the advent of blood transfusion and the vast majority of wounds were contaminated. Unless dead tissue was removed and the damaged area cleaned up quickly, infection invariably set in. Civilian casualties were undoubtedly helped by early first aid but many servicemen were not so fortunate. Infection was frequently well established and taking its toll. The men were often in great need of careful nurturing.

On the 'north side', casualties and 'clean' patients were cared for in separate wards to help prevent cross infection. The very ill were concentrated in one area to ease demands on the nursing staff. In the main block wards of the 'south', isolation of infection was easier in the cubicles, but on the other hand, keeping an eye on the very sick was far more demanding.

Infected wounds have to close from the bottom of the wound, or the inside of an abscess, to the skin surface. While the body healing processes took their time, the wound had to be kept open and well drained so that pus could not re-collect. If a broken bone was involved, particular effort was expended to prevent it becoming infected. If it did, convalescence was prolonged, painful and trying. Often the wound never completely healed and sometimes the bone didn't either. The orthopaedic surgeons employed rigorous aseptic 'no touch' technique in the operating theatre. Even gloved hands never touched the tissues, only sterilised instruments. Things like screws, plates or pins were not used if they could possibly be avoided. Immobilisation was achieved by external splints and plaster casts. When the stream up there in the 'north' turned white, any passer-by knew immediately that a plastering session was going on.

On the Thoracic Unit better ways were sought to manage collections of pus in the chest, or empyema. Methods of ensuring adequate long-term drainage by an indwelling tube were worked out. An innovative way was devised to secure the tube for the long period required for healing, and it became possible to supervise the patient at home. Having found sulphonamides ineffective against the staphylococcus, the commonest type of infection, Dr Roberts tried to sterilise the residual spaces with the chemical, azochloramide T, but found it of little value. Nevertheless, Holmes Sellors observed twenty years later, 'empyema was probably better managed then than now, as there were no antibiotics upon which to put undue reliance'.

The fight against infection was also waged in the Pathology Department. St Mary's bacteriologist Professor Fleming, distinguished morbid anatomist Merlin Pryce and expatriate Czeck Dr Eugene Nassau, an expert on the tubercle bacillus, took possession of the 'Cottage

Laboratory', as Matron's old bungalow had become known. Alexander Fleming devoted most of his time to studying the effects of his discovery on a wide variety of infections, including tuberculosis. It wasn't called penicillin then.

Eugene Nassau did some original work on the laboratory diagnosis of tuberculosis. His efforts resulted in the ability to grow the tubercle bacillus, though it took six weeks or more to appear on the culture medium. He was also searching for a tuberculosis immunity producing substance similar to BCG. Merlin Pryce, being particularly interested in inflammatory conditions of the lung, studied all the different types he could find. Even then he was postulating that viruses could transgress cell walls and enter the tissue fluids.

## The National Thoracic Service Unit

On the Thoracic Unit there was little to do at first. Holmes Sellors had been allocated Sector VII which covered Buckinghamshire, Cambridgeshire, Hertfordshire and Oxfordshire. He continued to visit the LCC hospitals north of the Thames as before, and also went as far as Leicester and Worcester. These traditional links were retained wherever possible. Vernon Thompson kept all his London Hospital affiliations. Soon other parts of London were also included through St Mary's colleagues. It wasn't long before a 'parish' developed and the need for non-tuberculous thoracic surgery demonstrated. Patients with all manner of chest conditions were being admitted and treated and 80 beds kept filled. In the space of a year the Unit became so busy that Drs Houghton and Roberts had to be evicted from their office on C Ward for a time to make room for more beds. During the course of the war the Unit had 1804 admissions and 501 major non-tuberculous thoracic operations were done.

Keeping an eye on the National Thoracic Unit was thoracic surgeon J. E. H. Roberts. He also had invented his own artery forceps. Visiting from time to time, the 'First War Horse . . . breathing fire and brimstone all over the place . . . was most helpful. He came and sat down and talked to you and pulled out of his pocket . . . reels of thread and said, ''Now if you are short of ligature material you use this, don't bother about catgut and things like that.'' '

Not many cases of acute chest injury came Harefield's way. Such wounds were often part of multiple injury and these patients 'were returned to hospitals near their homes'. The plan to send thoracic battle casualties to Park Prewitt near Basingstoke, where parts of several London hospitals had been evacuated, 'often proved impractical. Many . . . arriving from the battlefront were too ill to be transferred.' Anyway, specialist treatment of those that came to Harefield often been arranged in advance. Empyema was by far the commonest condition seen. As soon as these men were feeling better, part of their convalescent regime was an allotted number of circuits of the grass area outside F Ward before breakfast, physiotherapy and a PT class before lunch, then a long walk and more physiotherapy before tea.

Until 1942 Libero Fatti looked after the surgical needs of the Sanatorium patients. He became a familiar figure on the wards with book and card index of the patients under his arm. Then he left owing to ill health. In Middlesex, major operations for tuberculosis had doubled from 411 cases in 1941 to 845 in 1942. The MCC immediately offered contracts to Sellors and Thompson who agreed to continue the work. Wanting to admit the patients and get on with the job, they were constrained by the Council who were 'fighting hard to preserve their perogative' of keeping their TOs in control of these admissions. Being accustomed to take such decisions themselves, this arrangement did not appeal to the surgeons at all. But the system was firmly entrenched at Harefield and they could do little about it.

## Nursing

Miss Shaw, in charge of the greatly increased nursing and domestic workforce, took the wartime changes in her stride. Now having nurses from the Civil Nursing Reserve, the Red Cross, the Order of St John of Jersusalem and various Agencies, and general patients on the 'north side', she jumped at the chance to provide wider nurse training. She expanded the BTA Certificate and arranged for many of the student nurses to learn tuberculosis nursing. Within months she had also set up one of the national two-week Intensive Training Courses for nursing auxiliaries and shortly thereafter a complete General Nurse Training School for State Registration started. Running this was Sister Tutor Ann Dewar, to become a loved and respected figure to many generations of nurses.

The problems that gave rise to greatest concern were the terrible shortage of skilled nurses and the standard of nursing which had to be tolerated. Recruitment had been rapid and many of the new nurses had very limited experience. There was no possibility whatever of getting better – or more. 'The allocation of staff is insufficient . . . to enable special nurses to be allocated for very ill patients.'

In the cubicled wards of the Thoracic Unit the position was

particularly acute. . . . The post operative care of patients who have
. . . major chest operations demands special nursing for 48 hours,
particularly in a ward divided into cubicles. This standard has been
quite impossible to maintain. . . . The tempo of work has been slowed
down from time to time because the staff had been brought to break-
ing point.

Thankfully there was a nucleus of excellent senior nurses including
Sister Creed on A Ward, Sisters Breen, Grant and Kohn on the 'north
side' and Sister Sim on C Ward. Sister Johnson, a Scot 'who feared
no man and certainly no woman', ruled F Ward with a 'kindly rod
of iron'.

Running the operating theatres was also demanding. Sister MacGee
in 'north' hut 12 had four operating tables of which two were often
in action at the same time, but not with a mix of 'clean' and infected
cases of course. To get the work done at really busy times, two nearby
huts were also turned into theatres. Sister Kelly in the single 'south'
theatre coped with tuberculosis as well as infected and clean thoracic
cases, no easy task to organise. It helped that these operations could
invariably be planned, as they were usually not emergencies.

Ward nursing was heavy. 'We had to be strong to take in the
tragedy of it all.' Also, all wounds had to be kept clean and redressed
frequently. Patients with pressure sores, usually over the sacrum or
heels, had to be turned regularly every few hours to keep the body
weight off the affected areas. This caused severely ill patients much
pain and they dreaded it. It was physiotherapist Jocelyn Reed who
produced a method to help them, not to mention the backs of the
hard-pressed nurses. With Dr Stokes' blessing and the help of Mr
Sparrow, a 'total suspension apparatus', or 'balkan beam', was
devised. A bed was converted into a sort of 'four poster' by attaching
uprights to the corners. Cross beams on top and a series of ropes,
pulleys and slings, allowed the patient to be nursed in a hammock.
One nursed thus for six weeks had been so comfortable he was most
reluctant to descend.

## Hospital Perspectives

With an eye to the post-war years the Army Educational Department
ran various training courses for military patients. They worked with
the Hospital radio, which broadcast concerts and things like 'Any
Questions', and put together music educational programmes. One
such was 'the history and music of the Strauss family'. The music
was explained and discussed, and questions encouraged.

But there were others not interested in such things. One was a young Nazi officer prisoner-of-war with a bullet lodged near his heart. Instructed to stay in his single cubicle, he nevertheless gathered other prisoner patients together, harangued them and made them give the Nazi salute. He created considerable unrest and was not at all popular with the Poles, who had been forced to serve in the German army. Told by Holmes Sellors to desist or he would be sent back to his camp without surgery, he zealously continued – and kept his bullet.

On another occasion two Polish Cavalry officers, occupying a cubicle on F Ward, were impatient to get back 'to kill Germans'. They were granted permission to visit their Headquarters in London to make arrangements. On their return, resplendent in uniform complete with classic square topped hats, and bottles of champagne under their arms, they shut themselves in their cubicle and were not seen for a while!

Among the staff there were a number of characters. One who came to live along the 'Doctors' Corridor' in the Mansion was dentist Herbert Smale, just retired from St Mary's. The tall patriarchal figure, having lived in 'an upstairs/downstairs manner with kitchen maid, house maid, parlour maid, in-between maid and cook' in Harley Street, made the transition remarkably well. But he continued one particular habit. He always had an evening preprandial drink of sherry. As he would never drink alone he insisted on being joined by one of the residents with whom he enjoyed conversing. 'Papa' Smale 'with an upstanding military posture, a little white moustache and a croaky voice with which he would enquire . . . about such matters as the distance of the earth from the moon', was a favourite of the students. But they were not always among his, especially one day when he found Knobbie the carthorse in the Mansion tethered to his door knob.

The students, some of whom were coming up for their finals, did not let the place get dull. On one occasion they tied up the corridor doors of all the 'north wards' with bandages and string. They also enjoyed being outnumbered by over 200 nurses – and the Land Girls, especially one called Audrey. They could carefully select whom they took swimming in the nearby gravel pits!

Then there was 'Willie', SMO Dr William N. MacPhail, 'a most cultured gentleman with whom it was a pleasure to converse as he tapped his snuff box'. A Scot who loved his 'vin du pays', he was a leading expert on the bagpipes. Not only were his services sometimes needed to judge Highland Regimental Pipers and Highland bagpipe playing contests, but it was not uncommon to hear the skirl of pipes descending from the Mansion roof. He was a popular figure, his stature being particularly high with the children. He was one of the few who continued to carry his gas mask cardboard box and would open it from time to time only to dole out precious pastries hidden inside. Maybe he was one of those who, 'after two and a half years without gas being used, . . . had become careless; very few habitually carried their respirators (gasmasks), others had failed to maintain them . . . and some had lost them'.

## The War

Air raids didn't interfere with work one bit. The staff invariably ignored the warnings. The only drill they were required to follow was to drop to the floor wherever they were – if they thought the situation demanded it. Many recall the Battle of Britain, when the Germans lost 1733 planes and the British 915. The 'dog fights' were often clearly visible and fascinating to watch. Staff would count the number of British fighters taking off from the nearby airfields and, by counting how many returned, get a fair idea of how things had gone. But one thing mystified them. Occasionally a plane was seen flying high. It later transpired that it was a German Dornier 'silver pencil' on reconnaissance, using the crossbow shape of the Hospital, which pointed nearly north and south, to guide German planes to their targets.

Though only 15 miles from London as the crow flies, no bombs fell on the Hospital itself. The nearest was in some fields about ¼ mile away. Those which did fall nearby were usually from German bombers unloading when being chased by RAF fighters. On one occasion a house in nearby Gerrards Cross received a direct hit. It was then that the Hospital lost two of its staff. Two student physiotherapists from London lived there and, because they felt quite safe 'miles out in the country', did not go down to the shelter that night. It cost them their lives.

Communication with the outside world was a major problem. The Hospital switchboard was an internal one manned by Messrs Frost, James, Howe and Maishman. 'One of the greatest difficulties, especially at the beginning, [was] . . . that all the 'phone calls had to go through the small exchange at the village post office manfully operated by Mary Bishop. . . . She coped as well as possible with . . . the terrific increase in calls . . . and . . . the bombing, but inevitably the long delays caused much frustration.'

With this system there was no way secrecy could be ensured either. Harefield knew that D-Day, the day the Allied invasion of Europe was launched, was imminent because forty-eight hours before, official orders were received over the ordinary telephone. The thoracic surgeons at Harefield were to be part of teams, either going to Normandy with the armed forces, or to other parts of the country. Receiving the verbal message 'get your team together and go up to Leicester now – it's on', Holmes Sellors and Parry Brown duly went, to receive the first two trainloads of casualties. They wanted to take Jocelyn Reed as well, instead of one of the 'PT "rubber men" ', but Kenneth Stokes would not let her go. After about three months there, they returned to Harefield.

'In support of the medical services of the British 2nd Army and the Canadian 1st Army Group, a . . . small provision was made for the surgical treatment of chest casualties. . . . [It] . . . consisted of one fully constituted team (No. 3 Surgical Team for Chest Surgery)' and one other. No. 3 team included Harefield Thoracic Unit's Leigh Collis and chief assistant George Qvist, who crossed to Normandy on 27 June 1944.

## Peace

On 6 June 1944 wave after wave of planes going towards the English Channel, 'with gliders streaming out behind them', passed over the Hospital. Then came the period between 13 June 1944 and 29 March 1945 when south-east Britain was bombarded with unmanned planes, the V-1 'doodle bugs'. The main ordeal lasted about eighty days. Sadly one of the fatalities was a Harefield Sister killed when shopping in London. Finally the V-2 rockets started coming on 8 September 1944 until 27 March 1945. Though the range of these missiles extended as far as a line between the Wash and The River Severn, they did not produce many casualties for Harefield.

Germany capitulated on 7 May 1945. The war had brought about 300,000 combatant casualties and '146,777 civilian casualties of which 60,595 were killed, and 150,832 slightly injured. . . . Figures reveal . . . hospitalised air raid casualties for the whole period of the war were fewer than the number which would have required admission in a single week had the pre-war estimates been realised.'

The EMS was disbanded in 1945 and that autumn St Mary's returned to London. To express appreciation for his smooth and economic running of the wartime hospital, Professor Pickering presented the Medical Director with a set of biographies as a parting gift.

He knew his favourite subject was history both present and past, and that he was an avid reader. Dr Stokes had shown himself to have no axe to grind, to be fair and seen to be so, and

> exceedingly shrewd. He seldom made hasty judgements, and could always be trusted to give the soundest advice. . . . Above all, . . . one of his . . . characteristics was a Puckish sense of humour, . . . he was never unkind, and always succeeded in washing away the weights and worries of the moment.

He had been able to keep the hospital functioning happily, holding the reins lightly but firmly.

In recognition of all that Harefield Hospital had done for the Free French, Dr Stokes was proud to receive the Legion d'Honneur. Thomas Holmes Sellors and Lionel Houghton were awarded the wartime Medaille de Reconnaissance Français. The presentations were made at their Headquarters in Cavendish Square in London. The French Ambassador and about 200 gathered. Those to be honoured brought their wives. After the ceremony the party repaired to a room below to partake of a feast prepared by French military chefs and pastry cooks. Then it happened. The ceiling started to give. All the sumptuous patisserie and beautiful icing on the cakes became coated with plaster. Only the firmly fixed carpet on the floor above prevented the little gilt chairs descending too! No one was hurt and the happy occasion became one that few would ever forget.

Soon after the war, when electricity replaced the gas lighting, Harefield's lamplighter stopped making his rounds in the village. The smithy disappeared in the early 1950s, becoming a garage for the ever increasing number of motor vehicles using the now paved roads. Concern was now being expressed about lorries passing the Hospital at dangerous speeds. Motorbikes were doing the same within the Hospital precincts. One collided with a Hospital car, but fortunately no one was injured. Wartime evacuees had stayed in Harefield, the factories were busy and the Hospital staff houses, to which another six were added in Park Lane in 1947, soon became very much part of the growing village.

## Penicillin

Alexander Fleming (later Sir Alexander) had written first about his drug discovery in the *Journal of Experimental Pathology* in 1929 and again in *The Lancet* in 1943. He was a serious man whose conversation with colleagues in the Mansion usually related to his researches. He was so engrossed in studying the effect of his drug on tuberculosis, as well as the many other types of infective organisms, there was no doubt in anyone's mind what he meant when he entered the doctor's mess for lunch one day muttering 'it doesn't work in tubercle!' John Roberts and Merlin Pryce had also confirmed that even large doses did not save children with fatal tuberculous meningitis.

By 1944 Professor Fleming and Holmes Sellors were carrying out clinical trials using penicillin in non-tuberculous empyema. They also were administering it as an inhalent in saline for other suppurative lung conditions such as lung abscess. 'Fleming was our pathologist and the easiest man to talk to I have ever met. If you had a problem this was an important thing.' Sellors 'took . . . two or three cases of lung abscess to Fleming. . . . He said "sit down" and I did on a stool . . . and he said "What's your story?" ' When he was told of the success of treatment 'he said "Ay it shouldn't but it does." ' As more penicillin became available to Harefield massive doses were successfully tried where smaller doses had failed.

Penicillin's 'exploitation as a chemotherapeutic agent began . . . in 1940 and this stage of its evolution was the work of Florey and Chain . . . at Oxford. . . . Purification of penicillin was partly there by 1942 and, after a visit by Florey to the United States, they undertook the commercial production of it.' Sellors had been in the same year at Oxford with Florey, and the only thoracic surgeon at Oxford before the war. He had also co-operated with Lord and Lady Florey in their early empyema research and clinical trials. 'Fatti had some of the early trial ones with Lady Florey at the Central Middlesex Hospital and that somehow or other spilled over to me at Oxford.'

Penicillin was ready for use about 1943 and a year later American output was on a scale sufficient to allow almost unlimited supplies to be available for British and US servicemen. It became generally available in Britain in 1945. Thus, through Fleming and Holmes Sellors, Harefield contributed much to the study and development of a drug which 'revolutionised many problems of infection'.


*Politics*

The comparatively light demands made on its resources by air raid casualties enabled the EMS to provide adequate medical and surgical care for civilian sick and various categories of war workers, and to fulfil its main function, viz. the treatment and restoration to health of Service casualties from overseas. . . . A great experiment . . . in working a hospital system on a national basis . . . , [its] valuable lessons . . . did much to prepare the medical profession and general public for a State Hospital Service.

After the 1945 General Election campaign a Labour Government replaced the wartime Coalition one. The Socialists had made two promises. Fulfilling one, Aneurin Bevan, the new Minister of Health, presented 'a comprehensive . . . service designed to secure improvement in the physical and mental health of the people of England and Wales and the prevention, diagnosis and treatment of illness' to be funded by Government through general taxation. But he had problems with the medical profession and 'could only get the National Health Service (NHS) off the ground by making concessions to the powerful British Medical Association (BMA) and the Royal Colleges. He undertook that hospital consultants would not be compelled to join the Service full time.' This proviso allowed doctors to continue in private practice.

But 'in launching the Hospital Service of the NHS', the Minister had indeed applied the EMS 'knowledge, experience and practice'. The other two sections, involving General Practitioners and Local Authorities, incorporated the 1942 Beveridge Report recommendations. The NHS Act was promptly passed by Parliament in 1946.

The Hospital Service was to be run by fourteen Regional Boards whose unpaid members were appointed by the Minister. Hospitals were grouped together under Group Management Committees. These were responsible for all matters relating to them: finance including the administration of pay beds, maintaining premises, keeping the hospitals equipped, appointing and dismissing staff except for senior Medical and Dental Staff, and the Special Schools. As co-ordinators of local opinion, they also were the ones to transmit recommendations to their Regional Board.

Between 1946 and the start of the National Health Service on 'the Appointed Day', 5 July 1948, was a difficult period for the non-politically minded and relatively conservative hospital medical staff. They now had to accept medico-politics as a fact of life.

## · 7 ·

# The Changing Scene

THE second election promise related to another big national issue, the control of tuberculosis. The Socialists undertook to arrange for service men and women with the disease to receive treatment in Military Units before being demobbed. Harefield was designated for one of these Units. Thus it was caught in a political cross fire of manoeuvring over tuberculosis and the Health Service. At the end of the war more tuberculosis beds were occupied at Harefield than ever before. Now more had to be found for the Military Unit, and the only way this could be done was to close the 'north side'.

And so Harefield was no longer a general hospital. Nor was it purely a tuberculosis sanatorium because it had a Thoracic Unit treating all kinds of chest disease. There was great uncertainty as to its future. In the new, very different scheme of things, clinicians realised that the only way they would have any say in the shape of that future, was for them to learn quickly how to convey their views effectively to non-medical committees of management.

### Tuberculosis Again

Because 'the withdrawal of general medical and surgical work . . . led to the closing of the general training school for nurses', the imposition of the Military Unit was most unwelcome. But the first six 24-bedded 'north wards' had to be prepared. Staff were being provided: 11 Queen Alexandra Nursing Sisters and, in the charge of a sergeant, 50 newly recruited orderlies.

The Sisters wanted the Unit to be completely separate and self contained with its own Matron. But it could not be. Among the patients were debilitated repatriated British prisoners-of-war. Those terminally ill had to be moved from the open ward to cubicled E Ward. Further, Dr Roberts was physician in charge and Dr MacPhail closely concerned with rehabilitation. Both were much involved with the 'Military Boards held at the hospital . . . to determine how much the patients should have as a pension.' Vernon Thompson was the surgeon, doing cases in the 'south' operating theatre. Last but not least, Beatrice Shaw insisted on remaining in full charge of all nursing staff. That they had to report on duty to her, did not go down well at all with the QA Sisters.

When planning the NHS, the Minister had followed the advice of the Joint Tuberculosis Council on the contentious topic of tuberculosis. This body, consisting mainly of administrative TOs, had suggested that the tuberculosis service be co-ordinated regionally through the network of their Chest Clinics. Equipped to diagnose and direct prevention and cure, the Clinics would be backed up by Health Visitors to follow up patients at home, by specialist hospitals and sanatoria, and designated beds in general hospitals. Soon, in a blaze of publicity, the Minister was opening 'new' tuberculosis wards. These were often not new at all but commandeered from general physicians who greatly resented having their hospital beds taken over in such an arbitrary manner. Also, this apparent dissipation of beds seemed to threaten the existence of sanatoria, and their SMOs felt demoted.

Adding insult to injury, the Minister also accepted the Spens Report which proposed regrading of medical staff. SMOs, despite their clinical responsibilities of patient care and treatment, were regraded only Senior Hospital Medical Officers (SHMO) whereas the adminstrative TOs became consultant chest physicians.

The regrading was unsettling to Harefield. What were felt to be unjust decisions created a degree of local disunity, considerable annoyance and, in some instances anger. Harefield's medical staff were a mixture of SMOs and specialists of the Thoracic Unit and the 'north wards' during the war. They were accustomed to working as equals. Dr Stokes was given consultant status, but the other SMOs were not. Thus Dr McPhail of bagpipe fame, and pathologist Eugene Nassau became SHMOs. Three years of effort and protest corrected Dr Nassau's grading to consultant. 'Papa' Smale, now 70 years of age and providing emergency dental cover in return for board and lodging, became SHDO.

Politically motivated happenings such as these were most unpopular. Thus, at the outset of the NHS a climate of disunity between the politicians and the medical profession prevailed throughout the country.

## Streptomycin trial

Since its discovery in 1944 streptomycin had been used to treat tuberculosis with apparent success in the United States. The Government made it available for the Military Units. However it was not generally available in Britain until shown to be effective by a multicentre trial. The controlled clinical trial was set up in 1947 by the Medical Research Council's Tuberculosis Research Unit and the Tuberculosis Association's Research Committee, of which Lionel Houghton was a member.

Harefield took part but its Military Unit did not. John Roberts however, also in charge of Observation Ward which was taken over for the project, was very much involved. The trial was a complicated business. Forms had to be filled in for every patient in the trial indicating name, age, sex, diagnosis, prognosis, proposed dose, duration of treatment and calculated amount of streptomycin required. These were sent to the Ministry of Health who ordered the drug from Pfizer and Abbott Laboratories in the United States. The rubber-capped glass vials of streptomycin, thought to be unstable, were flown to London Airport and immediately delivered and stored in the refrigerated room by the kitchen.

Then it was Mr Mapstone's turn. Injections had to be made up for use within 24 hours. To prepare the several thousand needed each week, the MCC, who could be most helpful especially if tuberculosis was involved, provided the staff and equipment needed for the essential sterile area set up in one of the huts behind the stables.

The nursing staff found it very trying to have to give each patient his or her injection of the correct dose precisely six hours after the last. Dr Roberts spent much time explaining its importance. He also saw to it that blood samples were taken at the right times for the pathologists to measure drug levels. Clinical progress and radiological changes were also carefully recorded. The drug, though effective, was found to have important, unwanted side effects, such as deafness and other neurological manifestations. One well remembered patient, Connie Ross, suffered these to the full – but lived.

Towards the end of the trial an article on the use of streptomycin appeared in a foreign medical journal. The startled Ministry, having closely monitored the amounts of the drug used, immediately started an inquiry. After numerous questions and much correspondence, it transpired that the author, a medical ex-serviceman who had won the Military Cross in North Africa, had come to Harefield, been involved in the trial, and gone on to Canada. By collecting the residual liquid from several gross of the rubber-capped vials he had provided himself with enough streptomycin to use for the clinical content of his paper.

Before streptomycin became generally available, another medical registrar, because he had been told by someone in a pub that he had been cured of tuberculosis by onion soup and raw onions, thought it worth giving strong smelling allyl sulphide a try. The whole hospital knew which patients were having the treatment, but apart from the odour there were no ill effects or otherwise!

Tuberculosis remained a scourge for more than half the twentieth century. It was not until several anti-tuberculous drugs came on the scene that the seemingly miraculous decline occurred. Though still around today, especially among immigrant populations, the disease is now eminently curable.

## The Thoracic Unit

After the 1945 general election the MCC, previously of marked Conservative political leaning, had strong left wing affiliations. A committee, mostly of Public Health Department administrative TOs who had run the County Chest Clinics before the war, was formed to direct the County Tuberculosis Service. But they also tried to direct the surgical management of the disease. The independently minded part-time thoracic surgeons soon formed an advisory body to advise whether such advice was wanted or not! Several, still based at their teaching hospitals, retreated there.

Fortunately Thomas Holmes Sellors and Vernon Thompson did not, as particular pressure was being brought to bear on Harefield to stop non-tuberculous thoracic surgery. The Thoracic Unit had gained a considerable reputation through its work in the war years. Among the many wartime visitors who had come to see what was going on, had been Tudor Edwards himself and others of all nationalities: Chinese observers, a Free French team of thoracic surgeons, and groups of American Army Surgeons en route to their overseas units. Holmes Sellors recalled 'On one ward round towards the end of the war eight countries . . . were represented.' Forseeing that thoracic surgery would be in the forefront of medical advances in the future, they were determined that the Harefield Unit, a centre of excellence and a much sought after training ground, should continue.

Considerable competition for patients was ensuing because each of the several London teaching hospitals now considered it essential to have their own Thoracic Unit. The Harefield thoracic surgeons, including Kenneth S. Mullard after Libero Fatti finally retired at the end of the war, worked very hard to ensure that patients did not get referred elsewhere. They assiduously visited hospitals and Chest Clinics to which they were contracted and those with whom relationships had been established over the years. Holmes Sellors continued to visit 'his' LCC hospitals north of the river and those in his wartime Sector. Between them, the surgeons ranged from Ashford in Middlesex to Ashford and Benenden in Kent; Amersham and Aylesbury to Arlesey and Ascot; Hemel Hempstead to Hounslow; Rugby to Rickmansworth; St Albans to Slough; Windsor to Watford; and Leicester to London. The resulting busy Thoracic Unit had about 100 beds.

In 1948 Vernon Thompson was appointed to the London Hospital in Tudor Edwards' stead and had to largely withdraw from Harefield. 'Uncle Tom', as Holmes Sellors had become universally known, was appointed to his London training school, the Middlesex Hospital, but remained active at Harefield. Having contacts in the Ministry of Health since the war years, and seeing the trend of things in the Health Service, he also entered the realm of medico-politics. By 1950 he was Chairman of the local Consultants & Specialists Committee and a member of the Central Committee. Being privy to the Ministry thinking on Regional Medical Committees too, he was co-opted onto that of the Region in 1952. It didn't take 'Uncle Tom' long to become active in the British Medical Association (BMA) as well. No wonder he found himself unable to devote so much time to Harefield.

Holmes Sellors was to play a significant part in the formulation of the terms and conditions of service and pay of consultants throughout the country. He also took up the cudgels on one local bone of contention. At the inception of the Health Service, no provision had been made for private beds at Harefield. Because the Minister had been forced to agree to hospital consultants continuing to treat some patients privately, it was not a politically popular topic. As a result of everyone's efforts, Harefield private beds were designated in 1954.

## Local Administration

In July 1947, Harefield, Mount Vernon and Hillingdon Hospitals were relinquished to the administrative aegis of the North West Metropolitan Regional Hospital Board. Also covering Bedfordshire, Hertfordshire and parts of Berkshire and Buckinghamshire, its hospitals were '118 in number with an aggregate of 35,000 beds'. These comprised 'mainly teaching hospitals, . . . voluntary hospitals (many of them general practitioner hospitals of limited size), . . .municipal hospitals in . . . London and Middlesex, . . . mental and tuberculosis hospitals, . . . special hospitals for fever patients managed by . . . Joint Authorities and . . . public assistance institutions with hospital facilities.' Board Chairman was Mr Fred Messer, JP, MP, previously Vice-chairman of the MCC's PHC with Mrs Baker.

Harefield and Mount Vernon Hospitals became part of the Hare-field and Northwood Hospital Group. Offices were found in one of the EMS huts at Mount Vernon Hospital by relocating two remaining RAMC personnel. Mr F. A. Watson was appointed Group Secretary, 'the principal administrative officer and generally responsible for the administration of the Hospitals in the group and for the work of the Committee'. He remained so for 16 years.

The first Management Committee meeting, chaired by Mr Messer, was held on 15 June 1948. Mrs Ena Daniels, 'a smart, able and quick woman, a Socialist very averse to spending, but a talented organiser who always got her own way', was appointed Chairman a year later. Numerous sub-committees appeared: Finance and General Purposes, Staff, Land, Works & Supplies, Building & Maintenance, Medical Advisory and Nursing Group Committees, Co-ordinating, House and Medical Staff Committees for each hospital and the Joint Governing Body, Harefield Special School. Mrs Daniels and Mr Watson were to become familiar figures at Harefield.

In the new system, changes had to be achieved through one or more of these committees, and the Management Committee itself. Each resolution put forward by one committee usually had to pass through at least one other before going to the Management Committee. Decision making became slow and cumbersome. Few of the committees, other than the medical ones, had a medical member. Senior hospital staff soon realised that to get something done, the more of these committees that could be brought into agreement on a matter, the more effect it had. When disagreeing with administrators on what they considered important issues, clinicians found they had to be very vocal and work hard to make their views known.

'The presence of a Medical Director at Harefield . . . [with] . . . a humane and unbiased approach was a godsend.' Dr Stokes continued to exert his influence from his office at the left end of the central portion of the main block, beyond the admissions office.

## What Sort of Hospital?

The greatest concern of the Harefield staff was the immediate future of the Hospital. If it was to survive in the new Health Service, what shape should it take and what part should the Thoracic Unit play? There were a few, liking the old sanatorium regime and resistant to change, who felt it should revert to a tuberculosis sanatorium and the Thoracic Unit just cater for this disease. Many wanted it to become a general hospital again because of the problems of recruiting nurses. However, those on the Thoracic Unit, confident of a bright and innovative future for the Hospital, believed that Harefield should become a specialist hospital with expanded facilities for treating medical and surgical chest disease. But Hillingdon Hospital, with its older MCC Unit, was equally determined to become the principal Thoracic Unit in the Region. Consequently a coolness arose between the two institutions.

While the senior medical staff were making up their minds what should happen, the Management Committee, advised by the sub-committees, was forming its own views. A great deal of discussion, documentation and compromise ensued, which was sometimes acrimonious. 'It is with surprise and regret that . . . members of the senior medical staff read in the local press that far reaching changes are being made at Harefield. . . . It is further regretted that such decisions have been reached without consultation with the medical staff.'

There was no doubt that one of Harefield's major problems was shortage of nurses. Dr Stokes knew what he wanted. He produced figures in support of the view that Harefield should become a general hospital again, the 'north wards' reopening when the Military Unit closed in November 1949, and a Nursing School re-established. The majority of his colleagues agreed but those of the Thoracic Unit, including Holmes Sellors and Lionel Houghton, did not. In a Minority Report to the Management Committee, they strongly opposed these proposals stating that the figures related 'to a period during and immediately after the war and have little bearing on the present situation' and doubted that 'general beds and a . . . Training School would assist . . . recruitment of nurses'.

They felt Harefield should become a specialist chest hospital with some 700 beds for all conditions of the chest, including tuberculosis. 'The fundamental question is whether every person who wishes to care for the sick should be obliged to train for . . . State Registration, . . . or whether it is legitimate to recruit persons specifically for

78

the desperate needs of the tuberculous sick. . . . Those who are in nursing authority should have a real enthusiasm for this special branch of work and should not regard it as of secondary importance to general nursing.' They considered a better and less expensive option was to combine with the School of Nursing at Mount Vernon, not agreeing that 'the administrative difficulties would be insuperable'.

But the majority view prevailed. By 1950 the 'north side' had reopened and was soon in full swing again, with general medicine and surgery, outpatient, surgical and X-ray facilities. Sanatorium bed numbers had been restored too by using the wards vacated by the Military Unit. Because the Thoracic Unit was overflowing its beds in the main block, a few of these were allocated for minor surgical procedures for tuberculosis. A state of peaceful co-existence was gradually established.

## Nursing Problems

Well aware that the internal conflict revolved around how to recruit nurses to a hospital that treated tuberculosis, Matron 'Beattie' Shaw was among those convinced that the only real solution was for Harefield to become a complete nurse training school once again. She considered secondment for tuberculosis training, though of value, did not entirely solve the difficulties. She worked hard with Sister Tutor Ann Dewar to re-establish the School quickly. Even before the decision to reopen the 'north wards' was taken, the nurses library had been enlarged and School accommodation prepared in 'north' huts 19 and 20. A little further along, huts 22, 23 and 24 were being gradually converted, each into residential quarters for twelve nurses.

The General Nursing Council (GNC), the body responsible for nurse education, had agreed that a general training school could start if four wards for male and female medical and surgery were available, and arrangements made for gynaecology and paediatric experience for female students and genito-urinary for male students. Miss Shaw was very content when, in October 1950, provisional approval was given for a two-year BTA Certificate course combined with a further two years for State Registration (SRN). The course for BTA was started at once and for SRN the next year. Students were offered either combined training or tuberculosis training only.

Meanwhile Miss Shaw would not lower her standards of recruitment. All Sisters had to be SRNs. As employment of Agency nurses had been banned, she sought SRNs whether or not they wanted postgraduate training in tuberculosis nursing, those with the BTA Certificate alone, assistant nurses and ward orderlies. Study Days were arranged and Mount Vernon, Middlesex and Charing Cross Hospitals and King Edward VII Hospital, Ealing, sent nurses for tuberculosis experience, each receiving 5/- a week travel allowance. To encourage girls into tuberculosis nursing, there was an official £20 grant.

But nurses were not immune to the disease and 'when a break in service was attributable to illness contracted whilst nursing, the period of absence should be reckonable for incremental purposes'. Their salaries would be paid in full while on sick leave. Tuberculosis was particularly prevalent in Eire. General hospitals there, as elsewhere, would terminate the employment of any nurse who developed the disease. Dr Stokes would take them in, treat them and they frequently then joined the staff.

With a great awareness of the problems for these nurses, a band of enthusiastic and enterprising ones started The Harefield Fund. It was set up 'to provide those small comforts which make life easier during illness but which are so often beyond the pocket of the nurse'. In 1949 the Fund was handed over to the National Association for the Prevention of Tuberculosis (NAPT), having had its blessing and help at the start. Under the auspices of the Chest and Heart Association, The Harefield Fund continued for a while to help nurses suffering from all manner of chest complaints.

Some thought Matron not very easy going nor a very attractive person. But this little woman was much respected, above all by 'her nurses' whom she always carefully looked after. In recognition of her efforts and achievements at Harefield, and in the nursing world, Beatrice Shaw received the OBE for Services to Nursing in the 1955 New Year Honours.

## The 'Where-with-all'

'Everyone hoped . . . the NHS would take . . . the responsibility for hospitals from Local Authorities in 1948 . . . [and] . . . all . . . be provided.' But, with the Treasury now holding the purse strings, money was rigidly controlled. A Resource Allocation Working Party (RAWP) was set up to devise a formula by which distribution of money to the Regions in England and Wales could be achieved fairly. In the London Regions, the RAWP formula was a constant bone of contention. Considered to have been wealthy in comparison with other parts of the country, they were allocated minimum funds and

# The Changing Scene

invariably came off badly each time the formula was changed.

It was the duty of each Regional Board to see that their allocation was used to the advantage of all. Harefield, the last hospital to be built before the war, found itself low on the list of the North West Metropolitan Board's funding priorities:

> In London and Middlesex particularly, enlightened County Councils had gone a long way to achieving a hospital 'service' for their areas. There had been . . . building and replacement, a process tragically interrupted by the Second World War. . . . When it is realised that Middlesex County . . . spent more on hospital capital in the year before the war than the Board was allocated for the whole of the Region in any year, the extent of . . . pressures and . . . difficulties of priority selection can be understood.

A nationwide, regularly recurring problem in balancing the books was meeting any national pay award to hospital employees. Only the proportion in line with inflation was centrally funded. The balance had to be found locally.

To add to Harefield's difficulties, the Board could not, or would not, acknowledge how expensive thoracic surgery was. It did not accept that Harefield & Northwood Group might be underfunded, and found their consistent overspending untenable. With pressure being brought to bear on it, the Management Committee had to find extra money to stretch its meagre allocation. Some came from selling the silver extracted from thousands of old X-ray films stored at Harefield! Measures to contain expenditure were also imposed, and very unpopular. First came reduced spending on maintenance of the fabric of the buildings. Next came a freeze on the number of nurses allowed to be recruited, and spending on drugs and medical and surgical equipment.

There was no spare money at all for amenities for patients or staff. 'Miss Shaw . . . realised the need for continuing contribution from volunteers and approached . . . local ladies, asking them to set up a League of Friends. . . . This they did in 1953. . . . Affiliated to the National League of Hospital Friends, . . . [it] is an association of local people who, by personal service, raise money and help . . . patients, staff and relatives who live and work in the hospital.' So says Mrs Kverndal, previously Joy Cox, an early member of Harefield's League of Friends.

The 'Friends' took on management of the Hospital shop, previously run by the patients themselves, extended it to a trolley shop which went around the wards, initiated a library service, and a sale of work in 1956 realised £600. In collaboration with the authorities, they

81

helped finance things such as headphones and 2 channel wiring for the 'north wards' radio system, billiard tables for F and E Wards and the 'north wards' recreation hut, and television sets for A Ward and the Mansion. From 'very small beginnings', the 'Friends' quickly came to play an important part in the Hospital's life.

## Decisions

After the traumas over the short term future, there remained concern about the longer term. The Regional Board accepted that Harefield's Thoracic Unit 'has made notable contributions to the surgical treatment of tuberculosis . . . especially . . . pulmonary resection . . . [and] provided essential medical services for patients with non-tuberculous chest diseases'. It agreed that restricting the work 'would adversely affect . . . the treatment of patients with pulmonary tuberculosis, . . . the training of . . . consultants in chest diseases . . . [and] . . . student and postgraduate nurses [and] the recruitment of medical & nursing staffs'.

Then the Tuberculosis and Diseases of the Chest Group of the BMA, mostly former TOs now consultants, produced a report in 1951, stating 'the inadequacy of . . . present provision for . . . diagnosis, treatment and after care of tuberculosis . . . is a national scandal which can no longer be viewed with complacency. . . . The overall bed need for pulmonary tuberculosis is one bed per 1000 population. . . . The nursing of pulmonary tuberculosis . . . should be included in the training of student nurses.'

Harefield's Medical Committee, this time of one voice, responded quickly with a critique of the report. It was now experienced enough to know that Region could not ignore such a document, nor any official response to it. It also knew the Board had a waiting list for tuberculosis beds, and was surveying its chest hospitals and clinics to evolve a plan for treating both tuberculous and non-tuberculous chest disease. If Harefield was to influence things at all, this was a golden opportunity for views to be aired not only to the Management Committee but also directly to the Regional Board.

But it was another five years before the results of the survey appeared and the Board's deliberations and decisions made known. Incorporating some of Harefield's views, various aspects remained controversial. 'Harefield Hospital could not continue solely as a chest hospital, owing to the extremely difficult nursing situation. [It] should combine its nurse training with another', have closer association with Mount Vernon 'and the two hospitals . . . share a common specialist staff'. They also commented: 'There should be some rearrangement of hospitals in the area so as to include a general hospital such as Hillingdon . . . [as] . . . the present Group of hospitals is too highly specialised.'

The Medical Committee response, via the Management Committee, was again prompt. It accepted that Harefield would continue treatment of tuberculosis 'in the permanent buildings and the balance of the hutted accommodation' not needed for general work. It greatly welcomed the Board's statement that '100 beds should continue' to be used for 'surgery of non-tuberculous lung conditions and surgery of the heart', and Harefield 'become the Regional Thoracic Surgical Unit' (TSU). It did not agree 'that Harefield . . . has a diminishing part to play in the medical treatment of pulmonary tuberculosis. . . . There are more known cases . . . than ever before.' The suggestion to separate medical and surgical treatment of tuberculosis into general hospitals and special centres was deplored as a retrograde step.

## More Plans

In a joint appointment with the Middlesex Hospital, cardiologist Walter Somerville started coming to Harefield for 2 half-days a week in 1953. The Cardiology Department rapidly got going under his guidance. Initially the Hospital photographer doubled as ECG technician but soon the work was such that the load had to be shared. A cardiology technician arrived in 1958. Using the Middlesex Hospital facilities for invasive cardiac investigation in the first few years, these methods soon became routine at Harefield, and pacing the heart was planned. Techniques of bypassing the heart and lungs, to enable the surgeon to reach the heart more readily, were being developed and a cardiac perfusion unit was also planned. Parallel with this came the need for one of the first Intensive Therapy Units (ITU) in the country. In view of the developing non-tuberculous medical chest unit, a Respiratory Physiology Laboratory was also envisaged.

There was no doubt that Harefield's TSU was arousing great interest, speculation and activity. Most at Harefield greeted the Regional Board's plans for expansion of the Unit enthusiastically. The rest expressed a certain reluctance and others in the Hospital Group, considerable concern because of the financial implications.

Maintaining large centres were considered essential for nurse training and recruitment, medical training, research and major advances in treatment. It had become patently obvious that further radiological and operating facilities and more expertise in cardiac assessment were essential if the Harefield Unit was to keep abreast of developments. Theatre suite and X-ray unit improvements 'are long overdue. . . . The X-ray Department . . . should . . . [include] . . . an Angio Cardiographic Unit . . . available to . . . General Hospitals within a ten mile radius.' Cardiology and chest medicine required 'expensive apparatus and daily collaboration with a Thoracic Surgical Unit . . . [and] . . . techniques . . . required skilled technicians'.

The local idea to site the new X-ray Department and operating theatre suite in a two-storey block in front of the Hospital joining it to the concert hall, was countered by the Board with 'a single storey building between the main block and the children's unit, providing accommodation for two operating theatres with the ancillary accommodation and a 3-set X-ray department'. There was little alternative but to accept these proposals. The project was part of Regional capital planning and the required £250,000 was being provided. Also, when presented with an estimate of £20,000 for improved cardiac investigative facilities, the Board felt that an adequate Unit could be set up for half that sum, and that this amount 'they might be able to find'. Obstruction from those of the old sanatorium days who wished to retain the status quo, and bureaucracy at Board and Ministry levels, had delayed the desperately needed improvements long enough. Further discussion would only do the same.

# · 8 ·

# 'Dr Stokes' Hospital'

THE Medical Director, 'an original thinker . . . who could not be bound by formal doctrines or conventional ideas,' had to accustom himself not only to the Health Service but also to the plans being laid by the Regional Board for the future of the Hospital and its busy Thoracic Unit. Dr Stokes devoted his administrative skills to the day-to-day running of 'his' Hospital. 'His particular care was for the health and welfare of the staff as well as patients, and the cares and anxieties of both were of the utmost importance to him. . . . Thus it was over the years he earned the title of ''Father'' and always thoroughly lived up to it.'

## The Administration

Whether Dr Stokes liked it or not, there were now committees to be contended with. The House Committee was 'concerned with the comfort and well-being of patient and staff generally' as well. Two or three members visited various non-clinical parts of the Hospital regularly, including the farm. They recommended improvements, alterations, or redecoration. It wasn't long before they realised some of the effects of the siting of the EMS Hospital huts on the 'north side': the high cost of heating and provision of utilities to them, including the essential road lighting; the necessity for at least two electric ambulances for transport within the hospital; the problem of getting stores up there from the Pharmacy, and patients from there to the main theatre on time; and numerous other little inconveniences and difficulties.

It was the brief of the Co-ordinating Committee to arrange for the decisions, finally arrived at by the Management Committee, to be carried out. Two early ones, with which Dr Stokes had agreed, were very controversial. The crows inhabiting the trees around the Hospital were considered such a nuisance that they were shot, and the ancient cedar of Lebanon beside the Mansion was cut down. It was believed that the magnificent, majestic tree had fallen victim to some dreadful arboreal disease but, when the deed was done, this was found not to be the case.

In the postwar days of food rationing, 'catering arrangements had been a source of anxiety for many years due partly to rationing restrictions and to low staff rationing allowances. . . . Permission [was granted] to the Medical Director and Matron to exceed [the] ration allowance'. They had been the ones to adjust things accordingly and deal with friction over the Tea Account. Harefield staff had to pay for this issue of tea, sugar and milk from the stores to the various Departments, unlike the other hospitals. But now there was a Catering Officer responsible for things like this.

To help keep things running as smoothly as possible, John Henry Marks, 'a humourless man', Mr Gurney and Leonard Pearmund were still around. When Mr Catenach died in 1947, the latter moved into the Steward's house naming it Cathard, the first four letters of his wife's name and the last three of his. But, appointed Supplies Officer in the new Health Service, within the year he had to move again. Administrative Assistant F. J. Green now occupied an office at the front of the main building beyond Medical Records, to the left of the entrance opposite the admissions office.

Still there too was secretary Mrs Hand. Mrs Howard had replaced Olive Wintle at the end of the war. 'These two knew everything that was going on in the Hospital and a good gossip with them was quite fun.' Manning the telephone switchboard was the old team with the addition of Len Batt, and Mr Owen after Tom Maishman left in 1958. Now with external lines, calls no longer had to pass through the switchboard in the village!

## Old Hands

Harold Winwright was Head Porter and no longer living in the Hospital grounds. Son Richard, having started in the Stores Department had gone to war as a Marine commando, and returned to continue the tradition of 'a Winwright on the payroll' for the next 40 years. Kathie, the Frosts' daughter and Mr Mark's niece, worked for Dr Houghton from 1943, going with him to the various other hospitals where tuberculosis patients went to convalesce. Then she moved away for a time. Returning in 1957 as Mrs Norvall and Dr Stokes' secretary, she remained until 1963. Pam Durand had joined the ranks in 1944, was Dr Roberts' secretary and stayed for 42 years. To become old hands, the medical secretariat now included Miss Lang and Miss

Bedford on the Thoracic Unit and Miss Stevenson on the general side. Maureen Eggleton was another. Starting as a junior in the General Office in 1954, she was soon a medical secretary, going to the developing Cardiology Department.

'Papa' Smale, having 'been abandoned in Harefield . . . always had very good sherry' and a picture of Lady Hamilton on the wall of his room. Pathologist Gwyneth Hamilton, replacing Dr Heathcote, lived in the Mansion for a while in 1953. She was one he would 'waylay . . . to help him imbibe. He could never remember my name . . . and the boys told him to look at his picture. . . . That is how I came to be known as Lady Hamilton.' One day 'the dear old man' was found dead in his bath.

Merlin Pryce, a delightful Welshman, was a jovial, kind and helpful person, affectionately known as the Welsh Wizard. 'In spite of his maniacal laugh [he] was a very able morbid anatomist [and] always pretended he didn't know when shown a [pathology] slide, but always did'. However he was very absent minded. After leaving Harefield in 1954, he and his wife were to be guests of honour at a dinner in London. He remembered to get the car out and drive there, but forgot all about his poor wife!

Until SHMO Dr McPhail retired in 1955, he continued to exhibit his prowess on the bagpipes. It became his habit to parade on the grass by the main block wards 'long before dawn on a summer's morning' and unaccustomed new patients would be startled awake!

Harefield's 'Village-cum-Hospital' cricket teams were something . . . never to be forgotten.' Kenneth Stokes was a 'demonic fast bowler' and Dr Blair, a batsman. Before the cricket season Dr Stokes would lose weight to get into his 'slim' set of clothes. With Mr Snell and Dr Roberts, and Dr Harry R. C. Riches from 1952, matches were played almost every weekend on the field behind the Nurses' Home. Away fixtures were played too, 'cricket petrol' allowing in the continuing days of rationing. In one away match at the Epileptic Colony in Denham, John Roberts was knocked out while batting, astounding the home team. They were the ones who were supposed to lose consciousness during a match, not the visitors.

## The Farm

The Land Girls had gone. Mr Brady continued to run the farm and the enlarged orchard, a commercial venture, with his faithful band of workers. Described as tireless and one who 'devoted all his time to his work at the Hospital, and . . . well known for his cheerful disposition', he was also responsible for the upkeep of the grounds. By 1949 he had 'finished a bowling green for the staff, and . . . also constructed another for patients'. The cricket pitch was 'claimed to be one of the best in the district' and there was the 4 acre football, or hockey, field beyond the 'north wards'. He saw to it that the flower beds screening the 'north side' shelters and coal bunkers, and the rose bed outside the front door, were tended and spring bulbs planted in the lawn between the main block and A Ward. His death in 1950 at the early age of 53 was untimely.

Eggs, poultry and produce continued to be sold to the other hospitals in the Group at market price, but due to overproduction on a few occasions, crops had to be ploughed in. By 1951 the faithful horses had been sold, the farm workers having to transfer their loyalty to a new tractor. Then 'in 1953 they had fowl pest . . . [and] . . . killed off all the chickens. We had chicken nearly every lunch and dinner for weeks.' Two years later the geese had gone but more hens were purchased. 'The Steward bought two boars and 500 day-old chicks for the farm.' Breeding from about a dozen pigs, the piggery continued to provide pork for eating – and blood for Pathology's media preparation. Sometimes either a pig or several hens were stolen. An alsatian guard dog was acquired, but it didn't stay long after getting into one of the chicken houses and killing 64 birds! The egg supply fell dramatically for a time.

As the years passed and the faithful retainers aged, they were not replaced. Gradually the work became too much for the remaining eight men. By 1960 the farm was no longer paying for itself and it was sold as a small holding to the MCC. But while the farm was there, so there were rats. The wartime sandbagging had done little except provide havens for the Hospital's wild cat population to increase. They, and regular visits from the pest control officer, did a pretty good job keeping things under control. But with the farm so close, some rats took up residence in the Mansion. They could be heard behind the skirting but were not seen very often. On an epic occasion one had the audacity to appear in one of the toilets, making a 'slow moving' resident move very quickly indeed.

The old huts behind the stables, underneath which many of the feral cats had found new homes, were still in use. They now housed painter and carpenter workshops, quarters for male nurses, domestics and porters, the Records Office for a time, and Dr Roberts had his office there. Having come to the end of their useful lives, all but one were deliberately burnt down in 1959.

## The Wards

The first six 'north wards' were brought into use again in the 1950s when the Regional Board required Harefield to accommodate Chest Clinic physicians such as Peter W. Roe. Also, tuberculosis patients of Dr Nicol Roe were transferred there from Hillingdon Hospital. These wards were reminiscent 'of the barrack-rooms I had known in the army. The beds were arranged in the same regular, regimental lines. . . . Doors . . . were nearly always kept open [but] . . . the interior was clean and tidy and could have looked spartan but for . . . patients' belongings: coloured dressing gowns . . . across . . . ends of beds, locker tops . . . crammed with fruit, magazines, plants . . . the bane of the tidy-minded staff.'

Most of these patients had pulmonary tuberculosis but one of the best-known patients of those days spent five years on her back with tuberculosis of the spine. Sheila Potter was admired by all for her 'sunny disposition and sense of fun'. Children with tuberculous bone and joint infection were taken in as well, A Ward now having 66 beds and a nursery for six infants. As they could be in for several years, parents could stay at the hospital for a number of months too. Mothers slept on D Ward and Dads usually on Ward 6. Dr Roberts cared for the children and the patients of Observation and B Wards. Dr Stokes supervised the tuberculosis patients in the 'north' and Dr Houghton, those in the other chest wards.

The decline in tuberculosis in the 1950 decade was dramatic. At first, even with streptomycin, six months in hospital 'was a short time by the standards then prevailing'. Surgery was still required in selected cases because the organism soon became resistant to the drug. But tuberculosis no longer evoked such fear. When paraminosalicylic acid, (PAS) and the third drug to attack the tubercle bacillus, izoniazid, became available, resistance could be avoided. Using the three drugs together over periods of 18–24 months, cures were being achieved. Fewer patients were in hospital for shorter periods. As the need for these beds fell, they became part of the planned 'unit for non-tuberculous chest disease'.

In the second group of huts on the 'north side', next to the School of Nursing, were wards for general medicine in the charge of Dr E. Idris Jones. Mr David Levi, who 'prided himself on using very little blood', continued his skilled work as general surgeon in the 'north' operating theatre. Vincent Snell remained as orthopaedic surgeon. Very much part of the management of bronchiectasis, ENT care continued. There was a visiting ophthalmologist too, and by 1957 gynaecologist Mr C. A. Simmonds was coming regularly from Mount Vernon Hospital on a sessional basis.

The busy Thoracic Unit staff, the 'sort of interlopers', continued their work from F and C Wards. There were still beds for tuberculosis in Wards D and G most of which, for a time, were filled with patients requiring major surgery. 'After leaving Harefield to rest at home I returned to face the possibility of an operation, and this time I was found a bed in the main block.' These patients, as well as those who had had lesser surgery in the 'north' operating theatre, were cared for by the Unit.

## The Departments

Eugene Nassau and Dr Hamilton moved the Pathology Laboratory from the ground floor of the main block to the old Isolation Ward on the 'north side', biochemistry sharing 'north ward' 11 with the Out-patient Department. The 'Cottage Laboratory', having been given a new roof, remained part of the fragmented Pathology Department until it was demolished about 1960. The media making room remained in the old hut behind the stables, and the animal house in the rooms of the courtyard wall. Museum specimens, made by Mr McDonald when he wasn't taking photographs or ECGs, were housed in the Mansion itself.

For a while Pharmacy expanded into the room vacated by Pathology. Mr Mapstone still had some of the wartime half hundredweight of tannic acid in his stores, but persuaded the Ministry of Health to sell back the remaining stock to the original suppliers. But the original 11 lbs of gentian violet was still being used thirty-three years later! He continued to cope with the same old problems of getting supplies to the 'north wards' on time and efficient supplying of other hospitals and convalescent homes, such as Grims Dyke in Harrow Weald and Margate's Royal Sea Bathing Hospital.

The X-ray Department of 1951 had a considerable reputation for the high quality of its chest radiography. Despite its extremely cramped quarters, superb lateral chest films and bronchograms, which clearly outlined all sections of the lung, continued to be produced. A new processing unit had at last replaced the original one of 1937. It occupied part of the one X-ray room in the main block, the X-ray office being tucked in one corner. However, they did have a developing room, a screening room and a reporting room. But other special X-rays had to be done in two cubicles of C Ward. In these conditions nearly 11,000 chest X-rays and 1000 other types of investigations were done that year. Now joined by Dr MacPherson, Dr Blair also continued his lively clinical interest in the patients who came to the Department, and was frequently seen on the wards. But, with Dr Somerville, he greatly looked forward to the forthcoming new Department.

Screening was a much used radiological technique for checking the progress of sanatorium patients. Apparatus allowed physicians to view the X-ray of their patients' chests without having a film taken. Regular sessions were held in the Department and also in a room on the 'north side'. In 1951 there were some 9000. Maybe 'singing hymns in a cheerful, if unmelodious manner', Dr Stokes 'would preside in the dark, wearing a lead waistcoat, [as] one by one we chested the X-ray machine. . . . He was a lovable bear of a man, greatly loved by staff and patients alike.'

After the war the Hospital's Occupational Therapy Department went from strength to strength. Soon each ward had its own representative who liaised with the Department to the benefit of all. Annual exhibitions of patients' work were held. The exhibits would range from 'lovely toys made from felt in every imaginable colour, to fine etchings and water-colour paintings. . . . In the woodwork section . . . of Mr J. Day, . . . were some splendid examples of carpentry, including cupboards and tables [and] the astonishing surprise of a beautiful . . . table . . . in polished beechwood by a woman worker. . . . The embroidery, leatherwork and domestic articles were of a very high standard'.

## Patient Perspectives

There were still the Rules for sanatorium patients wherever they were. For those on bed rest in the 'north', windows 'were too high . . . to see much of the outside world. You could see the sky, . . . only a small square, . . . [but] . . . it was . . . my whole sky for the time being.' In the main block, however, the big windows of the cubicles 'afforded a splendid view of the grounds, and chaffinches used to peck for breadcrumbs on the balcony'. But fresh air was still the thing for chest patients. One 'night . . . the fog was in . . . the wards. . . . The patients could hardly see but the doors were still left open.'

Dr Stokes sometimes relaxed the Rules a bit. One patient, being allowed a typewriter, 'greatly appreciated the unusual concession that had been granted . . . in the wooden huts'. Occupational therapy was invaluable. 'Some patients were making lampshades . . . [and] . . . lamps . . . from bottles. . . . Doctors were regarded as a fruitful source of supply . . . and the only known source for . . . a prized . . .

Benedictine or Drambuie. Making cane baskets was another popular pastime. Some . . . made a small business out of it, selling them to visitors. . . . Others were not so gifted. . . . The ward Sister, stopping at one bed during her . . . tour, gazed at the shapeless . . . object, . . . tucked in a rebellious blanket, and inquired: ''And what's that we've got on the stocks today?'' . . . Supposed to be a shopping-basket, . . . Sister made some encouraging comment, [and] . . . passed on.'

'The patients were quite a cross-section of society. . . . Their helpfulness . . . towards each other was heartwarming. . . . Although some . . . were very ill, . . . the atmosphere was cheerful, with a restrained amount of leg-pulling.' There were also moments of spontaneous fun. Though 'the nurses were nearly always female,' there were a few male nurses on the men's wards. 'I . . . recall two . . . for their . . . acrobatic skills which they would show off to the patients when Authority wasn't about. . . . They were Poles, . . . very smart in their light grey, buttoned-up uniforms. They would perform . . . amazing acts of tumbling down the centre of the ward, . . . somersaults, leaping on to each other's shoulders and then spinning like catherine wheels. . . . The delighted patients applauded from their beds. . . . One wonders what Matron would have said had she . . . confronted this miniature circus in one of her wards.'

Before the days of television, entertainments still included radio via the hospital earphones, and film shows once a week in the 'north wards' and twice on Wednesdays in the concert hall. Entertainers still came, there being several pianos around, and sanatorium patients were still taken on monthly coach trips into the country. Visitors could come on Sunday and Wednesday afternoons. Children were not allowed in and had to wait for the grown-ups in the Memorial Hall, used as a waiting room for a time.

Catering for the patients' social needs now was Head Almoner Mrs Eva D. Robinson, and Mrs Toovey from 1958. For spiritual matters, Dennis G. A. Connor, Vicar of St Mary's Parish Church from 1952, was Hospital Chaplain. Regular services continued in the Chapel, where a stained-glass Memorial Window commemorating Queen Elizabeth's 1953 Coronation had replaced the old. For a time Northwood College of Divinity students held services on B Ward and Ward 6 on the 'north side' for those who could not go to the Hospital Chapel. Roman Catholic services were not held, but Father Long would visit every other Monday afternoon without fail. 'He would chat and joke. . . . One's faith or religion never came into the conversation. . . . Everyone was treated with the same compassion and concern.'

## 'Cogs and Wheels'

The 1950s were the days when the Hospital laundry laundered and starched nurses' uniforms, aprons and caps. Trained staff had five weeks annual leave and student nurses, four. An 88 hour fortnight was worked in 'split shifts'. They would start at 7 am, then off duty for three hours, either morning or afternoon, finishing at 8 pm. Other days would be worked through until 4.30 pm or 6 pm. Nurses had one day off a week, and, when on night duty, worked five nights with two off each week.

Each ward in the main block was staffed by two Sisters, a senior and a junior, most had two staff nurses and some, a few students. At night though, there were only two nurses on each 'north' ward and sometimes 'it could be a little scary'. Each had to go in turns to the dining-room for meals, only being relieved by an orderly if the ward position demanded it. Nurses had their main meals cooked and served in the Nurses' Home. In the dining-room adjacent to the Sisters' sitting-room, they sat at separate tables according to seniority.

Meals were prepared in the Mansion for the doctors who would come across to eat. Kosher food was also prepared there for a time, when Danewood ceased to be a Jewish sanatorium and these patients came to Harefield. The other patients' meals were prepared in the main kitchen where there was a Head Cook and Kitchen Superintendent. Everyone else used the 'north side' canteen with its adjacent kitchens. When these closed in 1958, half the dining-room below the concert hall was used by staff and half by patients who were up and about.

Though there were no longer medical students, Dr Idris Jones continued to hold a weekly teaching ward round. From 7 to 9 every Monday evening, it was a popular event which attracted 'all the registrars, some consultants and lots of general practitioners' and those doctors preparing for higher examinations. The first hour was devoted to patients. The second was spent in the Out-patient Department with slides and pathology specimens relating to patients just seen, or of previous rounds. It invariably finished before 10 pm so that all could adjourn to the Kings Arms for a pint!

If any of the staff wanted to see television in the early days, they had to obtain the key from the Nurses' Home and go to a room in one of the nearby huts where the one set was. It was through the League of Friends that television sets ultimately appeared for both the Nurses' Home and the Mansion. But, especially in the days before television, staff as well as patients took advantage of the Occupational Therapy

Department's knitting, rugmaking, sewing, leather and woodwork classes. In 1954 Mr Sparrow was joined by Art Therapist John Barsby. His wife, Polly, joined the TSU secretarial staff a few years later. 'John Barsby . . . had much success in this field and brought to light much hidden talent. In the 21 years he was there, 'several . . . doctors produced very creditable pictures'.

The Sports and Social Club opened a new social centre and recreation hall behind the gatehouse in 1952. There were tennis courts by the Nurses' Home, behind the Mansion and at the outside residence, the Lodge, a nine hole miniature golf course, a bowling green and a hockey or football pitch depending on how the ground beyond the 'north wards' was prepared. Another Entertainments Committee also came into existence to arrange social functions and organise trips to places of interest.

## Special Events

On Monday, 13 November 1950, Harefield had its third visit from a member of the Royal family. 'All . . . staff [were to go] about their usual duties so . . . Princess Margaret should see the Hospital under normal working conditions' during her two hour tour of 'north' and 'south'. Signing the Hospital Visitors' Book, the Princess made her way to A Ward but while she did so, the secretarial staff were locked in their offices so the proceedings would go without a hitch!

Some patients were to be busy with occupational therapy tasks because 'it was thought she would stop at the occasional bed'. Those 'who were given a clean top sheet and pillowcase knew that they were the "chosen" ones'. One was 'attempting to dabble in watercolours [with] . . . an art therapist at my bedside giving . . . advice on a picture I'd already completed.' But 'the day preceding, . . . "up" patients were sent off to the woods to look for foliage. . . . Patients who had not been allowed out of bed for weeks were up doing flower arrangements. . . . Even when the . . . HRH had arrived, our cleaner was . . . polishing. . . . The floors and windows sparkled.'

Having seen a physiotherapy class, the Nurses Training School and the operating theatres where tuberculous surgery was done, the tour ended with tea in the Nurses' Home. Three years later, Harefield celebrated the Coronation of the visitor's sister with a tea party for the children, a luncheon for adult patients, a nurses' dance, and coach trips to see the London decorations.

At Christmas time every patient who could, went home. The wards were still decorated for the benefit of those remaining, and

Colour Pl. 1  Stained-glass window in the Hospital Chapel commemorating the 1953 Coronation of Queen Elizabeth II.

Colour Pl. 2   The Australian Military Cemetery in 1988. A child remembering.

Colour Pl. 3   Cherry blossom time. Looking from the Mansion towards the hospital, *c.* 1965.

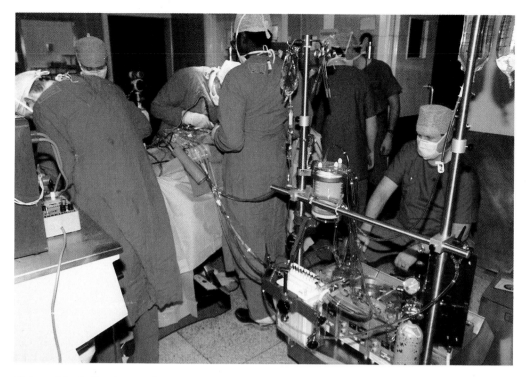

Colour Pl. 4 In the cardiac operating theatre. Getting ready to 'go on bypass'.

Colour Pl. 5 The Duchess of York and Professor Magdi Yacoub at the 1988 opening of the Eric Morecambe Department of Cardiology and ITU. The boy received the heart of the girl when she was given new heart and lungs – the Domino Procedure. The man on the bicycle has also had a new heart.

Colour Pl. 6 The Princess Royal and Dr Radley-Smith at the official opening of the Play-drome and Children's Ward extension in July 1989. In another Domino Procedure the blonde girl, having had a heart/lung transplant, gave her heart to the Japanese child playing at the table.

the staff. Few nurses took holidays at Christmas then as the results of their Finals often arrived with their Christmas cards. Usually there were more happy faces to be found than glum ones. The nurses, having been practising for eight weeks or so, led the Christmas Eve carol singing around the wards in which everyone joined. 'The carol singing by members of the nursing staff who toured the . . . wards . . . was a very affecting scene.' The party given for the children was highlighted by some sort of entertainment – a conjurer or piper. Santa Claus came too giving presents, but one year a near tragedy occurred. The doctor playing the part managed to set himself alight while warming his back by the open fire in the hall of the Mansion. He was very ill for quite a long time.

For the staff, the Friends 'gave a dance, . . . quite a social occasion [as they] managed to get a film star or . . . personality along. Afterwards there was . . . a "do" in Matron's flat.' Three other dances were also held: 'for ward maids, electricians and "lowly" staff with *lemonade,* for nurses, junior lab. and pharmacy staff with *cider,* and for . . . [senior staff] . . . with *wine*'! Also 'the Management Committee held a dinner dance . . . which was "anglo-classique", complete with small orchestra dominated by a saxophone. All the ladies in "frou-frou" and pearls, their perception of the latest fashion. The whole thing could have been written by Noel Coward.' A Christmas lunch was served for senior staff 'in the Sister's dining-room. It usually turned into a very "boozy" affair . . . [which] . . . was why it moved to dinnertime'!

Last but by no means least was the Pantomime. Producer and director invariably appeared from amongst the staff, and the cast from keen members of any or all the Departments. Everyone joined together for the occasion. Content and costumes, sometimes on loan from the West End theatres of London, always displayed hidden talent, great enterprise and wit. Usually based on a traditional story or pantomime theme, skits parodying senior members of staff were invariably included. There was always a remarkable, choreographed line of chorus girls too. Among these were several Sisters and Ward Clerks who would never miss the event if they could possibly help it. The Pantomime usually ran to packed houses of staff, relatives and local residents for four nights, with a matinée for patients who were up and about. After the last night performance, the whole cast celebrated its success (or otherwise!) at a party in the Mansion which invariably went on into the early hours of the next morning.

## Ambience

The close knit community, in which every member of staff became involved, returned. The senior staff always took part in all the Hospital events and activities and had time, and the inclination, to advise, answer questions, help and assist a newcomer in any way they could. It mattered not who you were or who they were. On one well remembered occasion Mr Levi, 'a wonderful surgeon with a very sharp wit who gave great parties at his home in Hampstead', came back from holiday in Switzerland when a Harefield nurse required an operation. Taking shorthand from the imposing Dr Blair in the X-ray Department could be an intimidating experience for a young secretary, but Mr Holder was on hand and willing to help. It was not uncommon for some tired person, slouching as they walked, to hear Miss Thacker call out 'stand up straight now'. The response was almost a reflex!

The Medical Director 'was outwardly bumbling and untidy, but one word from him would get things done.' He expected the grounds to be kept immaculate. Litter was an anathema to him. It was his practice to interview all new office staff. Though kind he was strict, demanding certain standards. He expected punctuality and not to see low necklines or open-toed sandals! Among his rules was that every message for a ward had to be handed directly to the Sister in charge. Delivery of daily operating lists, to the 'north wards' especially, was very time consuming, particularly if a subsequent change had to be made.

But Dr Stokes also had the 'human touch'. He and Beatrice Shaw cared for the staff in almost every way even acting 'in loco parentis' if need be when a nurse married. He would give them away and she would arrange receptions at one of the nurses' residences in the village.

With 'his love of cricket on . . . Village cricket grounds', Dr Stokes found time to go and watch matches when he was not playing. He would set off, carefully inserting himself into what he called the 'plucky little bus', a 'somewhat decrepit and bird spattered' Ruby Austin 7, HMV 198, which he shared with Beatrice Shaw. He invariably shared his evening meal with her also. For convenience, stepping stones were laid across the grass between her door at the end of the Nurses' Home and the drive to the front of the Mansion. They are there to this day. Perhaps it is no wonder that rooms in the coach house, which continued to be used as a doctor's residence, were in great demand by the younger members of the mess to 'get away from the Old Man'!

## 'Dr Stokes Hospital'

On 9 July 1959, Dr Stokes was 'seen in his car in the village. He had been in his office and . . . had called on his quarters in the Mansion.' The charismatic 'father of Harefield Hospital' and 'beloved friend and adviser to many . . . in the Hospital which he served so well . . . [and] . . . in the village . . . was suddenly taken by a heart attack from which he did not recover.' He was 58 years old. 'At the time the sky turned dark, the wind blew and it seemed almost like a sign from above. Lionel Houghton remarked . . . "a fitting epitaph for Kenneth".' The Hospital would never be the same. 'It will go on, of course, but one feels as a different place. . . .'

## · 9 ·

# Clinical Considerations

B EFORE the war the clinical concern at Harefield had been tuberculosis. But none foresaw that its surgical facilities and wartime National Thoracic Service Unit would widen the Hospital's horizons quite so dramatically.

Thoracic surgeons were a new breed: courageous, skilled and innovative, with inexhaustible energy and enthusiasm. Thomas Holmes Sellors and Vernon C. Thompson were two such men. These pioneers grasped the opportunity to create a unique Unit where frontiers of thoracic surgery, by then a specialty in its own right, were advanced quickly and effectively. When antibiotics appeared, no urging was needed for them to push boundaries yet further. By developing safer techniques and new methods, more diseases were encompassed. The Harefield Thoracic Unit became firmly entrenched and much sought after by those aspiring to a career in thoracic surgery.

### Surgery and Tuberculosis

Early tuberculous surgery largely consisted of draining an empyema, or lung abscesses by the method named after its inventor, Monaldi, or else producing conditions in which the affected, cavitated lung was made to collapse and rest. The lung and the cavity would collapse if air was deliberately introduced into the pleural cavity to take up space. Having less room in which to move, the lung was made to rest. As the air would gradually absorb, refills of this artificial pneumothorax were necessary until healing occurred. In difficult cases, where the lung was stuck to the chest wall, division of pleural adhesions was necessary to establish a pneumothorax. This was done under direct vision through a thoracoscope, a fine tube with lens and light attached, put into the chest through a small incision. These collapse procedures and air refills were carried out in rooms opposite the X-ray Department and operating theatre in Harefield's main block.

Another way to get a similar effect was to put the diaphragm, the sheet of muscle separating chest from abdomen, temporarily out of action by crushing its nerve through a small incision in the neck on the affected side. The paralysed hemi-diaphragm remained raised for some time afterwards, decreasing the space available to the lung. Phrenic crush was done under local anaesthesia, and often on out-patients. 'The record was ten in an hour. The patient came into theatre, jumped on the stool and onto the table, put their heads in the right position and you did the right thing.' It became a popular treatment in great demand. Also used was pneumoperitoneum. Air was intro-duced as often as necessary into the abdomen, instead of the pleura. The diaphragm was pushed up instead of being paralysed. In use for some years, these were the sort of procedures done in the 1950s in the 'north wards' theatre, from 'north ward' beds designated for sur-gical use to relieve pressure on those of the Thoracic Unit.

Tuberculous tension lung cavities, caused when air could get into the cavity but not out, were more difficult to deal with. To collapse the cavity, one technique tried in the very early days was to limit lung movement by lying the patient in a plaster cast on the affected side and then wait for things to happen. It was soon abandoned as it didn't work and was no joke for the victim! Then surgeons devised extrapleural pneumothorax. After opening the chest, and carefully keeping away from the lung and the cavity, an artificial tissue plane was developed outside the pleural layer. The lung and the cavity could then collapse and, again, air refills kept it that way.

## War Work

As well as the constant battle with infection, the St Mary's Academic Unit had pursued various avenues of research. One was the study of malignant hypertension, a condition of high blood pressure which had no obvious cause. Very difficult to control, methods of medical and surgical treatment were tried with varying degrees of success. They included cutting nerves which control most of the smaller blood vessels, the operation of sympathectomy, and induction of a high temperature with TAB.

Professor Pickering and Holmes Sellors managed to identify tuberculosis as an important factor in the causation of constrictive pericarditis. The pericardium, the tissue layer in which the heart is located, becomes very thick and fibrous. Gradually the heart is squeezed so much that it cannot function properly. The only heart operations Sellors hazarded occasionally was the removal of this thickened pericardium, and the closure of a persistent patent congenital ductus arteriosus by ligation.

Also on the Thoracic Unit, the surgeons were thoroughly familiar with the 'well established methods of drainage of empyema and of lung abscess'. But they realised that infection followed more readily when the lung was partly collapsed and there was a space in the chest. They found empyema could be prevented if a lung was persuaded to fully expand quickly. They studied the blood in traumatic haemothorax. Finding it remained liquid because it contained little fibrin, they discovered that early and complete aspiration avoided the secondary fluid collection, which clotted owing to a high fibrin content. The incidence of delayed lung expansion and infection fell dramatically.

As radiological assessment improved, making full use of lateral chest films, intrathoracic bullets or shrapnel could be located precisely. The surgeons were then able, through a small incision, to extract them quickly from seven or eight cases in one 4-hour operating session. With much encouragement and good physiotherapy these servicemen were fit for duty in about two months. As many as possible had to be returned to their units as quickly as possible. As a carrot, Holmes Sellors would have them use a flow meter to measure their vital capacity. Only if able to blow out a certain minimum volume of air could the soldier or sailor get a pass to go into the village.

Vernon Thompson proceeded with his chief interest, surgery of the oesophagus. He was the first British surgeon to carry out, at Harefield on 29 October 1941, a successful oesophageal resection with restoration of intestinal continuity at the same operation. It was at Harefield that Holmes Sellors carried out probably the first successful removal of a sequestration, a congenital lung malformation with an abnormal arterial blood supply. 'We had several of these.'

In the Pathology Department, while Professor Fleming was working away on his antibacterial discovery, Merlin Pryce and Eugene Nassau developed a method of culturing the tubercle bacillus using a blood medium. The technique became widely used in Great Britain. Merlin Pryce, much interested in lung pathology, perfected a method of making cast models of the bronchial tree. He also analysed the histological changes in a number of lung conditions, including cysts and tension cysts.

All this clinical experience was discussed at postgraduate courses, meetings and symposia arranged at the Hospital, sometimes with overseas Medical Service colleagues. Classic original papers appeared including one on suppurative pneumonitis from Merlin Pryce and radiologist Dr Blair. Dr Blair also wrote a detailed radiological, pathological and surgical study of sequestration: 'Broncho-pulmonary dissociation due to abnormal artery, visualised by bronchography.'

## Welding the Team

During the war the thoracic surgeons usually slept at the Hospital the night after operating. In those early days they considered that, with an experienced anaesthetist ensuring the necessary support, the actual surgery encompassed only half or less of the dangers. Every thoracic operation interfered with life support systems and post-operative care was every bit as important. As they frequently had to be absent, and anaesthetists had many other commitments too, each surgeon worked closely with a less peripatetic physician. They were willing to cover the post-operative period with the ever changing Unit junior staff. Holmes Sellors worked with Lionel Houghton and Vernon Thompson with John Roberts. The system worked well. Patients were soon being referred for treatment and the reputation of the Thoracic Unit grew quickly. It was the start of the closely knit team which developed, and has continued over the years.

Many aspiring thoracic surgeons came, trained and went. One post-war trainee was E. F. Chin, known as Paul. Of Latvian ancestry and brought up in Australia, he had been a Royal Naval Medical Officer, seen active service on destroyers in the Mediterranean and the notorious 'Murmansk Run', and was one of the few doctors to be awarded the Distinguished Service Cross. 'More British than the British', he had come to Harefield to get his Fellowship of the Royal College of Surgeons. Deciding he liked the specialty, he stayed to train. He was ready to take on some of the workload with Mr Mullard when 'Uncle Tom' and Vernon Thompson became busier elsewhere. But, having 'made a great impression on Harefield', this 'austere, kind man and neat with his hands', was to set out on his own to start a Thoracic Unit at Southampton.

Many became consultants in Britain: Birmingham, Blackpool, Bradford, Bristol, Canterbury, Cardiff, Edinburgh, Exeter, Hull, Liverpool, London, Manchester, Newcastle, Nottingham, Oxford, Plymouth, Portsmouth, and Southampton. Others took their experience and knowledge all over the world: to Australia, Canada, Egypt, Ethiopia, Greece, India, Italy, Malta, New Zealand, Nigeria, Pakistan, South

Africa, Spain and the United States. There are few places where the name Harefield is not recognised.

From the very beginning the importance of the team, which included nurses, physiotherapists and laboratory staff, was a fact of life on the Thoracic Unit. Even at times of acute nursing shortage, standards in the operating theatre and in ward care remained very high. The same applied to physiotherapy. 'Dear Uncle Tom was so encouraging to work for as he much appreciated the results we could get with persistent detailed work. He was always interested and keen for us to try out any new techniques that might be helpful and had many suggestions himself. . . . The team spirit that prevailed throughout the Hospital was a great attraction to staff.' So felt Jocelyn Reed.

Miss W. T. Thacker felt likewise when she followed on as Superintendent Physiotherapist in 1946. Her reputation, having a book on chest physiotherapy published which became a veritable handbook, was such that not only did she go abroad to teach, to Ceylon in 1952, but students and trained physiotherapists from all over the world came to Harefield. Though linked administratively with Mount Vernon Hospital from 1948, the needs of all Harefield patients, 'north' and 'south', general and thoracic, were met by Miss Thacker and her staff until 1974.

## Safer Surgery

Examination of the bronchial tree and oesophagus, only used with any frequency for diagnostic purposes a few years before the war, became routine. Either bronchoscopy or oesophagoscopy, or both, were considered essential preliminaries to operating on the chest, and done using rigid tubular instruments. Local anaesthesia was used for bronchospcopy, but as time passed general anaesthesia was employed, and much preferred by the patients. To be done quickly and safely, the examinations needed to be carried out in the operating theatre with staff accustomed to the procedures.

In its early days, thoracic surgery was dangerous. Aided by blood transfusion and improving anaesthetic techniques, successful removal of a lung by the standard snare and mass ligation of its root had also became possible just before the war. Most lung conditions needing operation then resulted from infection. Bronchiectasis, a relatively common sequel to infection in lung which had collapsed, was one such condition. Characterised by copious infected bronchial secretions, removal of the affected part had a high mortality and morbidity. Invariably the cut bronchus did not heal properly. The consequent leak, or broncho-pleural fistula, produced an empyema and up to two years in hospital. The Harefield surgeons advanced rapidly to resection by dissection in these cases.

Holmes Sellors and Parry Brown, the senior thoracic anaesthetist, developed and popularised in Great Britain Overholt's method of operating with the patient in the 'face down' or prone position. It protected the 'good' lung by achieving constant dependent drainage of infected secretions through the simple, single bore anaesthetic tube in the trachea. It also allowed the busy surgeon to sit down while he worked.

Taking another approach, Vernon Thompson developed his 'bronchial blocker'. He preferred to operate standing, with the patient lying on his side. A fine tube was threaded beside the anaesthetic tube into the bronchus of the lung to be operated upon. The balloon near its tip, when inflated, confined the secretions but still allowed their removal by suction. He also devised a bronchial clamp, the curve of which conformed to the anatomical shape of a bronchus. For use prior to bronchial division, again confining secretions to the part being removed, it caused practically no tissue damage.

Using their various methods, post-operative morbidity in bronchiectasis was reduced and mortality gradually fell to 6 per cent, an astonishing achievement for those days. In 1944 the work was recorded in *The Lancet* in a classic original paper by Sellors, Thompson & Qvist, 'Dissection lobectomy for bronchiectasis'.

Physiotherapist Jocelyn Reed contributed much. She developed effective methods of post-operative chest physiotherapy: postural drainage, the technique of primarily moving the chest wall as opposed to just 'taking a deep breath', localised chest expansion exercises against pressure, training the patient in diaphragmatic breathing, and supporting the painful chest wall with a 'cough lock' webbing belt.

Until the late 1940s, general anaesthesia was administered by 'bag squeezing', a tiring and trying occupation for the anaesthetist in a long operation. Ventilators to deliver the anaesthetic gases mechanically were being developed and one of the first prototypes was tried out at Harefield. Gradually, 'techniques made thoracotomy [operating on the chest] a safe, routine procedure, instead of one which carried a sense of adventure and hazard'. By 1949, Holmes Sellors had resected a tracheal stricture, and lung resection by dissection was routine and straightforward.

## More Tuberculosis Techniques

Thoracoplasty, a more drastic surgical method to achieve collapse of a chronic cavity at the top of the lung, came on the scene in the 1940s. Carefully dissecting the diseased lung free, portions of a pre-determined number of ribs were removed and the chest wall 'fell in' to a specified degree. The anatomical size of that side of the chest, and consequent movement of the lung, was decreased permanently. First carried out under local anaesthesia, the operation was done in one, two or three stages. It caused considerable deformity. Though the anaesthetists were expert in putting in the anaesthetic, patients thoroughly disliked the experience – but not as much as broncho-scopy! As time went on and anaesthetic methods advanced, the operation started to be done under general anaesthesia, which they much preferred. A less deforming one stage modified thoracoplasty, devised by Semb, was an operation at which 'Uncle Tom became dextrous and visitors from all over the world would come and see him do it.'

> Thoracoplasty was one of the most successful operations that has ever been devised. . . . [The patient] with an open . . . cavity . . . had an 80 per cent chance of being dead within five years . . . If they had a successful thoracoplasty which closed the cavity, they had an 80 per cent chance of being alive and well and working in five years. There has been little in the field of surgery which alters the prognosis for life as that. . . . The patients knew it and the decision as to whether or not thoracoplasty was advisable or practicable . . . was the turning point in their lives.

Jocelyn Reed's strict postural exercises produced excellent cosmetic results in these patients. In the war years, impressed with post-operative results only a day or so after surgery, visitor Capt. Dwight E. Harken arranged for American 'physical therapists' to come to Harefield for short courses.

With the advent of chemotherapy, there was 'a tendency to lung resection instead of thoracoplasty' and, for tuberculous strictures, good results were obtained with removal only of the 'sleeve' of bronchus in which it lay. Even so, in the first half of 1951, though there were 88 lung resections, 110 thoracoplasty stages were also carried out. It was not until the end of the decade that the disease had declined so dramatically that only a very occasional patient needed surgery.

Meanwhile, to avoid the deforming thoracoplasty, other collapse methods had evolved. Known as plombage, oil or plastic sponge or plastic balls were put into the extrapleural space instead of air. The latter became known locally as 'Paul's Balls' as Mr Chin used them most. These spheres, hollow so to be light in weight, were supplied in two halves. Preparing them was a complicated and tedious business. They had to be sterile when inserted of course. Before every operating list where a plombage was due to be done, the theatre Sister set to work. Carefully gloved and gowned she would ensure that the sterile halves were completely dry and, immersing their rims in ether to make the surfaces adhere, fit two halves exactly together. Fifteen or more had to be prepared for each case.

But the method did not 'catch on'. Often the body will not tolerate the presence of foreign, though inert, material. The rate of infection was high and most plombes had to be removed within a few years. But sometimes it worked well and a few late complications of plombage are still being seen 40 years later.

## Thomas Holmes Sellors

Energetic Holmes Sellors recorded much of his wartime work in numerous papers: a new mask for giving oxygen 'made of a disused X-ray film with a padding of strapping folds' in *The Lancet* in 1940; on the Monaldi method of chest drainage in *Tubercle*, in November 1942; on treatment of lung abscess, chronic empyema and pneumonitis; on surgical treatment of patent ductus and, towards the end of the war, lung cancer. He also somehow found time to write chapters for *Surgery of Modern Warfare*, the 15th edition of *Pye's Surgical Handicraft* and, for *Modern Trends in Radiology*, 'Post-operative Complications'. He created the drawings for another book he and Lionel Houghton had written: *Aids to Nursing TB*, published by Ballière Tindall and Cox in 1945 and, in collaboration with Dr J. L. Livingstone, edited *Modern Practice in Tuberculosis*.

When Holmes Sellors was also on the staff of the Middlesex and London Chest Hospitals he continued to record his activities, initiating papers on all manner of topics. But these papers invariably did not originate from Harefield. Because much of the clinical work they reflected had actually been done there, some feel that the contribution of the Harefield Thoracic Unit to thoracic surgery at that time was never adequately recorded or recognised.

Knighted in the New Year Honours of 1963, Sir Thomas was appointed to the National Heart Hospital, relinquishing two more sessions at Harefield. After officially opening the new theatre and X-ray building in 1967, he left Harefield altogether. Subsequently he was elected President of the Royal College of Surgeons of England,

President of the International Society of Surgery, President of the BMA and was awarded their prestigious Gold Medal in 1979.

John W. Jackson, senior registrar from 1952, was appointed to the expanding TSU in 1959 'to have full charge of 3 beds'. Also in 1959, Paul Chin was killed tragically in a road accident. Kenneth Mullard moved to Southampton and was replaced by H. C. Nohl. These two, C. A. Jackson and Holmes Sellors were the thoracic surgeons at the end of 1960. Anaesthetic support came from Drs Parry Brown, L. O. Mountford (Monty), Brian A. Sellick from 1948, and E. J. (Johnny) Leighton and J. (Joe) W. Lewis from 1952. The first three left a few years after Sir Thomas when Drs Leighton, Lewis and R. E. M. Maclaurin were joined by Robert W. Hall, an erstwhile registrar, and Ann P. Triscott.

'Uncle Tom was a very well-liked man. He was kind and helpful. I never heard him be rude to anybody,' said John Roberts. He was 'the epitome of the English gentleman – cultured, kindly and wise'. By the time 'Uncle Tom' left Harefield, his spirit of adventure, progress and caring had been imbued upon many, not least his successors. These things were now an integral part of the Thoracic Unit.

## Progress

After the war co-operation between all the departments of the Hospital continued and more ideas and techniques were developed. Harefield went on attracting visitors from all parts of the world to see the new work being done in the investigation and medical treatment of tuberculosis. Lionel Houghton produced the Houghton Index. Calculated from the results of several blood tests, he postulated it indicated progress of treatment. He pioneered the use of steroids and adrenocorticotrophic hormone (ACTH) in tuberculosis and, with Eugene Nassau, investigated the modifying effect of steroids on the tuberculosis vaccine, BCG. Numerous papers on this subject received wide recognition.

Dr Houghton also started the use of respiratory function tests at Harefield and of skin testing, a dangerous exercise in those days. Being skilled in hypnosis also, and having obtained some creditable results, he advocated its use in the management of asthma, writing other papers on these studies.

With Dr Roberts, Dr Nassau worked out methods, in 'sputum negative' tuberculous patients, to obtain infected material for culture from stomach washings and swabbing the larynx. Because of his reputation and knowledge of the organism, Dr Nassau was sent to India to set up bacteriological laboratories. With the aid of grants from the World Health Organisation (WHO) and the Regional Health Authority, he was also able to continue his research on 'fluorescent techniques in the identification and classification of mycobacteria', as well as immunology. Also, when long-acting penicillin appeared, at the request of the manufacturer and the Chief of the Treponematosis Section of the WHO he studied its use in animals and/or volunteers.

It was John Roberts' contention that one form of lung damage in children, obstructive emphysema, was often due to pressure from enlarged tuberculous glands. He also observed that the lung changes persisted after the obstruction had been removed. Having been taught how to examine the bronchial tree by Holmes Sellors, he would bronchoscope such children himself and draw the material from the glands with a needle through the wall of the bronchus. He was further convinced that secretions trapped beyond an obstruction were a potent cause of secondary infection and bronchiectasis. Concerned about the effect of all this on the heart, he and Dr Parry Brown developed a method of measuring pulmonary artery pressure in these cases.

Parry Brown introduced the double bored, or double lumen, endotracheal tube, giving the surgeons much more flexibility. It allowed an anaesthetic to be given via both or only one lung, but gave access to both for secretion removal by suction. Using the tube, Kenneth Mullard studied the value of assessing function in each lung separately. He also fashioned a 'trap' in which sputum could be collected at bronchoscopy for culture and malignant cell examination.

By the end of the 1950s management of infection had been transformed by the advent of a number of antibiotics. The incidence of lung abscess, bronchiectasis and empyema had dropped dramatically. Tuberculosis all but disappeared and the Tuberculosis Service became the Chest Service, the Clinics becoming places where all forms of chest disease were investigated.

## Later Work

The thoracic surgeon has become much involved in assessment, diagnosis and treatment of lung cancer. When it first reared its ugly head, the patients' only hope was to have the tumour removed. The same applied to cancer of the oesophagus. He visits Chest Clinics and hospitals to see the patients and discusses their problems with the physicians. Responsible for deciding if surgery was possible, he carries out most of the preliminary tests and biopsies himself. The advent of fibre-optic lighting, and then flexible fibrescopes, has greatly enhanced and expanded the possibilities for treatment during the procedures. When the latter instruments appeared, many physicians began to master their use under local anaesthesia.

The thoracic surgeon is also available to help manage chest injuries, now usually resulting from road accidents. Harefield has never had an Accident and Emergency Unit of its own, but the TSU becomes involved when such patients are transferred from other hospitals which do. Conditions also within the Unit's surgical orbit are many and varied. They include repair of hiatus hernia, total gastrectomy for stomach cancer, resection of most types of thoracic malignant and benign tumours, dealing with oesophageal and tracheal strictures, management of spontaneous pneumothorax, and some thyroid surgery.

The Thoracic Surgical Unit had between 70 and 80 beds in 1967. In the new theatre complex about 400 major thoracic operations and 100 heart operations were being done each year. Numbers rose to over 500 by the early 1970s, with a similar number of heart cases.

Research in thoracic spheres of interest was pursued. There was another trial with the BTTA, this time to test short course tuberculosis chemotherapy, and a study of the effects of other drugs in asthma and industrial lung disease. From the surgical side, when lung cancer incidence had reached 600 per million population, came a comparison of patients presenting in 1953 and 25 years on. There followed a review of multiple primary pulmonary malignancy, and papers on the relative merits of flexible and rigid bronchoscopes, methods of oxygen administration for the procedure under general anaesthesia, chest trauma, and a variety of unusual thoracic surgical problems. John Jackson edited the third edition of the Cardiothoracic Volume of Rob & Smith's *Operative Surgery*, and H. C. Nohl-Oser with others, wrote a textbook, *Surgery of the Lung*.

The 'nutritional status and metabolic consequences in patients undergoing lung and oesophageal surgery' were investigated with the aid of a £7000 Regional Research Grant; nitrogen balance and gastric emptying of patients having oesophageal surgery, and the use of new antibiotics in thoracic surgery were studied; and Harefield cooperated with researchers elsewhere, providing samples of lung or other tissue appropriate to their needs. A study of various methods of treating one form of lung cancer was done in conjunction with the Regional Radiotherapy and Oncology Centre at Mount Vernon and another trial was undertaken, this time on the effect of cytotoxic drugs after surgery for lung cancer.

## Clinical Considerations

Following in 'Uncle Tom's' footsteps of 25 years before, I was awarded a Hunterian Professorship by the Royal College of Surgeons of England in 1969. While senior registrar at Harefield, I had spent a year studying the use of diaphragm muscle in cardiac surgery at The Hospital for Sick Children in Toronto, Canada. The following year John Jackson attained the honour too, for his study of 'Surgical Approaches to the Anterior Aspect of the Spinal Column' in the management of diseases of the spine. The third was H. Chris Nohl-Oser who, being particularly interested in mediastinoscopy, then a relatively new surgical method in the assessment of operability in lung cancer, presented 'An Investigation of the Anatomy of the Lymphatic Drainage of the Lungs'. Over subsequent years a number of other members of Harefield's surgical staff have also been honoured thus.

## The Thoracic Surgical Patient

People coming to the Thoracic Unit have always been fearful but, because they know many advances are being made there, remain confident that their life threatening lung or oesophageal cancer, heart disease – or tuberculosis – will be treated, even if it means the discomforts of major surgery. The 'Unit . . . acquired some of the old sanatorium regime in not hustling patients out of hospital but rehabilitating them for normal life as part of their post-operative treatment. Yet in spite of the apparent absence of ''rush'' the turnover . . . steadily increased year by year.' For a time, a patient would be in hospital for three weeks or more but with advancing techniques, such as using staples instead of needle and thread and stitches which do not have to be removed, the time has gradually decreased. With ever improving facilities, 'turnover' has continued to rise.

Post-operatively most thoracic patients find themselves in a very uncomfortable position, especially for the first 24 hours or so while the necessary drainage tubes are still in the chest. Pain is controlled by drugs, but it is still uncomfortable. In their apprehension there is a great tendency to compare their lot with that of their neighbours. An unfortunate but real event. Do they have one drain, two drains or no drain? It could tell them what sort of operation they have had. Was part of their lung removed – or all – or none? The truth is that no two patients are ever the same, no two surgeons have exactly the same methods, and no patient can ever make accurate assumptions about another. Children are much better than adults. They probably won't have lung cancer, are not so analytical nor are they aware of all the implications. One was so proud of *his* big chest scar, he told all his mates that it 'was where the shark got him'!

Those with swallowing difficulties often feel particularly poorly when they come in. Perhaps they will best be helped by placing a tube in the narrowed portion of oesophagus and leaving it there. Alternatively the affected segment is surgically removed. This takes several hours to do but can transform the patient's life. But it is not without cost. Not only do such patients have to go through extensive surgery but also they need careful nurturing and their convalescence may be prolonged. Their greatest moment, even greater than when the chest drain is taken out, comes a week or so after the operation when they find they can eat without their food getting stuck.

Physiotherapy is an essential, but not popular, pastime for every thoracic surgical patient. The inevitable post-operative secretions are often difficult to shift because coughing feels unsafe with the big wound. John Jackson had a standing wager with the physiotherapists. Lung collapse, to be prevented after a lung operation now-a-days, still can occur due to thick secretions obstructing the bronchi. If they, by working with the patient, could re-expand the lung and avoid the secretions having to be removed by suction at bronchoscopy, then he would give them 2/6d and, if it was a child, the child got 6d pocket money. More often than not the physiotherapist and patient won!

## · 10 ·

## Another Era

WITH the death of Dr Stokes and the retirement of Beatrice Shaw, a phase in the life of Harefield Hospital was over. The farm, piggery and kitchen garden were no more. The 'Cottage Laboratory' had been pulled down and the spectacle of the three huts behind the stables being put to the torch was imprinted in many minds. Tuberculosis had almost disappeared and Harefield's sanatorium beds were being used to treat other forms of chest disease. The emphasis of Harefield's work had well and truly shifted to thoracic surgery and medicine. One way or another the 1950 decade had been a momentous one.

### New Administration

Having a Medical Director, Harefield had been able to hold the NHS hospital administrative structure at bay. Now it had no alternative but to conform, and accept 'that a Hospital Secretary be appointed to take charge of the lay administration . . . who shall be responsible to the Management Committee through the Group Secretary'. This resulted in the appearance of Mr Vernon H. Green. A succession of Hospital Secretaries followed. Each stayed two or three years before being promoted and moving on. Mr F. A. Watson, who left in 1964, was similarly replaced by four Group Secretaries, one staying as long as five years.

The Medical Committee became 'aware [of] . . . the policy of . . . Management to reduce the administrative influence of the medical staff . . . viz., the abolition of the post of Medical Director. It was assumed . . . that the lay authority, . . . previously exercised by the Medical Director, would be transferred to the Hospital Secretary but . . . this has not taken place.' They were very sceptical, and very uncertain of their relationship with the Group Management Committee. But at least Mr Staveley Gough, FRCS, a retired surgeon,

111

had taken over as Chairman in 1966 and, remaining so for eight years, established some continuity.

The new arrangements had been made a little more palatable when 'a Medical Administrator [was] appointed from among the consultant staff . . . to advise the Hospital Secretary on medical aspects of the lay administration'. Lionel Houghton was selected. But the post proved to have little or no executive power and was discontinued by common consent in 1969. The first Cogwheel Report of a Government Advisory Committee for Management Efficiency had appeared two years before. The imposed new medical administrative structure gave the rôle to the Chairman of the Medical Committee. The Report received a lukewarm reception from clinicians because of its wide administrative implications: 'when a doctor makes a clinical decision about his patient he decides in effect on the allocation of the resources of the hospital, whether human or material'. Nevertheless Harefield formed the required clinical Divisions of medicine, surgery and cardio-thoracic surgery, and each selected its chairman.

The many Group committees were becoming inundated with statistics on bed occupancy, waiting lists and 'Deaths and Discharges', expenditure lists, financial arrangements, staff establishments and changing terms and conditions of work for employees. An ever escalating number of 'guidance' documents were coming from the Regional Board. These related to such things as Acts of Parliament, like the Factories Act which 'required authorities employing more than 20 building and engineering staff to appoint Safety Supervisors . . . to ensure that the working conditions complied with the provisions of this Act'. Also received were about 100 circulars from the DHSS each year on subjects ranging from activity analyses and battered babies to welfare milk and wigs. It was not too surprising that Minutes had become long and much less personal, and decision making extremely slow.

## Future Prospects

Harefield Hospital was now one of two major chest hospitals in the Region. But the North West Metropolitan Regional Hospital Board was not planning to expand them. Instead it preferred the establishment of close working relationships with surrounding Chest Clinic physicians. Also proposed for Harefield was a Geriatric Unit, a Gynaecological Unit to be run by Mr Simmonds and, based on the premise that new Northwick Park Hospital would reduce pressure on the Harefield & Northwood Group for general work, closure of some

112

general beds and transfer of others to Mount Vernon Hospital. To specifically advise on the plans, the Management Committee set up a study group which included medical representatives of both hospitals.

It was still Holmes Sellors' view 'that whilst the suggested form of integration of the general medical and surgical work at both Hospitals was acceptable, the emphasis on the future . . . should lie in relation to thoracic (lung and heart) work . . . and . . . expansion in the respiratory field (chronic bronchitis, asthma etc.)'. Eventually Management concurred: 'Harefield should be developed as a specialist hospital for chest diseases [with] a thoracic and cardiovascular unit for the investigation and treatment of medical and surgical heart disease, a . . . specialist unit for non-tuberculous chest disease, respiratory failure and respiratory physiology, and the medical and surgical treatment of tuberculosis of the lung, spine and kidney.'

Even so, Harefield's medical staff were still uneasy. As it was the future of the Hospital under discussion, they felt consultation had been inadequate, their views not seriously considered and they had not been kept informed of very significant decisions. Some were concerned that, once again, removal of Harefield's general beds would not only threaten the status of the Hospital but also nurse training and recruitment. The concerns were expressed in a Memorandum to the Management Committee. 'We suggest a closer liaison [with] the Group Management Committee . . . , would appreciate information on the . . . reactions to our proposals and . . . hear progress of our projects and . . . of proposals made . . . to the Regional Board concerning Harefield. . . . It would promote goodwill and understanding . . . if senior staff were . . . [kept] informed . . . and their priorities submitted to . . . Region.'

But everyone agreed that the Geriatric Unit proposal should be rejected. Although such a unit might help keep some form of nurse training, it was not considered proper use of tuberculosis beds. Mount Vernon Hospital would be more appropriate. Even with this advice from the Management Committee, the Board was adamant. Within the year a Geriatric Unit, in the charge of the consultant geriatrician of Hillingdon Hospital, was established at Harefield.

In the early sixties, the Regional Board 'confirmed that Harefield Hospital should remain the main regional thoracic centre and that the catchment area for the thoracic unit at Harefield . . . should be: . . . Windsor, West Herts, Staines, Hillingdon, Harefield & Northwood, south west Middlesex and Central Middlesex'. The prospects for Harefield seemed a bit brighter for a little while.

*Nurses*

Miss Shaw's successor in 1960 was Miss A. T. Monteith. Having been an assistant matron in 1952, she was well aware of Harefield's shortage of nurses. But she knew who the 'backbone' of the nursing staff were. They included Sisters Coyne, Garbett, Hopwood, Hughes, Pilling, Randle, Reay, Sheldon, Skelton, Charge Nurses Dale and Moon, and Harefield trained Sister Demulder had taken charge of the operating theatres.

She was also aware of the several local factors hindering recruitment efforts. Available accommodation was not all it should be. Facilities were not very good and some rooms had to be shared, especially those in the 'north side' Nurses' Home. Married accommodation was very limited, creche facilities were lacking, and local property was expensive to buy or rent. Geographically the Hospital was not close enough to London to be attractive and yet its proximity to London tempted school leavers living locally to go there for training. Local transport was unreliable and there was no formal attachment to a civic community. Working conditions had not improved. Nurses still had to do many domestic duties in badly designed and out-of-date wards. And the Hospital had become known only for its specialty thoracic service.

Numerous recruiting avenues were pursued. Several girls had come from overseas, especially the Phillipines. Much time and effort was spent expediting work permits for others. Visits were made to various places such as Dublin, and lectures given to local schools, Girl Guides and Girls Brigade, Boy Scouts and the Red Cross. Competitors for the Duke of Edinburgh Award were tested in first aid and home nursing. However, the Cadet scheme, starting in 1961, proved very successful. School-leavers came and tasted hospital life to see if nursing was 'for them'. Ten years later there was a waiting list.

Miss Monteith was also very anxious to keep the School of Nursing going. Almost immediately she had taken over, recognition of the combined State Registration and BTA Certificate course was withdrawn, followed by that for the BTA Certificate only. Then, a year later, the GNC only agreed to 'continuing . . . general training for the time being . . . if . . . satisfactory occupancy of the general beds, particularly of general surgery and gynaecology' was maintained. A training hospital had to have 300 general beds and it was their opinion that Harefield should either join with another school or have only Pupil Nurses for State Enrolment. Despite everything, Principal Tutor Miss G. H. Graham, who succeeded Miss Dewar, continued

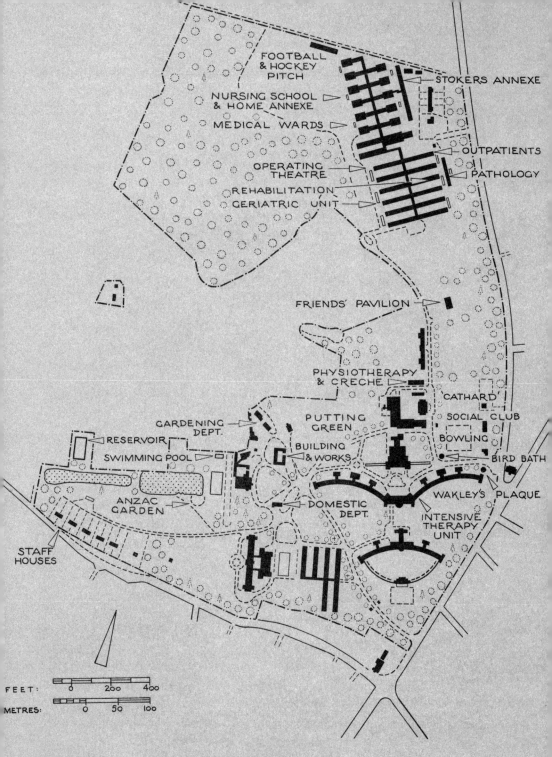

FOOTBALL
& HOCKEY
PITCH

STOKERS ANNEXE

NURSING SCHOOL
& HOME ANNEXE

MEDICAL WARDS

OUTPATIENTS

OPERATING
THEATRE

PATHOLOGY

REHABILITATION
GERIATRIC UNIT

FRIENDS' PAVILION

PHYSIOTHERAPY
& CRECHE

CATHARD'
SOCIAL CLUB

GARDENING
DEPT.

PUTTING
GREEN

BOWLING

RESERVOIR

BUILDING
& WORKS

BIRD BATH

SWIMMING POOL

ANZAC
GARDEN

DOMESTIC
DEPT.

WAKLEY'S PLAQUE

INTENSIVE
THERAPY
UNIT

STAFF
HOUSES

FEET:        0      200      400

METRES:      0      50      100

Fig. 8   1964: Harefield Hospital

the high standards of teaching between 1962 and 1971, and excellent State examination results were attained, 100 per cent qualifying in 1966.

But the number of general beds was gradually decreasing. By 1967 Harefield no longer met requirements. The Harefield and Mount Vernon Preliminary Training Schools had already joined, using the School in the 'north wards', and when a new building opened at Mount Vernon, Harefield once again lost its School of Nursing. In 1970 the first combined Prize-giving was held. The Deputy High Commissioner of Australia, Mr R. W. Boswell, and his wife were Guests of Honour.

## The 'North Wards'

In the early sixties Harefield was still providing medical and surgical services of a general hospital, with patients in Wards 4 to 10, and 14 to 17. The latter four were general medical wards and Wards 5 and 6 the Geriatric Unit. Conditions on the old temporary 'north side' had been improved and the patients found themselves in less spartan surroundings. The covered way was resurfaced and enclosed, given fluorescent lighting, and then part of it received a new roof. The days of constant stoking of the stoves, especially in those huts used as wards, were over when a 'north' coke boiler house provided central heating. Living in the Hill End Road staff houses became a little easier too when a new electrical supply and immersion heaters were installed, and all the puddles disappeared from the path when concrete access was laid down. A new road to the 'north side', with an adjacent car park, was completed in 1967. Other car parks appeared next to the concert hall and between the main block and A Ward.

But there had been no gainsaying the Regional Board's policy decisions. Clinical use of the 'north wards' began to diminish. Paradoxically the changes were helped partly by shortage of nursing staff with consequent bed closures, but mostly by the great decrease in incidence of tuberculosis. Even when Pinewood Sanatorium closed and the chest physicians had brought some work to Harefield, these beds were not nearly in such great demand.

Over the course of several years, much of the general work went to Mount Vernon Hospital. Wards B and C in the main block had been 'upgraded', incorporating the balconies. By 1969 they housed the general surgery, orthopaedics and gynaecology that remained. Then the latter two went as well. But Mr Snell and Mr Simmonds continued to work at Harefield until they departed in 1971, and Mr Snell's successor stayed on for a time.

Mr Levi had been replaced by Mr J. W. P. Bradley. With his interest in vascular surgery, the Hospital began to see such cases, including emergencies like ruptured abdominal aorta. This expertise was greatly welcomed as it not only complemented the cardiovascular service, but was also important for nurse training and continued recognition for surgical training by the Royal College of Surgeons.

In 1966 the Occupational Therapy Department, and the art section from the old Australian Chapel, shifted to Ward 3, Mr Sparrow remaining at the helm until he retired in 1971. Gradually the Department merged with the 'north side' Physiotherapy Department forming a Rehabilitation Unit in Ward 7 for the geriatric patients. By 1972, two of the 'north' general medical wards had moved to the main block, leaving two up there with the Geriatric Unit. Also remaining on the 'north side' for the time being were Medical Records, the Medico-social Workers and the Out-patient Department. Though various administrative departments, such as Stores, Area Supplies, and the Catering and Domestic Departments, took over vacated huts, the shrinking clinical use of the accommodation had a very bad effect on morale.

## Overcrowding

Building of the new X-ray Department and twin operating theatre suite extension, put where the Board had decreed, commenced in 1964. It was officially opened by Sir Thomas on 22 July 1967. Meanwhile the intrepid team of Drs Blair and McPherson and Mr Holder continued to cope in the tiny main block X-ray Department next to the single operating theatre, using the 'north' Department less and less. But their screening room had moved to E Ward to make a space for the recovery area necessary for special post-operative nursing of cardiac patients. Needless to say, immediately the new Department and all its facilities were ready in the January, X-ray moved in. Just before the move, Harry Westbury replaced Dr Blair, who retired after 30 years. A year later, after 31 years, Mr Holder departed.

Both 'north' and 'south' operating theatres were under the eagle eye of Theatre Superintendent Sister Demulder. As the thoracic work became more specialised and activity increased, she too had had to work in cramped quarters. New techniques and apparatus, including heart/lung bypass, were all mastered in the single 'south' thoracic theatre. The bulky Mayo-Gibbon heart/lung machine, acquired in 1960, filled the original dental room. As dentistry was regaining considerable importance with the developing cardiac work, the Department moved to the room over the Board Room. The displaced ophthalmic service went to the 'north' Outpatient Department.

But the thoracic theatre could not move into their palacial quarters until July 1967 as the new ceiling was defective and had to be replaced! But when the move was complete, the old X-ray room was converted into a second theatre and the main hospital corridor, which had run right outside the theatre doors, was at last closed off. The 'north' theatre transferred to the now twin main block theatres in 1969 and, for a time, the space was adequate.

Part of the plan to concentrate all surgery in the 'south' was to ease the serious nurse staffing problem. But there was a valuable nucleus of experienced theatre nurses and the 'stalwart, indefatigable theatre technicians Jordan and Cokeley' to whom 'there was no question of trade union hours or rates or attitude. Everything was done as fast and as efficiently as possible.'

Then, when Clare Hall Hospital closed, there was another upheaval to enable thoracic work to be done in the now 'general' theatres. For a time, all surgery had to be squeezed into the 'new' theatres. The 'light room' above the Board Room was needed for a larger recovery room. The dentists had to move again, this time to prepared quarters on A Ward, and at last the front hall stairway, which now led nowhere, was removed. By 1975, thoracic surgery was once again being done in the main block.

## Relocations

In 1960 the Pathology Department was disseminated all over the place, a very unsatisfactory state of affairs. When the courtyard rooms were demolished, the animal house had to move to the 'north' Isolation hut. Another part was next to the 'north wards' theatre and yet another in the old 'north' kitchen behind the Out-patient Department. The increasing number of technical staff battled on with Eugene Nassau and Gwyneth Hamilton until the custom-built laboratory, opposite the garage, opened in 1965. But even with integration of some pathology services with Mount Vernon, the new building was not big enough. The Isolation hut had to remain in use until 1970 by which time the new quarters had been extended and the animal house no longer needed.

Pharmacy was also relocated, in Ward 2 on the 'north side'. With more space and the ordering of many items transferred to Supplies, Mr Mapstone no doubt found life a bit easier. Also, he no longer had to prepare sterile intravenous fluids. But being on the 'north side' had its disadvantages. As activity there decreased, more and more supplies and drugs had to be transported 'south' and security had to be tightened because of its increasing isolation. In 1972, when a Group Pharmacy service was formed, Mrs Gill Kitto succeeded Mr Mapstone.

Physiotherapy was another fragmented Department in 1960. There was an exercise room in the converted roof garden on the central main block until 1968, and one on C Ward for the thoracic surgical patients. Then the Department was moved to G Ward, with a cubicle on F Ward. The part in 'north' Ward 2 was shuttled first to Ward 1 then to Ward 3 and then to Ward 7. In an effort to ease these problems it was decided, despite Miss Thacker's considerable reservations, to provide a building on the south side of Observation Ward, roughly midway between 'north' and 'south'. To achieve this as economically as possible, the already hard pressed gardening staff had to prepare the site. The new Department appeared in 1964.

The 'Shed' did not prove a success. A service had to be maintained in the 'north' for the geriatric patients and, to get to Physiotherapy now, patients as well as staff were exposed to the elements. Three years later it was used mainly as a crèche, helping to get staff. Despite physiotherapists still coming from all over the world to gain chest experience under Miss Thacker, recruitment was not very good. Then came unpopular moves to amalgamate the Department with Mount Vernon. For a time obtaining staff became even more difficult and students stopped coming. When Miss Thacker, and Freda Barlow who had come in 1968 to look after the general wards, left in 1974, the diminishing general work had to be curtailed further as the only staff left were part-timers. Somewhat reluctantly Paula Walker, Mount Vernon's Superintendent, took over.

By the beginning of 1961 a Respiratory Physiology Department had been established. Run by physiologist Peter Lockwood, it shared the room on the ground floor of the main block, which Pathology and then Pharmacy had occupied, with Cardiology. As the work developed and more equipment was acquired, the space soon became very crowded. But the two Departments had to continue working almost on top of each other under increasingly difficult conditions for many years. As time passed, there were several senior cardiology technicians until Mrs Gina Perera took over in 1972, but Peter Lockwood continued to preside over Respiratory Physiology.

## The Patients' Day

The administration made great efforts to smooth the patient's sojourn in hospital. From time to time, a detailed analyses of 'The Patient's Day' would be carried out. The aim was to try and make as much of each day as normal as possible – ensuring enough sleep, that tests and investigations were completed in an orderly way with an explanatory word, and meals served at reasonable times. Patients who were up and about could eat in the dining-room or, from 1963, have a snack in the Friend's Pavilion. To those confined to the wards, and to ever decreasing numbers on the 'north side', a choice of meals was delivered in heated, insulated trolleys. Low fat or salt or protein or residue, reducing, gastric and diabetic diets were available. Subsequently a 'plated tray' service was instituted.

The introduction of name badges removed the anonymity of the staff by telling patients to whom they were talking, and the appearance of lay Ward Clerks in the mid 1960s gave them someone to go to for their day-to-day concerns. Also doing wonders for patient morale in the main block wards was that they could keep their clothes with them, get dressed whenever possible and, if not needed for some test or other, go into the grounds or the village.

Visiting, though still restricted for G and D Wards, became easier from 1964 when Bus 347 and Coach 703, later replaced by Bus 309, came through Harefield. For patient entertainment, a new Radio Harefield came into being in 1967. The transmitting equipment was bought by the League of Friends and set up in an 'eyrie' above the concert hall. A year later a second station, Radio 390, started. Both were manned by volunteers, including one of the Hospital telephonists, a Charge Nurse, an ambulance man, and a member of the Medical Records staff. The patients were once again receiving information about Hospital amenities and activities. Amongst the programmes were Desert Island Discs with local celebrities and, from 1969 for the next 14 years or so, the Inter Hospital Quiz. By 1973 the radio system had been rewired, this time at the expense of the Regional Board.

Until about 1975, the radio also relayed the regular non-denominational Sunday services from the Chapel. For both mobile patients and staff, these were held either by Rev. Dennis Connor, or the Free Church Chaplain. Communion was also celebrated each month. During these times of change with the shrinking of the Hospital, the Chapel was used less and less. However, even though for smaller numbers, services were continued in the Board Room.

Those patients who were getting better did not change much. They continued to get up to all sorts of things, especially on the tuberculosis wards while they existed. There, the day-time rest periods were needed because 'the ward at 2 am was a bustling active affray. All . . . on strict bed rest were not at this hour, but up and about and

119

visiting'! The men had a Christmas tradition as well. Having the co-operation of a taxi firm, some of them, via the G Ward fire escape, would be spirited by a fleet of cars to their homes late one evening. Spending a little of the festive season with their families, they returned the same way before dawn the next day! And sometimes 'a fox passed the rear of the main block. It was fed by the patients who left out food overnight – all very unofficial of course'.

## The Place

With the end of the 'family' and an entirely different administration, it was inevitable that Harefield would change. But some things didn't. Unchanging were the gardeners' efforts to care for the grounds, lawns and cricket pitch. Each spring they continued to plant bulbs and herbaceous border plants in the gardens to complement the cherry blossom and roses. Many came from the greenhouses of Grimsdyke until it closed in 1963. After that, supply continued only as far as finances would allow. By 1968 the hospital covered 79 acres. Part of this was Old Park Wood, 'probably the finest remaining ancient woodland in Middlesex'. The Herts & Middlesex Wildlife Trust took it under its wing as a Reserve in 1964 and purchased it outright in 1978. It is now a Site of Special Scientific Interest. Also, as faithful retainers retired, they were not replaced and the upkeep of the rest of the grounds was arranged on a Group basis.

Until the early 1980s when it was pulled down, the remaining Australian hut behind the stables was the gardeners store and home for the feral cats. In 1963 homes were found for 30 of the kittens in the continued effort to control their number. Some other things remained unchanged too for a while; such things as the skyline landmarks of the boiler-house chimney and the familiar stock pile of 420 tons of coal behind, and the water tower on the farm, now belonging to the Greater London Council.

Some things disappeared. Among them were the colonnades either side of the concert hall because of lack of funds to repair them; the roof garden on the main block; the old Chapel in the courtyard, followed by the courtyard walls; the Memorial Hall from opposite the Hospital entrance to make way for private houses, and 32 trees. Twenty-seven, including some of the old fruit trees, were considered dangerous. They were followed by six elms with Dutch Elm disease in 1972.

New things appeared: an extension to the stable block, housing the Building Department, and a new incinerator behind the Maintenance Department. Almost unnoticed during conversion to oil-fired heating, was the piecemeal removal of the old sanatorium chimney and its replacement with a new. More obvious to the staff in 1962 was the appearance of the swimming pool behind the Mansion, as pool parties could be added to the social menu. But breeding in the lakes, and in shallow pools in Old Park Wood by the 'north wards', were several species of mosquito. Their control was crucial, but now their presence in the Mansion precincts was even more unwelcome.

For a little while longer the gentle life continued there, the residents being awakened with a cup of tea and the gas fire lit by one of the maids! Then the Mansion itself received a face lift as it had become victim to dry rot and needed a new damp course. The work was funded by Region. 'Bearing in mind its architectural merit . . . removal of the blacking out on the front windows would improve the appearance. . . . It was noted that these would be painted to tone with the outside on the decoration of the Mansion.' Inside, mahogany toilet seats were replaced with plastic ones, and the magnificent 'barley sugar' balusters of the main stairway exchanged for new because a few had been broken! Central heating was installed and, no longer needed, the tall chimneys disappeared. The original drainpipes were supplanted by plastic ones and, pulling the creeper off the walls, the south wall plaque disappeared.

## Light Relief

Around the Hospital at various times would be seen either the familiar figure of Miss Monteith in her red uniform on her upright bicycle, or a physiotherapist or nurse trundling along the road to the 'north'. A doctor on the way to Out-patients by car, would use the mirror at that awkward corner about half way along to see that all was clear on the narrow road. Or there might be a porter in an electric cart or ambulance covering about 125 miles a week taking staff or patients or supplies to and from the 'north side'. Sometimes in one of the car parks a patient might be found cheerfully carrying out his allotted form of treatment. 'To wash and clean [a doctor's] car was part of physiotherapy. Many benefited in more ways than one!'

From time to time strange faces appeared on the scene. On one occasion in 1960, a Russian delegation of half a dozen physicians and surgeons interested in tuberculosis were shown around, much to the curiosity of all the staff. 'To demonstrate British democracy, they were given time just to wander around the Hospital entirely on their own.' Also in the 1960s, being so near Denham and Elstree Studios, the

Hospital was known as a place where scenes of films could be taken. One never knew when a team of actors, cameras and technicians would invade – with permission of course. On one occasion caravans were parked all around the roundabout outside the front door and even the switchboard was moved and signs changed!

Films included 'Life for Ruth', scenes for 'The Raging Moon', a story of how two young people confined to wheel chairs found happiness with each other, and parts of several 'Carry On' films. The rehearsing of two actresses, playing nurses walking in the highest heels imaginable, caused much mirth. Then in 1974 came a BBC film 'Cross Your Heart and Hope to Live'.

Christmas was still celebrated in traditional fashion with a Carol Service at which the Lessons were read by representatives of all grades of staff, both clinical and ancillary, from consultant and senior nurse to technician, pupil nurse and porter. For the children's Christmas party the teachers contributed presents and decorations, and the Hospital provided the tree, cake and party food. One of the doctors still represented Santa Claus. A Christmas turkey dinner was served on the wards to remaining patients by senior medical and nursing staff. The staff Christmas dinner was served another day.

For a few more years the highlight of the festivities remained the Pantomime, followed by the traditional Mansion party for the cast. Then, to welcome the New Year, the residents would transform the Mansion. It would be turned into a mini-casino, or a setting for a Gilbert and Sullivan operetta, or some other novel entertainment would be arranged such as candle-lit tours – which included the cellar. The ensuing party was usually lubricated by punch, often mixed in one of the baths. On one occasion it was so strong that one glass took care of the Works Officer when fresh air hit him!

# · 11 ·

# Into the Heart

'Of all the main surgical advances made in the last 50 years surely the most remarkable have been within the thorax, and you, Sir Thomas Holmes Sellors, are one of the pioneers who led the way into this new realm of surgery. Innumerable diseases of the heart and lungs which formerly defied treatment are now accessible to it. Operations on the heart and great vessels and on the lungs and bronchi have given life to the young and comfort in later years on a scale hardly dreamed of when you were a surgical registrar. . . . You are among those whose work brought a special lustre to British Medicine and made London one of the world's leading centres of Cardio-thoracic Surgery.' Part of the citation for the BMA Gold Medal 1979.

## Early Cardiac Surgery

The resourceful nature of the thoracic surgeon was such that it was a natural progression for the heart to come within his purvue. Very little heart surgery had been done during war other than tying an occasional patent ductus arteriosus, the first congenital cardiac defect to come 'under the knife', and pericardectomy, removal of thickened pericardium with release of the restricted heart. It was not long before a unique experience of this operation was acquired because of the many of cases of pulmonary tuberculosis at Harefield.

Holmes Sellors was among the first to ligate an infected patent ductus. The dramatic improvement of the patient's clinical condition and physical signs immediately the ligature was tied impressed staff and visitors alike. Coming round from the anaesthetic, the patient invariably said something like 'How nice there is no more drumming.' This was dubbed the 'Sellors sign'.

A Harefield visitor in 1947 was Alfred Blalock, originator of a bypassing operation for 'blue babies' with Fallot's Tetralogy. In this congenital malformation not enough blood gets to the lungs to gather oxygen, often because the pulmonary heart valve is narrowed. On

4 December 1947, Holmes Sellors carried out the world's first direct pulmonary valvotomy on a young man with such an abnormality. The patient also had tuberculosis and the associated pleural adhesions made any other procedure impossible. After the successful operation he lived for eleven years before succumbing to his lung disease.

Rheumatic fever, a common disease then, was often followed by narrowing of another of the heart valves. At 'closed' valvotomy, the mitral valve was stretched, or cut by a knife fitted closely to the surgeon's exploring finger. Harefield's first was in January 1951 on an 8-year-old boy with mitral stenosis. In 1955, Sellors started to correct coarctation, a congenital narrowing of the aorta, the main artery leaving the heart. The short segment containing the stricture was cut out and the ends joined up again. Because the body tries to get blood around the blockage by enlarging other arteries in the chest wall, the great hazard is haemorrhage. By 1959 the diseased and narrowed aortic valve had also come within Holmes Sellors' sights.

It was known that by lowering body temperature, blood circulation could be stopped for about ten minutes without causing brain damage. Inducing hypothermia was quite a business. The anaesthetised patient was immersed in a bath of cold water to which ice was added and stirred around with a large wooden spoon! It took quite a time for body temperature to fall to the level at which circulation could safely be stopped for the allotted time. The heart pump was then taken out of circuit, mended and put back again. As in the days before anaesthesia, surgical speed came back into fashion.

Using the method in the 1950s, Holmes Sellors added closure of atrial septal defects to the Harefield list of treatable congenital heart conditions. He also ventured further inside to close a ventricular septal defect on at least one occasion. His technique was flawless. He first checked that all the instruments he needed were laid out in their usual places. Then he stopped the patient's circulation by clamping the aorta and the large entering veins. Never taking his eyes off the heart, and reaching for or being handed the appropriate instrument, he sewed up the hole with deft, dancing fingers. Ten minutes were usually more than he needed. His peers considered Holmes Sellors 'the uncrowned king of cardiac surgery', and cases were being referred to him from all over the country for operation. It was no wonder that trainees were still wanting to come to Harefield.

Pl. 40   Harefield County Sanatorium, *c.* 1935. View to the north. Observation Ward is going up opposite the old dining hall and kitchens. The men's old F Pavilion lies beyond the trees on the left.

Pl. 41   Harefield County Sanatorium, *c.* 1935. View to the south. With the old Special School lying beyond, the new children's ward goes up just in front of the old. On the right is the driveway to the old sanatorium entrance.

Pl. 42  Aerial view of Harefield County Sanatorium, 1937. Little trace of the old sanatorium remains.

Pl. 43   A sputum disinfector. These obviated 'the disadvantages of conveyance of sputum mugs over long distances'.

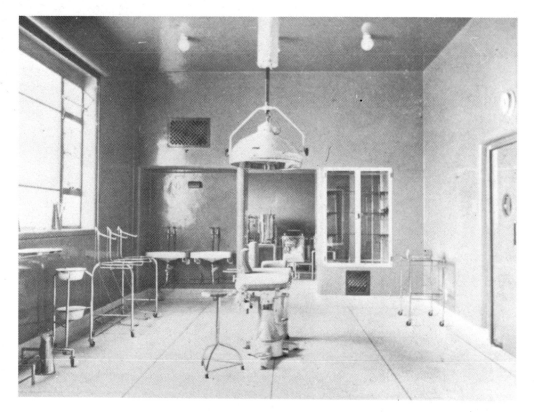

Pl. 44   Middlesex County Sanatorium's new operating theatre 'with its modern equipment'.

Pl. 45   The new Sanatorium wards had 'open . . . balconies in front obtaining . . . full benefit of a southerly exposure'.

Pl. 46 The last of 'Aussie huts'. Behind the stables, most were still in use as offices, maintenance workshops and some staff rest-rooms, c. 1955.

Pl. 47 HRH Duke of Gloucester being greeted at the 'opening of the new buildings of the County Sanatorium Middlesex, on Monday, 18 October 1937'.

Pl. 48 Aerial view of Harefield Emergency Medical Service Hospital. The two groups of 'north side' huts lie alongside the staff house in Hill End Road at the top of the picture.

Pl. 49 Wartime patients and staff posing outside one of the 'north wards'.

Pl. 50 The 'north side'. Photograph taken *c.* 1978 when the first hut housed the Pharmacy.

Pl. 51 Bird-bath Memorial to a Second World War Polish refugee. It is to be found a short distance inside the Hill End Road entrance on the right.

Pl. 52 Patients, staff and local inhabitants enjoying the annual Fête at the Hospital in 1949.

Pl. 53 HRH Princess Margaret, escorted by Dr Stokes, Matron Shaw, Mrs Daniels and Sister, talking with a patient and the Occupational Therapist, Mr Sparrow, in 'north' Ward 1, 13 November 1950.

Pl. 54  Kenneth R. Stokes and Beatrice A. Shaw, *c.* 1958.

Pl. 55  'The plucky little bus', which Dr Stokes shared with Miss Shaw, in front of the Mansion, *c.* 1955. The house still had its creeper and chimneys.

Pl. 56 The Hospital ANZAC Garden south of the lake behind the House. Landscaped in 1969, the stepping stones lead to a 'little stone bridge' over a 'man-made stream'.

Pl. 57 Dr Stokes and his intrepid cricket team, c. 1950.

Pl. 58  Final curtain. The 1951 Christmas Pantomime on stage in the concert hall.

Pl. 59  Nurses' Prize-giving 1967. The guest of honour is flanked by a laughing Mrs Ena Daniels and Matron, Miss Monteith. Dr H. R. C. Riches is seated on the left.

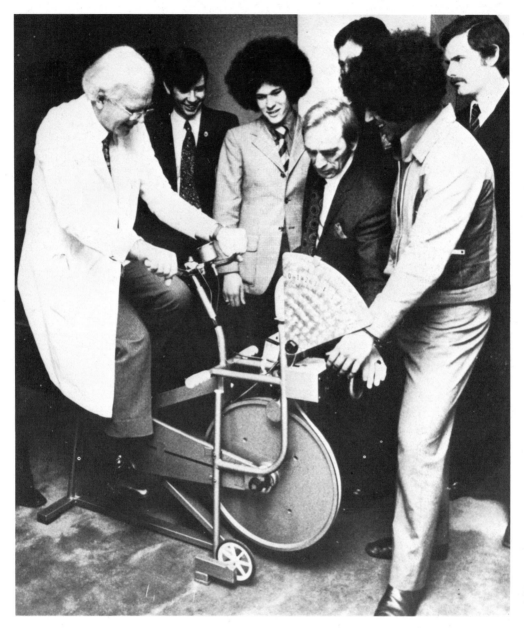

Pl. 60   John W. Jackson on Harefield's first exercise bicycle, presented to Hospital in 1973.

## Cardiology

In the early days the thoracic surgeon would happily deal with all aspects of surgical disease of the chest, both cardiac and thoracic. He was surgeon, physician and cardiologist rolled into one. He would undertake himself, mainly by clinical examination and fairly simple radiological assistance, the assessment of patients with cardiac conditions he felt he could deal with.

Developing in parallel with the increasing skills and experience of the surgical team, were advances in the methods of diagnosis and assessment of heart disease, started so effectively at Harefield by Walter Somerville. Horizons were really expanded when it became possible to pass a fine tube into the heart via a vein or artery in the groin or arm under X-ray control, cardiac catheterisation. Blood flow through the pump, and the lungs, could be assessed. By angiography, injecting radio-opaque liquid visible under an X-ray screen, the chambers of the heart, the coronary arteries and the great vessels could be outlined. It was the cardiologist with this expertise who now investigated the patients, producing the information a cardiac surgeon needed to safely correct the abnormality.

Cardiologist Malcolm K. Towers joined Dr Somerville on Dr Houghton's retirement in 1964. With the opening of the bigger X-ray Department in 1967, the range of cardiological and radiological techniques increased dramatically. An active pacemaker service was established. The electrical device to stimulate flagging hearts was first implanted by the surgeons in the operating theatre under general anaesthesia but, as equipment and techniques altered, cardiologists came to implant them quickly and effectively under X-ray control and local anaesthesia. The only problem with this was that more were done and costs rose. One year when ninety-two were inserted, the Administration commented 'It was hoped that fewer pacemakers would be used in the current year'!

Children with congenital abnormalities require special expertise. Recognising that increasing numbers of these little patients, both thoracic and cardiac, would need to be nursed separately, thoracic surgeon Chris Nohl-Oser and the paediatrician at Hillingdon Hospital, Harry Finlay, devoted much time and energy in discussion and negotiation. Beds on the 'boys side' of A Ward, made available for non-tuberculous chest conditions a few years before, provided the space. Their efforts resulted in a nine-bedded Paediatric Surgical Unit (PSU) opening there in 1969. Two years later paediatric cardiologist, Rosemary Radley-Smith, replaced Dr Roberts. Though a very occasional child with tuberculosis was still being admitted, most were now suffering from one of the many congenital heart defects which were coming within the surgeon's realm.

Radiologist Dr R. B. Pridie replaced Dr MacPherson in 1970. He brought a particular interest in newer invasive, and non-invasive, methods of cardiological investigation. The case load of cardiac catheters and angiograms was rising about 10 per cent per year and more space dedicated to cardiac investigation became desperately needed. As a provisional measure, one of the X-ray screening rooms used for barium studies was converted for multiple use. Eight years later Region finally approved a £½ million X-ray Department extension. Providing ultrasound facilities, it was in use by 1980 and officially opened the next year by the Health Minister. Now many cardiac abnormalities could be effectively diagnosed and assessed without invasive catheterisation.

## The Heart/lung Machine

Using the knowledge gained with hypothermia, along came another method of surgical cardiac support. The function of the lungs and heart is taken over temporarily by a heart/lung machine. By-passed and cooled, the heart pump can be taken out of circuit for longer than ten minutes, giving the surgeon time to repair or replace any of the four heart valves or correct more complicated abnormalities. To help orchestrate the development at Harefield, came Perfusionist George W. E. Wiggins in 1958.

Two years later a Mayo-Gibbon heart/lung machine, one of the first types available, was obtained with the financial assistance of the Regional Board, and a grant of £30,000 from The King's Fund. Of gleaming stainless steel with enclosed glass screens standing as high as a man, it took Mr Wiggins quite a while to prepare the machine for each use. The numerous screens had to be absolutely clean and sterile before venous blood could flow over them, to be oxygenated by the oxygen gas to which they were exposed. The tubing to carry the anticoagulated blood also had to be clean and sterile and the several pumps in perfect working order. These worked by a milking action, with rollers intermittently compressing the tube, pushing the blood along. Blood flow was controlled by adjusting the speed of the pumps. The whole machine had to be 'primed' before use and, having been filled with almost fresh blood, it was stabilised at a specific temperature by the inbuilt heat exchanger.

The machine was used first for congenital heart defects. On

30 November 1961 a 12-year-old girl with Fallot's Tetralogy had an 'open' pulmonary valvotomy and, on 13 December, a ventricular septal defect was closed in another 12-year-old girl. But it was not very long before the Mayo-Gibbon machine was superceded by simpler, less bulky, disposable apparatus. Using a heat exchanger to retain the ability to raise or lower the temperature of the blood, the principles remained the same. But now oxygenation was achieved merely by bubbling oxygen through a reservoir of blood. The most important preliminary to this advance was the development of filters sufficiently fine to prevent even the tiniest bubble entering the patient's circulation and causing a stroke.

It also takes time for the anaesthetist to prepare the patient. A drug is injected to send the patient to sleep and another to relax his muscles. A tube is placed in his trachea to provide nitrous oxide anaesthetic gas and oxygen. Another goes through his nose into his stomach to keep it empty, as the acid could be dangerous if he vomited. A further tube drains his bladder allowing a constant watch to be kept on kidney function. An intravenous drip is established and, to keep an eye on the pressure in the veins near the heart, another fine tube is placed in one of the jugular veins in the neck. An arterial line is put in his wrist to monitor blood and perfusion pressure. Wires are used too, on arms and legs for a constant ECG trace, and in the oesophagus to measure temperature.

Then it is the surgeons turn. The chest is opened, usually from the front. Then the patient is given an anticoagulant. Before 'going on bypass', appropriate sized tubes have to be placed to divert all blood draining back to the heart into the machine, and another put in the aorta to direct oxygenated blood back to the patient. Only then, co-ordinated by the surgeon, can the circuit be completed and the operation commence.

## Special Care

After cardiopulmonary bypass the heart has to take over from the heart/lung machine within an hour or so of the surgical insult. Though invariably improved by the corrective surgery, its function has to be monitored very closely in the immediate post-operative period, and any treatment needed administered at once. In the early days patients presented for surgery were often extremely ill with diseased valves and failing hearts which could not be supported medically. Valve replacement was considered a last resort.

Such patients might need careful observation for as long as a week or two after operation. Some might go into renal failure and others, liver failure as well. For these, expert advice was essential and the services of a nephrologist were arranged. But as experience with extra-corporeal circulation and confidence in management were gained, surgery as a treatment came to be considered earlier in the course of the disease. Unless the underlying condition was extremely complicated, the critical period gradually became less protracted. Today most cardiac patients spend about 24 hours in the ITU.

This essential post-operative care had to be provided initially in a single recovery room. As numbers rose, a six-bedded Intensive Therapy Unit was opened on 6 April 1964. Conveniently near the operating theatre at the central end of F Ward, it also catered for any Harefield patient needing special care, including children at first. Such units were just becoming generally recognised as extremely valuable for nursing ill patients. Concentrated in one area, specialist staff and equipment could be provided effectively and economically.

In 1965 a separate coronary thrombosis unit was proposed but the Regional Board would not support the plan 'as a research project, because the . . . usefulness of such units was accepted. . . . However . . . [Harefield was] a particularly suitable place for this work to be developed and as the unit . . . urgently required two monitors . . . it was agreed these be purchased from free monies at a cost of . . . £488.' Thus the existing busy ITU had to be used for these patients too. When the new ground floor theatre block opened, E Ward was altered to accommodate both the ITU and the female thoracic surgical beds from C Ward. Both E and F Wards had been enclosed but, except for the ITU sections of both, in the prevailing economic climate the balconies had not been incorporated and the single rooms were very small.

Obtaining nurses for the specialised work was very difficult. Coping with all the problems over the next 20 years or more, guiding both the ITU and PSU from the beginning towards the standards of today, was Sister Ellen M. Tompsett. Committed to this type of work she was selected in the early days of ITUs to be a member of the Royal College of Nursing working party on staffing them. When the Joint Board of Clinical Nursing Studies (JBCNS) was set up by the DHSS, she was also a member of the groups working out their postgraduate Cardiothoracic and Paediatric Cardiothoracic Courses.

## Attendant Alterations

The enterprise and innovation of George Wiggins contributed considerably to progress in the earlier days. It resulted in improvisation, improvements to equipment, and economies. 'The Technician in the Heart-Lung Department . . . serviced and brought back into use the heat exchanger supplied with the Mayo-Gibbon blood bypass apparatus ten years ago. . . . Using this . . . it has been possible to use . . . oxygenators costing £10 each instead of . . . oxygenator and heat exchanger costing £40 each.' Despite his ever increasing work in the operating theatre, he found time to devise methods to sterilise apparatus, including suction pumps and ventilators. He then initiated at Harefield the ethylene oxide gas method of sterilisation.

Obligations of other hospital departments also increased, particularly Pathology. Estimation of the levels of chemicals in the blood, such as potassium and sodium, were needed frequently in cardiac surgical patients, often out of hours. In the early days, one such test, for potassium, had to be done repeatedly throughout the first post-operative night on very ill patients. It was one of the jobs the ITU duty registrar did in a small room adjacent to the Unit. As patient numbers rose and pressures on the junior surgical staff increased, this became impractical and was done as required in the Pathology Laboratory. Haematology became so busy providing blood for transfusion and for the heart/lung machine, that a Transfusion Section had to be formed.

From the start of 'open heart' surgery at Harefield, the essential monitoring of blood gas levels during every operation using the heart/lung machine had been done in the Respiratory Physiology Laboratory. The cramped quarters it shared with the ever busier Cardiology Department became untenable. When the Special School closed in 1976 it moved there, leaving Cardiology space for a second laboratory.

Between 1964 and 1969 about 100 'open heart' operations were carried out each year by the thoracic surgeons. But their rôle was gradually changing. As cardiac techniques, knowledge and skills widened, so there was a tendency to lean towards one or other aspect of the specialty. Some elected to do both as before. When 'the Uncle' left Harefield he was followed briefly by J. Keith Ross (now Sir Keith). Then in 1968 I was appointed and a year later, to a new post to allow expansion of cardiac surgery, came Egyptian born Magdi H. Yacoub. Suddenly the number of cardiac operations trebled, becoming the second highest in the country. But there had been no equivalent expansion of facilities. The impact of this dramatic rise on the staff was so enormous that Harefield was hard put to cope. The goodwill of everyone, not least the nurses, was tried to the limit.

## Developing Techniques

With more time available using cardiopulmonary bypass, 'closed' mitral valvotomy became an operation of the past. A better job could be done safely under direct vision instead of by feel. If it is at all possible a valve is always repaired. For those that have to be replaced, artificial valves were used at first. As these could cause several serious problems resulting from turbulent blood flow and coagulation effects, Mr Yacoub proceeded to homograft valve replacement. This meant negotiation with Coroners to obtain human hearts, from which the valves were garnered and stored. He used such valves, both stored and freshly obtained, very productively in both adults and children, producing 'brilliant results stimulating world wide interest. . . . Patients treated between . . . 1969 and . . . 1971, [had an] overall hospital mortality . . . [of] 7 per cent . . . compared with an . . . average for . . . similar institutions of 15–25 per cent. Follow up . . . indicated a high level of success.'

Harefield also took part in an international multi-centre prospective clinical trial on 'alternative treatments of survivors of mycardial infarction'. Starting in 1972, the trial investigated whether surgery could protect patients at risk from further heart attacks. Those that suffer ischaemic heart disease, with its attendant angina or myocardial infarction, have narrowed coronary arteries. The surgical methods used were endarterectomy, or 'coring out' the narrowed portion, and bypass grafts. At this operation, a vein graft is inserted to carry blood to the heart muscle around, instead of through, the obstructed artery. Depending upon how many are blocked, so the number of vein grafts is determined. As many as five or six can be placed at once.

General surgeon Mr Bradley was operating on aneurysms of the abdominal aorta and the Thoracic Unit dealt with those of the thoracic aorta. The affected portion of the vessel is replaced with a tube of woven cloth acceptable to the body. The latter cases need the support of the heart/lung machine. Now the few people surviving a ruptured aorta in a road accident also survive surgical repair.

Most research now related to the heart, any with clinical aspects being approved by the Hospital Ethical Committee. Many studies were made possible by grants from the British Heart Foundation (BHF) and other research funds. They were pursued with the help of research posts which had also been created. A plethora of papers appeared in the medical journals. Some were on drugs used during cardiac catheterisation, and anaesthesia for coronary artery surgery; on late (10 years or more) results of heart valve replacements, and use of valves constructed from stored dura mater (a tough membrane taken after death from around the brain); on the value of echocardiography, or ultrasound, in the investigation of heart disease; on the effect of the game Squash Racquets on the heart, and the use of the gamma-camera; and on bacterial endocarditis, tumours of the heart, dysfunction of its muscle, and 'the absent pulmonary valve'. A cardiologist, radiologist or surgeon presented Harefield's results at clinical meetings in Great Britain and worldwide.

## More Pioneering

As Holmes Sellors and Vernon Thompson had hopefully foreseen, Harefield continued to provide an innovative, extensive cardiothoracic service. In Mr Yacoub, Harefield had a surgeon who not only had a prodigious capacity for work but also a particular interest and expertise in correcting congenital heart defects in tiny people.

One of the more complicated abnormalities is called transposition of the great vessels, in which the aorta and pulmonary artery leave the wrong side of the heart.

> This means that . . . blood short of oxygen is recirculated back to the head and body without passing through the lungs . . . in an almost closed loop. Children . . . can only stay alive (if) some blood . . . mixes either through a hole in the heart or through a duct . . . which normally closes in the first few hours of life. . . . Although . . . not the first in the world to carry out a successful switch operation, we had been developing (it) for three years prior to our first . . . one in 1975. We . . . developed the two-stage operation for anatomical correction for children with [transposition and] an intact septum. . . . [This] we . . . pioneered and have the largest experience in the world. We first started . . . doing anatomical correction in the first few weeks of life in 1982 and . . . were probably the first . . . in the world to do [one] successfully.

Another surgical method had been devised to correct another defect in which the heart has only one ventricle. Possibly the first person in the world to have the operation, in 1974, was working in a research capacity at Harefield 14 years later.

A constant search to treat other complex abnormalities has resulted in innovative procedures such as that in which a coronary artery, arising from the pulmonary artery instead of the aorta, is placed in its correct anatomical position. The defect in which the pulmonary veins drain into the wrong part of the heart can be put right too.

Occasionally a Harefield innovation has been controversial. In 1975 an attempt was made to improve the condition of a 13-month-old dying child with severe heart, kidney and liver failure, so that corrective heart surgery could be achieved. It involved linking the circulation of the infant with that of an anaesthetised baboon, hoping that the organs of the animal would help the failing ones of the child. 'It was a last ditch effort. . . . At one stage they . . . were disconnected because we thought the child had made it, but he had a relapse.' Both died. There ensued quite a heated public debate. 'People may be upset at the idea. But from what we have done . . . there is hope for a lot of people' said Mr Yacoub.

Harefield had always been enterprising and forward looking, and the fact that it was under fire was nothing new. The Board's Senior Medical Officer, having agreed that 'the long term future of Harefield lay in cardiothoracic and chest work', wrote in May 1972:

> I am greatly concerned . . . that a heart transplant should be performed at Harefield. . . . I am doubtful whether the necessary nursing strength, laboratory . . . and isolation facilities for post-operative care could be allocated . . . without prejudice to the other responsibilities of the hospital.

Nevertheless, on 8 September 1973, Harefield's first heart transplant was carried out.

## Cardiac Patients

In the early days, for the man in the street to be told that his lethal cardiac disease could be treated by surgery seemed nothing short of miraculous. Though frightened, he would accept the offered lifeline with unquestioning thankfulness. As methods advance and attitudes alter, he retains great interest in the marvels of technology. But now better informed, when an ethical aspect arises relating to this 'seat of human emotion' and its other intangible attributes, he will question. Nevertheless, when faced with his own mortality, he will still accept and is still afraid.

This does not apply to very young patients who have not yet learnt to communicate. It is estimated that 'almost 1 in 100 babies born in Britain has a heart defect'. Infants and children are first seen by the paediatric cardiologist who 'is responsible for sorting out what the

problem is. . . . The baby that has very complicated things wrong
. . . tends to come . . . very early in life, perhaps on the first day.
If things are less complicated, then the baby may come . . . at two
weeks, one month or later.'

Treating children is very exacting. They 'become extremely ill very
much more quickly than an adult . . . and therefore one cannot stand
and wait and watch as one can with an adult. On the other hand
they . . . recover more quickly than adults. . . . Dealing with very
tiny people . . . [who] don't have as much blood as an adult . . . you
have to be very careful . . . about bleeding. They also tend not to be
as fat as adults and have to be kept warm.' In the early 1980s there
was a 2-year-old patient with Fallots Tetralogy. Almost unnoticed
was the fact that the child was a descendent of Thomas Wakley, a
link with Harefield's past. His operation was a total correction, done
almost exactly 33 years after Holmes Sellors' first epic one.

Most patients coming into Harefield are those who live within
the Region. But as knowledge of the work and expertise of the TSU
spread, so they came from further afield. This applies especially to
those adults and children suffering from cardiac conditions not yet
treatable elsewhere. They include ordinary people and famous ones:
from miners to royal princes, from media personalities to industrial
magnates, from housewives and mothers to prime ministers. They
come from Britain, Europe, Scandinavia, the Middle East, and from
all over the world. Once again there are times when the Hospital
seems like the United Nations.

A fair proportion of admissions are emergencies. For these, and ill
patients flown in from abroad who cannot be turned away, beds have
to be found quickly. Among them are infants and children coming to
the PSU in ever greater numbers. The pressure for beds is sometimes
enormous, especially as many from abroad cannot receive treatment
under the NHS. 'Many Private Patients were sent directly to the
Hospital and the PSU because of the fame of the Hospital.' During the
precarious years when the children's work was developing, it was
felt that if these patients were refused, the Unit would not survive.
But at times 'distress was caused by [the "booked" patient] being
told that no bed was available when they arrived . . . especially when
detailed domestic arrangements had had to be made'. Nevertheless,
many confronted thus take the disappointment with remarkable fortitude, even though they are facing the biggest trial of their lives.

133

## The Surgical Experience

In the beginning a cardiac surgical patient could expect to be in hospital for several weeks, the first three after surgery in bed. As years passed a 'quiet revolution' occurred. He has got out of bed and gone home earlier and earlier, until the duration of admission for the average patient had fallen to about six days.

But as Harefield has become busier, the person with heart disease usually has to be subjected to more than one admission. During the first the diagnosis is confirmed, details of the problem discovered, and the course of treatment planned. The need for cardiac surgery engenders in patients such reactions as: 'The medical term would be "instant panic".' But unless the patient is very ill, it is impossible to proceed to surgery immediately because of the numbers being investigated. They have to wait their turn. 'Home for a month . . . then the journey . . . back to Harefield . . . was so unreal I cannot remember my feelings.'

> Finally 'admission was brisk and businesslike and I was allocated (a) ward. . . . My wife was with me. I joked that she had come because I wouldn't tell her where I had put the insurance policies! The truth is that the Harefield system of the next of kin staying at the hospital is of great comfort to the patient. . . . The League of Friends' . . . accommodation there was a very great kindness.
>
> There followed a couple of days of . . . tests . . . done very professionally by all sorts of people, with a pleasant word and little fuss. There was even a visit to ask what request I had for the Hospital Radio! It was all done so very well. . . . One very important happening was repeated at several stages prior to surgery, . . . making sure the patient and family knew exactly what was going to happen and how the patient would look and react in the Intensive Therapy Unit and immediately after.

The operation is not a pleasant experience. After having coronary artery bypass grafts one patient

> had double vision, my speech and thoughts were out of synchronisation, my judgement of distance was hopeless, . . . and I wondered if I would ever walk again. [There was] the added delight of breaking into tears every time I sneezed!
>
> The care and attention shown before surgery was excellent and so professional, increasing greatly [post-operatively] – nurses on the ward, the surgical teams on daily rounds, the physiotherapists, . . . people bringing books and food, the Ward Clerks, one's own visitors with cards and flowers – all the morale boosters needed. The visits to X-ray, ultrasound, another angiogram, more blood sampling, exercise

and targets that I can only describe as 'get well targets', the steady progress from walking to the door of the Ward to making it to the end of the corridor and then to the outside world. Another important step was casually meeting people who were coming in for their annual [check] at Out-patients, and seeing that the operations were so very successful.

# · 12 ·

# The Years Between

'As a hospital, Harefield has had its full share of the problems common to any hospital "built without the city walls". Difficulty of access provides problems of staffing and in visiting. Domestic staff is not easily available in a country village and many nurses would prefer to be within easy distance of a city centre. Relatives and visitors also find that distance is an inconvenience, though complaints on this score are surprisingly few. But, having looked at the disadvantages, what are the assets? They are obvious – better atmosphere in all senses, better outlook and better surroundings. Patients do not live in a confined ward in a dressing gown and carpet slippers. When fit they are fully dressed and walking about to whatever extent their physical condition permits.' Sir Thomas Holmes Sellors 1965.

That Harefield continued to progress under the weight of constant difficulties over money, nursing staff shortage and recurrent uncertainty about its future, was due to the extraordinary, ever changing group of people that gathered there.

## Money

'This conference deplores the action of the Ministry of Health in so restricting revenue allocations . . . as to endanger . . . essential services and . . . prevent . . . overdue improvements' was part of a resolution put forward for the 1962 conference of the Association of Hospital Management Committees. But it was not accepted 'in the absence of support from . . . outside the Metropolitan regions to which the financial restrictions were confined.'

The Management Committee was under constant pressure. In addition to pay awards, monetary consequences of other unpredictable national events were rarely completely met from central funds either. Happenings such as devaluation of the £ in 1968, policy changes after general elections, increased postal charges and inflation compounded funding problems. 'The Board feel sure that they can rely on the full co-operation of . . . Management Committees in . . . taking . . . steps to meet the . . . price increases and . . . restrict . . . expenditure . . . within the approved allocation. I must emphasise the . . . seriousness of the matter . . . [and] the need for . . . action to be taken immediately . . . [to] . . . deal with [it] in confidence and without publicity.'

Strikes had their effect too. In 1966 a Seamen's strike increased some food prices, and in 1972–73 a rash broke out: postal workers, miners, National Union of Public Employees, and hospital ancillary staff. Industrial relations at Harefield had always been good and the Hospital was never overly affected. When visiting the laundry, Management Committee members 'were impressed by the . . . happy working atmosphere amongst . . . staff who had . . . recently been involved in the industrial dispute'. And this was when chronic staff shortage prevailed and antiquated equipment was still being used. Things changed, however, when Harefield was chosen to provide the Group service.

One recourse to economise was continued curtailment of maintenance. The Regional Board thoroughly disapproved of this. But they found £12,000 for repairs to the 'crumbling' concrete structure of Harefield's main block because it was due to the original method of building. The local press observed: 'Regional cuts hit hospital standards. Because the Harefield & Northwood Hospital Group is being kept short of money, . . . savings are having to be made by lowering already low standards and . . . by restricting non-clinical services.'

From time to time the TSU was given small extra amounts by the Board but it was by no means enough for the ever increasing work load. Attempts to impose constraints seemed to be by curtailing the money supply. In 1970 'the Board considered that existing commitments should be covered before new developments were financed.' The Management Committee, in difficulties just maintaining the activity of the Unit, let alone its increase, were told: 'I do not think the Board has stipulated that the number of operations should be restricted, but your Management Committee cannot anticipate . . . any further money . . . for this unit. . . . It is a matter for them to decide what service they can provide from within the resources available to them.'

When 'asked if they could make any economy in the cardiothoracic service provided', Harefield agreed that money could not be taken from other areas. They responded unanimously that, as the Unit provided a Regional service, 'the Board should accept full responsibility

137

as to the amount and type of work to be carried out. . . . The Board is apparently unwilling to recognise that the Cardiothoracic Unit was expensive.' Whatever the cost, no clinician at Harefield was going to refuse patients a new treatment. Thus their opinions and those trying to exert some sort of control frequently differed.

## Adaptations

If Harefield was to advance in the prevailing financial climate, it had to be by piecemeal development and making the best use possible of existing accommodation. In juggling around what was done where, non-clinical areas were affected most. Because the gate house, as well as 'Cathard', was needed for staff accommodation in 1961, the telephone switchboard was moved into the main block again. It was vastly improved when a much needed automatic telephone exchange appeared, with a small brick building outside to house the wiring. In 1966 Medical Records was moved to the 'north' and Mrs Toovey and the Medico-Social Department from the 'north' to a room on G Ward. A little later it went back again next to the Records Department!

Between 1958 and 1963 the Pathology Department's work more than doubled. A Control of Infection Sub-committee had been set up in 1960. As chairman, bacteriologist Eugene Nassau supervised prevention of any type of infection and, should it arise, advise on management. But even though more morbid anatomy and cytology, and some haematology, biochemistry, and bacteriology, was gradually being done at Mount Vernon Hospital, the Laboratory had to provide an ever escalating service.

Both thoracic and cardiac patients required blood chemistry studies, often out of hours by technicians called from home. Those in the Transfusion Laboratory, having the task of obtaining and cross matching blood, were affected too as the number of emergency cardiac operations rose. Also, as operations became more complex, more fresh blood was required. Donors had to be contacted, invited to the Hospital and the blood collected.

By 1971 Dr Hamilton was expressing her concern. 'The stress amongst the staff . . . is building, especially with the growth of open heart surgery which requires very demanding lab assistance. The work load . . . has increased tremendously. We have had to handle emergency work as well as regular tests which grow in complexity each year [and] need at least six more technicians to cope. The biggest problem is funds. If these are available I foresee no difficulty in finding qualified people.'

Paradoxically the removal of clinical work from the 'north wards' enabled essential adjuncts, especially for heart disease, to be accommodated very economically. The old 'north' theatre was turned into an animal research and Homograft Laboratory. 'Soft' money was forthcoming through various research grants from bodies such as the BHF, and technical help was obtained to collect fresh hearts and prepare the valves.

By using B West Ward as a 5-day cardiothoracic investigatory ward from 1973, clinicians were able to use their time much more effectively. Many patients could have necessary tests at Harefield instead of at the referring hospital where facilities were often not as good or not available. But it also meant quicker 'turnover' and more patients coming in. The same year, Management noted 'great savings . . . made by the dramatic reduction of average length of stay resulting from improving techniques. These may seem . . . more apparent than real in that . . . expenditure . . . will naturally increase as work load increases.'

## Hospital Profile

The Special School was in existence until 1976. Its Joint Governing Body comprised Dr Houghton or Dr Roberts while they were still there, Dorothy Whiting and then Mrs McLoughlin, and other officials including someone from the Local Authority and its Education Committee. Mrs Daniels was a member for many years and Mr Watson was Secretary. Early on the School had joined the Special Schools Association. It had developed contacts with the Youth Employment Exchange and formed a magazine and Art Club. Extending its scope over these years, it came to provide such things as languages, typing and secretarial skills in addition to the basic '3Rs'. The average number of pupils, both children and adults, varied from 16 to 37, and they had various examination successes.

Though Harefield was still providing some general hospital services, the bulk of the work was being done on the Thoracic Unit. In 1970 Harefield was officially recognised once again as the Regional Cardiothoracic Centre. This was greeted with only tentative sighs of relief. Even though Harefield was providing cardiothoracic care to one third of those in need of it in the London area, no firm statement had been forthcoming about either the short or long term future.

The effect of this omission was profound, and morale plummeted. In 1973, having been repeatedly pressed for a commitment, the Regional Board remained evasive:

> It is . . . not possible to reach a conclusion on the . . . duration of Harefield . . . as a . . . centre . . . until the Board has knowledge of the developments at Brompton Hospital, . . . and . . . the Department of Health's decision on the . . . future of the National Heart Hospital. In the meantime, . . . any . . . major schemes at Harefield beyond those already in the capital programme should be deferred.

It didn't help either that Harefield had gradually shrunk to just over 400 beds. 'It was reasonable to expect some reduction in staff establishments. . . . Heads of Departments said . . . they were already working under pressure and . . . could not make any reductions.' They needed an idea of what the overall development would be 'in order to plan . . . future work'.

There is no doubt that the hard working enthusiastic junior staff, surgical, anaesthetic and cardiological, made very material contributions to the developments. Harefield has never been affiliated officially with any teaching institution, but, because of the experience available there, rotation arrangements were established with several London Teaching Hospitals for the senior anaesthetic, cardiology and surgical registrars.

## Nursing Shortage

In the 1970s, nurses 'just could not be recruited'. Apart from extensive advertising, several new measures were tried. 'Return to Nursing' courses were put on at Hillingdon Hospital, and nurses' Study Days started again. Uniforms for Sisters and staff nurses were modernised and a new badge, introduced for the joint Nursing School, replaced the engraved Hospital badge which every nurse qualifying at Harefield had received since 1958. Harefield established 'in service' specialty training courses in the ITU and PSU. Unfortunately the former could not continue after Harefield's JBCNS Cardiothoracic Course started. Other local ideas to attract and keep nurses included a suggestion that those with appropriate postgraduate qualifications should receive more pay, in line with geriatric, mental & district nurses. The Thoracic Unit surgeons established an annual Nursing Essay Prize of cash, open to any student or trained nurse who had worked, or was working, at Harefield.

With the work of the Unit continuing to increase, embargoes imposed on staffing to save money and the gradual reduction of hours in the nurses' working week from 44 hours to 40, the pressures increased. Adding to the problem, the GNC had introduced a new training syllabus in 1962 and again in 1969; and about 1971, the Asa

Briggs Report appeared. Each resulted in student and pupil nurses spending more time away from the wards, and restricted the type of ward upon which they could work. 'Cardiothoracic wards were too specialised.'

It was perhaps the nursing staff above all who exhibited the 'spirit of Harefield' to the full. The stresses on them reached a peak in 1971, when rumours of closure of the Hospital were rife and morale very low, and went on into 1973, a year when 571 patients were admitted to six ITU beds and 195 into nine PSU beds. In an effort to help, the three-shift system of working was instituted in the two Units. Unpopular measures, but necessary from time-to-time, included curtailment of operating theatre time. Once the situation was so bad that the main block theatres had to be closed for a while and both general and cardiothoracic work done in the cardiac theatres. Sometimes bed numbers in the ITU or cardiothoracic wards had to be reduced temporarily. Occasionally a nurse left. That general beds were rarely affected caused considerable

> misery and bitterness. . . . The waiting lists were long and patients . . . dying before they could be admitted. The nursing staff were also very unhappy. . . . [The] decision [was] taken to reduce beds on F [Ward] . . . [with] no consultation. . . . No cuts were made on medical wards, which provided a local service with no waiting list, whereas the thoracic wards provided a regional service and had long waiting lists. . . . [It was] explained it was difficult to shut . . . medical wards as nurses . . . [had] . . . to receive basic training in such areas, whereas a set time only was allowed on specialised units.

Nevertheless the short-handed nurses, trained, in training and the invaluable nursing auxiliary, always gave to the utmost of their effort and goodwill to overcome the difficulties. They struggled on to provide ever more precise care to an ever increasing number of patients with conditions of ever increasing complexity.

## Nursing Reorganisation

Meanwhile, until she left in 1967, another of the nettles Miss Monteith had to grasp was the 1964 Salmon Report. This outlined a new structure for senior nurses, dividing them into ten grades and three levels of management (top, middle and first line). The Group Nursing Committee felt this 'Decentralisation of Nursing Administration' provided

> an excellent career structure. . . . Many able nurses . . . reluctant to move from patients would be willing to advance to middle manage-

ment. . . . Recruitment would be enhanced. . . . Posts in matron's office . . . [would have] . . . specific spheres of responsibility. . . . Nursing schools would be satisfactory if . . . in close proximity to wards and departments . . . for experience. . . . Nursing administrators would help select recruits and supervise . . . practical work. . . . The uniform grading will remove present anomalies in . . . status and . . . reduce discontent. . . . It is logical to have one charge nurse for each ward with definite spheres of authority . . . supported by . . . closely available middle management.

For this grade, 'the opportunity for promotion to . . . Nursing Officer (NO) widens prospects for . . . ward sister upwards. . . . The . . . proposals would involve considerable change in the present procedures, [and] would need to be carefully introduced.' With this Miss Monteith agreed. Sure implementation was inevitable and be much disapproved of by many doctors, she welcomed a pilot scheme for middle and first line management. Now all would get an idea of what was in store.

Harefield medical staff were indeed much against the change, convinced that not only would it do nothing to help the major problem of lack of nurses, but also it would take extremely valuable senior nurses away from the bedside. By making them Nursing Officers (Salmon No. 7) the position would become one of 'all chiefs and no indians'. The idea of 'Salmon' was for these NOs to remain in the clinical area, but in a small hospital like Harefield they had to take on administrative duties as well.

Grace Schofield, 'one of those fortunate people to whom responsibility appears to come easily, . . . efficient and with personal natural charm', was Matron of both Mount Vernon and Harefield Hospitals when she was promoted under the Salmon structure. Succeeding her as Chief Nursing Officer (Salmon No. 10), was Dorothy A. Hunt. Miriam Tucker had followed Miss Graham as Senior Nursing Officer (SNO) Education (Salmon No. 8). Then, on becoming Principal Nursing Officer Education (Salmon No. 9), she had to deal with the preliminary negotiations for the now planned amalgamation of the Harefield and Northwood School of Nursing with that of Hillingdon Hospital.

Mrs E. M. Hughes succeeded Miss Monteith in 1967 until 'Salmon' was implemented. Betty Froud took over as Harefield's SNO from 1970 to 1973, to be followed by T. Myrtle Holbrook for the next 14 years. By 1972 the system was in place at Harefield and all 'new' officers, including the NOs and Ward Sisters, sent on management courses. The clinical areas remaining on the 'north side' were now in the over all charge of NO Michael Allen, and those that had been moved to the main block were supervised by NO Miss Sybil Jones. Another NO was appointed for the cardiothoracic wards, Miss Demulder became NO of the operating theatres and Miss Tompsett, NO in charge of the ITU, PSU and the postgraduate courses.

## Volunteers

Harefield's League of Friends was by now occupying a very special place and becoming invaluable to the working of the Hospital. Having completed a Refreshment Pavilion about half way up the road to the 'north' in 1963, the 'Friends' went on to raise money to provide a Visitors' Bungalow. Achieved with the financial aid of the King's Fund, the building lay to the north of Observation Ward and opened in 1967. To lodge there, relatives of patients who lived far afield only had to make a contribution to the Hospital.

Other amenities for patients and staff would also appear. Provided through the 'Friends' were such things as the Hospital Library service, taken over by the Red Cross in 1967; furniture for the Bungalow and chairs for the Physiotherapy Department and concert hall; table cloths for the dining-room and linen, counterpanes and curtains for the geriatric wards; bedside lamps and hair driers for the Nurses' Home and paintings for the School; hire of at least seventeen television sets for the wards and residences; entertainers for the children's Christmas party and gifts for the patients; and a grant towards refurbishing the tennis courts.

The Management Committee acknowledged their help in 1970. 'Each of the hospitals in the Group is fortunate in having an active "Friends" or similar association to help with service and extra facilities which cannot be provided out of our ordinary allocation.' With the aid of a grant and loan from the Management Committee, and the King's Fund again, a new Pavilion opened in 1974. Next to the concert hall with another car park behind, it is run by a band of 30 or so willing helpers. Provided with a telephone, this Friends' Pavilion quickly became a popular venue for snack meals and a place to hold 'thank you' parties for the various voluntary helpers.

Individuals would help too, doing things like making curtains or a notice board, and one gave freely of her time in the Occupational Therapy Department, declining any payment. Legacies were left to the Hospital and patients contributed to the various funds. These included the Cardiac Research Fund, the Cardiothoracic Unit Fund and the PSU Fund.

Other organisations also took the hospital, or parts of it, under their wings. In 1968 the Young Volunteer Force Foundation was set up by the Government, who strongly supported and encouraged personal voluntary service. One group of boys from Merchant Taylor's School helped Harefield patients settle in at home after a long period in hospital. Lions International of Hillingdon, Uxbridge and Harrow made major contributions. By 1969 they had financed the redecoration and furnishing of the day rooms of C, E, F, and G Wards, which contained, on C and G Wards, billiard tables previously given by Middlesex Education Department. The sanitary annexes of these wards were somewhat spartan, and the rooms available for private patients also left much to be desired in the way of comforts and amenities. Repeated tackling of the authorities by the medical staff, constant pressure on the Regional Board, and with the help of the 'Friends' and various charities, things improved greatly.

Many charities, large or small, such as The Not Quite Perfect Golf Club, helped. The Antedeluvian Order of Buffalo would provide fancy dress entertainment for the children at Christmas time. The Independent Order of Foresters made the PSU one of its charitable interests. Much needed equipment was provided from time to time and funds were forthcoming for a ward extension. Without all these good people Harefield Hospital would not be the place it is today.

## The Atmosphere

Throughout all its vicissitudes Harefield remained a friendly place. 'The staff generally in Harefield were a very happy staff and the atmosphere was a friendly one' said a member of one Committee in 1967. 'The Hospital as a whole had a very cheerful atmosphere,' said another in 1971. A year later an erstwhile patient put his views in the local paper: 'There is at Harefield a large, busy and important establishment where it is impossible to pass anyone who has not a cheerful word and a happy smile. These are so infectious it is impossible not to reciprocate. . . . I . . . pay tribute to all who work there. There must be many . . . who would wish to be associated with these sentiments.'

The Entertainments Committee continued to arrange trips to places of interest at home and abroad for the staff. It organised the Inter Departmental part of the Inter Hospitals Quiz. This cup was won by

Harefield's clerical and administrative staff in 1974. With the League of Friends and the Harefield Community Association, it also ran the annual Fête. There was a Gymkhana in the 'north' field on the same day until the late 1970s. The TocH Fair and the Michaelmas Fayre were usually held in the Hospital grounds too. By sponsoring these events, the Committee shared the profits and were thus able, among other things, to provide Christmas parcels for retired members of staff.

The Social and Sports Club, who took over the old Friends' Pavilion on the road to 'the north', ran badminton, keep fit classes, 'olde tyme' dancing and film shows, bingo and a bar, mostly in the concert hall. There was a photographic society, a football team, tennis and hockey clubs, and the toxopholites of the archery club furthered their skills in the field behind the Pathology Laboratory. The bowling green inside the main gate was still in use too, the Hospital team winning the Hospitals' Cup in 1965. For many years the cricket club arranged matches most weeks, with tea in the Mansion afterwards. The pavilion, which is still there, finally became so decrepit that players had to change in the Domestic Department which now occupied the coach house. Recording these activities from 1964, another monthly magazine appeared, this time called the *Harefield Gazette*.

Happily, in what had become difficult and changing times once more, the faces around the place were often familiar ones. Apart from the medical staff, Pam Durand, Helen Stevenson and Maureen Eggleton were there, Loraine Long (later Mrs Neuhoffer) had come to Matron's office in 1960, Jennifer Hill had joined the secretarial ranks, and in 1964 Betty Westbrook came to the TSU office. Miss Hillson had come as Domestic Superintendent in 1957 when Stanley Browne first arrived. Head Porter from 1963, he was another helpful connecting link. There too were Mrs Joy Kverndal and Mr Sid George of the League of Friends.

## Life Before 1974

In the Mansion, the bay window room had become the sitting room, the medical library having been moved into the previous one, the small room to the right of the front door. Subsequently it was transferred to the main block, with a quiet room for doctors to read in peace. For a little while longer meals were still served in the Mansion and the Nurses' Home, and the kitchen still baked bread, but a 'pay-as-you-eat' system was introduced for staff in 1969. While cooking facilities remained in the Mansion the residents, aided by willing friends, gave monthly 'cordon bleu' dinner parties to which consultant staff were invited as guests. Eventually meals could no longer be cooked there and it all stopped. Then everyone had to use the main dining-room under the concert hall, or the Friends' Pavilion.

Links with the village were maintained by the ANZAC Day service at St Mary's Church which staff faithfully attended. Strengthening ties further, married doctors were living in Parkside and the village High Street, as well as Newdigate Road by 1967, and more of the nursing staff had found homes in the village. Then, for good or ill, further links were forged when responsibility for staff health went from the charge of a Hospital staff member to the general practitioners of the Harefield Group Practice.

Running the general office were Mrs Eccles and Mrs Webb, with F. J. (Slasher) Green. Mr Pearmund remained in charge of the Supplies Department 'up north' until 1973. Over the years he had gradually developed a panel of regular suppliers and, as time passed, more and more supplies of all kinds were bought in bulk for the Group. This decreased choice, but it was cheaper that way. Eventually the purchase of many supplies was centralised further, to a Regional basis.

If administrative continuity was needed, Mrs Daniels, known by many as 'the lady with the hat', was frequently at Harefield. Chairman of the Management Committee for fifteen years, she also served on many sub-committees: the early Group Contracts & Supplies, General Purposes & Finance and Nursing. As a member of Harefield's House Committee too, sometimes in the Chair, she was very aware of the problems of the 'north side', which kept Mrs Baker's ghost alive! Appointed to the Regional Board in 1963, Mrs Daniels received the OBE in 1967.

But even in these low years, Harefield was not to be deterred. It continued to investigate and operate upon more thoracic patients, and almost as many cardiac, than any other centre in the Region. By 1974 more than 1000 patients were having cardiac catheter investigations and over 2000 were being admitted to the 70 bedded TSU each year. A similar number of major thoracic and major cardiac operations, both exceeding 500, were being done every year.

*Reorganisation of the Health Service*

Toward the end of the 1960s, Harefield staff read a newspaper article with understanding nods:

> Management Committees are too big, some have more than 25 members, (and) are bogged down in a morass of sub-committees [which] interfere in the day to day work of professional administrators. . . . Too many . . . members are passengers with little or no medical or administrative experience. . . . Experienced [people] are discouraged from serving . . . because the committees are too slow and inefficient. . . . [They] are responsible to no one. They decide every policy decision and control the spending . . . for the running costs of the hospitals. . . . Another . . . fault is . . . , like rabbits breeding offspring, they keep breeding subcommittees. The . . . Health Ministry must . . . stop this worsening situation.

The Government was well aware of the problems in the NHS. A reorganisation to rectify things was being planned to achieve 'unified administration of the medical and related services in an area by one authority'. As the plan also involved re-arrangement of Local Authority boundaries, it was a complicated business. Deciding to retain the Regional Authorities, they proposed '85 Area Health Authorities (AHA) . . . providing all health services in areas co-terminal with the new local authority councils . . . [to be] responsible for . . . social and environmental . . . services'. Depending on population, Areas would be divided into Districts forming a third tier. Each tier would have an advisory Team of Officers –Administrator, Treasurer, Nurse and Medical Officer. Management would be by consensus.

'To determine and express public needs and preferences', the Government also decided that Community Health Councils (CHC) should be formed of '18–30 people with particular interest in the health service, . . . who represent voluntary organisations already working in support of health services.' As their effectiveness would depend entirely on the calibre and attitudes of members, and the understanding established with Health Authorities and their officers, this was greeted with some scepticism.

As plans for reorganisation went ahead, countrywide concern emerged about: the methods of, and limited time available for, consultation; the proposed reduction of health profession and medical representation on the Authorities; that Authority members would still be appointees and not representatives; and there was no recognised 'boss' of the multi-disciplinary organisation. Though welcoming the co-ordinating proposals, another of Harefield's concerns was that 'the larger areas and populations . . . were . . . likely to lead to even more impersonal administration and . . . be unsatisfactory'.

Local press again summarised the position: 'Seven Area Health Authorities one being Hillingdon, will make up the new Region . . . replacing the North West Metropolitan Hospital Region. . . . One of 14, . . . [it] will have 600,000 fewer people within its boundaries than the . . . present Regional . . . Board. The . . . health areas will correspond to county . . . or London Borough boundaries. . . . Management Committees . . . will disappear and control [be] streamlined through Areas.'

The first changes occurred in 1972 when the Chairman of the new North West Thames Regional Health Authority was appointed, followed by the members and selection of the Regional Officers. Numerous directives then started to appear and, as seemed so often the case, time was of the essence. One letter of 6 April on the important matter of Area and Regional Boundaries requested a reply by the 19th. The reorganisation Bill received Royal Assent in June 1973. By December the 15-strong shadow Hillingdon Area Health Authority (AHA) had held its first meeting. The Chairman had been appointed by the Secretary of State, ten members by the Regional Authority and four by the Local Authority.

# · 13 ·

# Survival

IF Harefield thought preceding years had been trying ones, the next few were to prove far worse. Having just become accustomed to a very different administration, the Hospital became embroiled in the biggest medico-political controversy it had ever faced. The essence of everything Harefield was, and that which had made it so, was to be put to the test.

## Local Reorganisation

In the reorganisation process, Harefield & Northwood and Hillingdon Hospital Groups and Hillingdon Local Authority had participated in a 'Management Study'. Harefield & Northwood Management Committee made 'recommendations . . . which would make the Borough of Hillingdon one complete Area bringing in Hillingdon Hospital'. In discussions to decide whether the Area should be divided into Districts, 'the medical staff of the Hillingdon Group felt there was no advantage in Hillingdon, Mount Vernon and Harefield Hospitals coming under the same management team'. But Joint Liaison Committees, set up to monitor and co-ordinate the many alterations, favoured a one district Area because of 'the geographical position of the Group . . . with its lack of maternity and psychiatric facilities. . . . The population served would be between 200,000 and 250,000'.

On 1 April 1974, Hillingdon Area Health Authority and its Management Team took over. The Harefield & Northwood Group Management Committee and all its sub-committees disappeared in a flurry of farewell dinners. The clinicians had been unanimous that there must be a strong Area Medical Advisory Committee. A 'shadow' meeting on 14 February 1974 comprised seven consultants from Hillingdon Hospital, two each from Harefield and Mount Vernon Hospitals, plus one from each Regional specialty – cardiothoracic, radiotherapy and

149

plastic surgery – and five general practitioners of whom one represented the Community Health services. The Chairman and Vice-chairman were elected from the consultant and general practitioner ranks respectively. Chaired by Dr Idris Jones, the Group Medical Advisory Committee held its last meeting on 15 March 1974.

The concept of being in a single district Area was confusing at first, especially when Hillingdon AHA deemed the Area geographically unwieldy and divided it into South and North Sectors! Sector Administrators replaced Hospital Secretaries but Harefield, in the North Sector with Mount Vernon Hospital, was to have but a Unit Administrator. The Medical Committee rose quickly to defend the Hospital's status: 'A revised management structure had been agreed at Regional level, . . . brought into being as present staff left . . . and new appointments made. . . . Again, changes were being made without consultation.' A year or so later, the Hospital and Harefield's Community Health Centre, soon to be resited adjacent to the Hospital, were assigned to a West Sector.

The new style administration and different method of decision making took a little getting used to. No longer did it mean persuading committees. Now it was individuals on the Area Management Team who had to be convinced of the validity of a plan or development and, with their help, approval of the Authority obtained.

About this time, relationships between Government and medical staff deteriorated countrywide, mostly over conditions of service and pay. Senior doctors in Hillingdon withdrew administrative co-operation for a time, and juniors actually went on strike between December 1975 and January 1976. Gradually, as people in Hillingdon Area got to know each other, a good working basis for the future was established. It became evident, even with its severe financial problems, that the Hillingdon AHA wanted more or less the same future for Harefield as did the Hospital staff. This was as well, because a series of events would soon threaten the Hospital's very existence.

## The Old Problem

In the meantime, reorganisation had not improved the meagre Regional money supply. On the contrary. The RAWP formula was changed yet again: the 'future "yardstick" for allocation will be population served and case load.' North West Thames, with a smaller population, became a 'nil growth' Region and 'in future years . . . can expect less money than . . . in recent years'. Also, for 1976/77, the 'main innovation will be that . . . cash . . . from the DHSS will be

. . . tightly controlled and . . . overspending . . . carried . . . to the next year'. That year too, a 5–10 per cent cut in administrative costs was ordered, so penalising Authorities who had already shown good stewardship. Hillingdon recorded 'that AHAs . . . should be allowed to determine the manner . . . its finances were managed [and were] not convinced that arbitrary constraints . . . led to the most efficient use of resources.'

With continued underfunding of pay awards, price increases and inflation, Hillingdon AHA had to find £½ million during 1976–77. Harefield staff learnt of this, and the local decision to cut all budgets by 2.6 per cent, through a press release! Various measures were imposed to economise. Judged by savings made during the three week strike of junior doctors, all three hospitals were closed to admissions, except for emergencies, for a like period over Christmas. But this time it was not nearly so effective and the unpopular exercise was not repeated. Funding problems were getting worse each year and in 1979, except for nursing staff, many posts were frozen and a one month delay put on advertising others. Then the Area Medical Officer undertook to save about £150,000 by eliminating the need for locum junior staff. Altering contracts to arrange cross cover did not prove easy. The measure was very unpopular and did not last long.

Harefield Medical Staff Committee had already commented 'on the dire financial straits of the . . . Health Service. In almost every hospital there was evidence of lack of maintenance, disrepair and old buildings. . . . Extra funds should be made available . . . before considering any reorganisation of administration which would, at best, lead only to minor economies and more probably, to increased expenditure.' Also criticising the existing annual budget system, 'it was felt that a triannual or quinquennial scheme would lead to broader planning and to less wasteful spending. . . . Supplying and organising . . . specialised units, such as cardiothoracic and burns units, would need to be discussed in more detail.' However the changes inexorably came about. As it had been feared, there seemed even more administrators around and the annual budget system did not change.

Voluminous papers laying down guidelines had been issued, but none had been forthcoming about Regional Specialties. Funding these was an aspect which the Government considered a matter for Regional Authorities. The brand new North West Thames Region decided to adjust the allocation to each Area according to their specialty services, and leave distribution to them. Senior medical staff were very concerned. They had no confidence that Hillingdon's allocation would prove adequate for three Regional Centres, two at Mount Vernon and the expensive TSU at Harefield. Events proved them right. Competition for money intensified as the work of Harefield continued to escalate.

## Financial Management

The Government, itself not satisfied with financial arrangements in the NHS, issued 'Patients First' in 1979. The document laid out details for strict budgetry control

> designed to facilitate functional budgeting. . . . An institutional budget will consist of . . . sub-budgets. . . . This in . . . turn will form part of a district budget. . . . A budget allocation is . . . in terms of . . . cost levels of . . . resources. . . . [Thus] what are controlled are resources translated into financial terms. . . . Whatever authority the manager . . . be granted . . . it should not permit him to alter the level or quality of the service . . . or make changes resulting in a more costly service without the authority of higher management.

Before the changes, which were to be instituted in 1982, Hillingdon AHA decided to explore the potential of local budget devolution. Harefield, though just about to enter its time of trial, welcomed greater local responsibility and control. It agreed to form a 'shadow' Unit Management Group (UMG) comprising the Sector administrator, Senior Nursing Officer, the Chairmen of the Medical Committee and of the Cardiothoracic Division of 'Cogwheel', a Professional & Technical staff member and a financial adviser.

With executive control remaining at Area level, Harefield's money allocation was divided between designated budget holders in the various Departments. The exercise was for the UMG theoretically to control these and ensure Harefield remained within the confines of its overall allocation. The UMG was to review the devolved budgets, investigate under- or overspendings, recommend use of savings to purchase equipment for non-recurring use, or the diversion of funds to another budget. If overspending was found they had to have the agreement of the budget holder before any action was recommended. 'The UMG . . . [had] authority to spend up to £1,000 of any saving' without consultation with higher management.

During this period Jeremy Millar was Harefield's Administrator. He co-ordinated the fledgling UMG while it dealt with constant calls to retrench. Cutbacks on Harefield were so severe that the Medical Committee, monitoring the activities of the Group, made a strong plea for . . . equitable share of economies between hospitals and services . . . , for strong nerves, a little time to see the fruits of economies already started, and consideration of . . . alternatives to severely reduced patient services. Let the Regional Strategy evolve . . . so that the efficiency of the hospital and the morale of its staff be preserved.

The 'shadow' experience proved invaluable in various ways, not least gaining the confidence of higher management by showing that Harefield was capable of controlling its own expenditure.

## The Hospital

Though Harefield still accommodated some general surgery and medicine, far and away the greatest emphasis was, in 1979, on the 'full facilities . . . available for the investigation and treatment with all types of medical and surgical cardiothoracic disease'. These included the X-ray Department of course, where Drs Westbury and Pridie held sway with Superintendent Radiographer Mrs Parnell. Apart from cardiac work, including running a national echocardiography training course, they continued to provide a full radiological service to the thoracic surgeons dealing with lung and oesophageal disease. But to cope with the ever increasing cardiac load, a 'purpose built extension, costing in excess of £½ million [was] about to be commissioned. This will make the . . . facilities at Harefield the most up-to-date in the country with a capability to carry out 2000 angiograms per annum.'

The Cardiology Department had two laboratories after Respiratory Physiology moved out. More appropriately called the Cardiac Investigation Laboratory, it was the Regional Centre for training cardiology technicians and equipped for not only recording ECGs but also a wide range of non-invasive tests such as pacemaker and computerised exercise testing, 24-hour ambulatory monitoring and a variety of other forms of cardiography.

Meanwhile the horizons of the Respiratory Physiology Laboratory had been expanding too. Peter Lockwood, providing an 'in service' training scheme for technicians, had two graduates to help him carry out the many lung function tests available. All types of pulmonary disease could be investigated, including industrial disease. Furthering clinical assessment of oesophageal function and disease, an Oesophageal Laboratory was also established there, with facilities for 24-hour ambulatory pH monitoring and intra-oesophageal pressures. Respiratory Physiology gave a Regional service and had become a secondary referral unit providing a sophisticated range of results to physician and surgeon alike.

Pathology, ensconsed firmly in its 'custom built building a short distance from the main block', provided an ever increasing range of haematological tests on a 24-hour basis. Likewise microbiology, which still had a media preparation room. 'All diagnostic, epidemiological and surveillance tests are carried out except viral studies.' Though most biochemistry was now done at Mount Vernon, 'the Harefield Laboratory provides a 24-hour service for all patients in ITU, theatres and Paediatric . . . Ward (routine and emergency) as well as the remainder of the patients in the Hospital outside office hours'.

There were the four operating theatres – two cardiac which had opened in 1967, and two in the first floor converted accommodation in the main block. The ITU of six beds, with adjacent sleeping quarters for the duty medical officer, occupied a portion of E Ward, and the PSU of 11 beds was in the east end of A Ward. 'Over 900 major cardiothoracic operations are done each year, at least 350 of which are cardiac procedures requiring cardiopulmonary bypass. One third of these are children.' The drop in the latter, from the 500 or more done five years before, was resultant upon Mr Yacoub transferring three sessions to the National Heart Hospital in 1975. In the existing financial climate this factor was the basis for obtaining Regional approval for a second cardiac surgeon.

'Over two thirds of the cardiothoracic admissions are people residing within 10–15 miles of Harefield and in the North West Thames Region.' But Harefield also provided a national and international adult and paediatric cardiology and cardiac surgery service and was a national, as well as Regional, secondary referral centre for both acquired and congenital complex medical and surgical cardiac disease.

## The Threat

In 1977 'Cardiothoracic Surgery in the North West Thames Region' once again came under discussion and extensive negotiation. Then, in its Strategic Plan of 1979, Region stated that Harefield should be one of three Regional Cardiothoracic Centres. Just when it seemed the short term future at least was assured, other events intervened. Quite apart from its constant battle over funding, Harefield found itself embroiled in a even greater one. This time what was at stake was its survival no less.

The Department of Health and Social Security (DHSS) had set

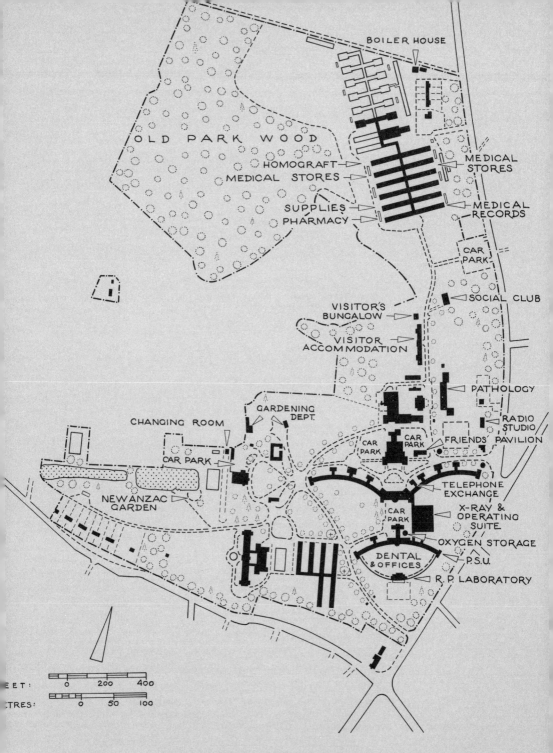

Fig. 9   1976: Harefield Hospital

up the London Health Planning Consortium (LHPC) 'to identify . . . issues relating to health services and clinical teaching in London . . . ; to decide how, by whom and with what priority they should be studied; to evaluate . . . options . . . ; and to recommend means of co-ordinating planning . . . in London.' The LHPC comprised lay and medical representatives from the London Regions, London University and Postgraduate Teaching Hospitals. The fruits of their labours was 'Towards a Balance: a Framework for Acute Hospital Services in London reconciling Service with Teaching Needs', and reports from specialty Study Groups.

One of the LHPC Study Groups, for cardiology and cardiothoracic surgery, was

> to review the existing provision for adults and children . . . in the Thames Regions, to consider the likely need . . . over the next decade . . . to evaluate options for achieving a rational distribution of units . . . taking into account . . . current planning . . . the implications for undergraduate and postgraduate teaching, and to make recommendations on the preferred siting and size of units.

Harefield received a two hour visit from the Group. From various parts of the country a cardiologist, thoracic surgeon, nurse, an administrative medical officer and two lay people in the Health Service, came in October 1978. They departed with a completed questionnaire of details relating to cardiology, cardiac and thoracic surgery: of staffing, bed numbers and occupancy, sources of patients, workload over the previous three years and waiting lists.

In preparing its Report, the Group also took note of opinions expressed by other bodies. All had issued Reports in 1979: the Royal Colleges of Surgeons and of Physicians 'on Combined Medical and Surgical Units for Cardiac Surgery'; the British Paediatric Association's 'Cardiac Services for Children in England and Wales'; and the 'Flowers Report – London Medical Education' from the University of London.

The 63-page Report on Cardiology and Cardiothoracic Surgery was issued a year after the visit. It stated that 'no more paediatric cardiac surgery should be carried out at Harefield' and advised 'the transfer of adult (cardiac) work to a general teaching hospital elsewhere in the Region.' These draconian conclusions caused the local press to state: 'Harefield heart surgery unit . . . is in dire and urgent danger of being moved.' Being so severe and unexpected, Harefield was galvanised into concerted action.

The whole Hospital united as never before. All problems and

disagreements were forgotten as staff girded themselves to defend Harefield. Nurses and Heads of Departments, as well as medical staff, got together. Each drew up a careful analysis of the Report. A working party of the Medical Committee, comprising Drs Pridie, Radley-Smith, Triscott, Westbury and me, co-ordinated Harefield's effort, which proved a prodigious task.

## Closing Ranks

All the critiques remarked on teaching hospital influence: 'all the Group . . . has shown is regret that an effective, integrated and . . . economic unit could . . . exist outside a teaching hospital' and 'the . . . closure of cardiac work . . . [is] solely for the benefit of . . . programmes in the London Teaching Hospitals – not . . . improvement of . . . service to the patients.' These 'shop floor' opinions were reflected in the 17-page Harefield response.

'The report . . . seems . . . to treat as axiomatic propositions which are far from self-evident and still further from general acceptance in our profession.' Facts were provided to support each opinion expressed. When commenting on the Report's lack of evidence for cardiac centres located in general or teaching hospitals performing better than those which were not, it was pointed out that,

> on the contrary, the available evidence suggests otherwise. . . . The proposals . . . for relocation . . . are not based on the preservation and development of existing standards of excellence for the benefit of the public [but on] . . . the sterile logic of planning and perhaps the personal prediliction of the authors . . . For service to patients, teaching should be a subordinate . . . consideration.

The view was also given that, in general or teaching hospitals, competition from other specialties placed a limit on development of excellence. The combination of research and teaching with treatment did not necessarily produce the highest quality of service to patients either, nor the greatest effectiveness in 'throughput and economy'. That cardiac centres not so located 'suffer from the lack of supporting services and academic influence is . . . positively contradicted by . . . their throughput and quality and their worldwide contribution to the state of the art'. Regarding paediatric cardiac surgery,

> there is no evidence that children treated in cardiac centres not located in paediatric centres fare less well. If . . . adult and paediatric divisions of the specialty are to be torn apart for the sake of planned tidiness, there should be evidence . . . that children will benefit. . . .

Some of the best and most innovative cardiac surgery for children has been achieved in centres which do both adult and paediatric surgery.

The Harefield response also noted that, though it had been within their brief, the Group had not studied thoracic surgery. 'If they had, . . . they would have found that thoracic surgery has difficulty in surviving separately. . . . Isolated from cardiac surgery [it] is not sufficiently challenging or interesting to attract young surgeons to do it.'

The working party also had something to say about the Hospital, its team spirit and the fact that patients come first:

> We must point . . . to a simple truth . . . nowhere acknowledged in the report, . . . the peculiar genius which inspires a team in our demanding specialty cannot be uprooted and expected to flourish elsewhere. . . . Talk of transplanting this excellence . . . is simply a euphemism for its destruction.
>
> Industrial relations and . . . service to the public are . . . excellent. It has the space and ability to expand. Its location is more convenient for . . . patients who come from all over the country and the world than any of the hospitals amongst whom it is proposed to divide its work. . . . The quality of its treatment and the quiet peace of its surroundings outweigh all other considerations. . . . The public is entitled to hear better reasons for its destruction.

The response ended: 'We suppose that in the course of the next decade, excellent units could be developed. . . . But we have assumed . . . any sensible plan . . . in the Thames Regions would . . . preserve the ground so laboriously gained in the past decade. Perhaps we were wrong.'

## The Fight

The working party met at a set time almost every day. Because of the Study Group's 'hasty and superficial visit', they prepared a second 33-page document to back up their response. While describing the Hospital and its work in more detail, it reiterated the facts that 'the closeness of Harefield to the M1, M4 and M40 Motorways, Heathrow and Northolt Airports, British Rail at Watford and Denham' make it easier to get to 'than from . . . the centre of London', and 'that Mount Vernon Hospital, . . . is only 2½ miles from Harefield'. Staffing had not been accurately described either. It was pointed out again that, in addition to Drs Towers and Radley-Smith, 'three . . .

157

cardiologists . . . to neighbouring hospitals, . . . each undertake one or two sessions a week in the . . . catheterisation laboratory . . . [and] . . . five (others) attend the clinical meeting on Mondays as well as referring patients for investigation and treatment.'

A description of the Heart Transplant Programme, which was just getting under way, was also included. The Programme tended to confuse the pertinent issues, but there is no doubt that it came in the nick of time to be a potent factor in the survival fight. The resurgence of a previously failed technique involving the body's most precious organ, highlighted Harefield in the public eye just when it greatly needed support.

The two local Members of Parliament were approached personally. They helped a great deal, one asking a question in the House on 6 May 1980, duly recorded in Hansard. Letters were also written to the Prime Minister, leaders of other political parties, the DHSS, the BMA, the Royal Colleges of Surgeons and of General Practitioners, ex-patients, their general practitioners and constituency Members of Parliament, hospitals who sent patients to Harefield, active and retired colleagues and ex-staff the world over. All were encouraged to write to the Chairman of the Regional Board and anyone else they wished, including their MP if that was appropriate. The responses were overwhelming, a great surge of support coming from far and wide.

Sir Thomas, now Past President of the Royal College of Surgeons of England, entered the fray too. Among other things, he pointed out to the Secretary of State that 'Harefield dates its tradition from its Sanatorium days and an EMS Chest Unit in 1940 to its present position as one of the largest and most prestigious centres in the country. It has an international reputation and more than 34 overseas surgeons and some 29 UK consultants owe much of their training to the Unit.' He also came to support Harefield at one of the open meetings arranged by the Community Health Council.

The Hillingdon CHC, an articulate and active body with good relationships in the Area, had immediately come forward to help 'with the full support of the AHA'. Using their publicity budget, with the League of Friends helping out when that ran low, the CHC 'planned a carefully structured campaign to gain maximum support'. They put out press releases and posters; prepared exhibition material showing facts and figures and reports of Harefield's success stories, especially children; co-operated with orderly demonstrations such as a 130 mile walk to Harefield from Nottingham by two ex-heart patients; and mobilised ex-patients, adult and children, to public meetings where medical staff spoke. At one, the Health Minister accepted a Parliamentary Petition of 100,000 signatures. These had been collected through hours of effort by past and present patients, staff and their relatives, and local people.

## Course of Events

To counter a valid criticism of the threatening Report, the second cardiac surgeon, already agreed by Region, had to be appointed. But, because of the serious lack of money, the AHA was exerting pressure on Harefield to limit the amount of cardiac surgery. It was with considerable difficulty that agreement for the appointment was obtained. Only when the Area Medical Committee received a written undertaking from Harefield to 'restrict the workload to the 1978 level until . . . the AHA can financially support an increase', i.e. 359 bypasses a year, would they, in January 1980, 'advise the Authority to advertise for a second cardiothoracic surgeon on the understanding . . . that applicants . . . will be advised of this restriction before acceptance'. Mr Alun Rees, already a locum consultant at Harefield, started on 20 October.

With the extreme uncertainty and apprehension about the future, morale at Harefield was again very low. It did not help any aspect of the fight or the work in 1979 that nurse staffing levels were also low, 10 per cent below establishment. Half the vacancies were filled with Agency nurses. To make things worse, a year later when the pressure was really on them this time with the Transplant Programme, the nurses' working week was reduced from 40 to 37½ hours. Once again the nurses rose to the occasion and struggled on. Ironically, though under staffed, the nursing budget itself was frequently overspent giving the UMG some headaches. It was due partly to underfunded pay awards, partly to expensive advertising and partly because of the cost of the number of Agency nurses required to provide adequate nursing cover.

But the Harefield working party had realised that it also had to keep an eye on Region. It happened to find out that the Authority was reviewing its 1979 Strategic Plan decisions. In the final analysis, it would be the Regional Health Authority (RHA) who would be the arbiter of whether Harefield survived or not. They had set up a feasibility study to determine alternatives to Harefield 'should it be considered that the appropriate solution is to move from Harefield'. The Regional Team of Officers wanted still another 'specialist group . . . to advise whether Harefield . . . should be the proper centre; . . .

When these studies are completed the RHA will . . . determine where the centre should be located.'

But now Harefield's fledgling Transplant Programme had to be taken into consideration. The Regional Chairman 'asked a panel of experts . . . to advise . . . on the . . . state of provision. . . . It has not been recognised by the Transplant Advisory Panel of the DHSS. . . . In view of Magdi Yacoub's very considerable success in this unit it is not an easy problem to solve.' These experts visited Harefield in August 1980. At their request, Harefield's working party drew up yet another document of 29 pages of further information. By October the RHA had accepted the favourable report of this group 'in principle. However, there were financial and staffing implications and the Regional Team of Officers would be . . . reporting back to a later meeting.' Harefield had to continue its anxious wait.

It was at the end of 1980 that Region 'agreed that Harefield . . . merited retention on a long-term basis. . . . That the cardiothoracic surgery unit remain . . . as one . . . Regional Centre . . . ; an approach be made to the DHSS regarding financing of supra-regional services . . . and . . . improvements to the Harefield unit be considered for . . . the Regional Capital Programme.' Harefield breathed again.

## New Management

Hillingdon AHA recorded 'appreciation of the efforts of all staff concerned. . . . The findings were . . . due in no small measure to the teamwork which had gone into the presentation of Harefield's case.' Its Management Team had also 'accepted that Harefield . . . made major contributions to the economies . . . in 1979–80'. Then, just when stability was vital to Harefield, the 'area tier of management' was removed. Apprehension prevailed again.

The 1979 'Patients First' document had outlined this reorganisation, proposing 'establishment of . . . district . . . authorities, and . . . strengthening of unit management . . . to ensure . . . decisions are taken quickly . . . at local level . . . [and] . . . doctors . . . involved in . . . planning and running . . . the NHS'. The Government did not believe great upheaval would be caused. But administrators were compelled to reapply for their own jobs with no guarantee of reappointment and, in Hillingdon, though it helped considerably to be a single district Area, the changes proved more disrupting than the reorganisation of eight years before.

By 1982 the new Hillingdon District Health Authority (DHA) had inherited all the underfunding problems. In addition, it continued to come off badly under old friend RAWP. Not only was capital invest-ment there to be the lowest in the Region, but also Region 'continued to plan for the withdrawal of funds . . . without commensurate plans for reduction in workload'.

Fortunately good relationships with the incoming administration were soon re-established but Harefield was not allowed to sit back on its laurels. There was now 'very little fat left to trim. We can maintain the cuts . . . so far achieved . . . but it is not possible to increase them . . . further. . . . It is . . . hoped that savings . . . will not . . . be used to offset overspendings at the other units.' But what the new Authority did want was renewal of the 1980 undertaking about cardiac workload.

Apart from transplants, which were separately funded, Harefield's 'UMG could not support the view that cardiac surgery and other activities should be reduced. . . . It felt . . . it would [have to] take instruction from District to enforce such a move.' Confirming this, the Medical Committee strongly 'opposed curtailment of clinical services . . . to trim expenditure to achieve the target set'.

With its extra year 'shadow' experience, the UMG had shown itself 'able to influence, control and co-ordinate spending so that budget limits were readily met, . . . yet allow . . . cardiac workload to [increase] without a decrease . . . elsewhere in the Hospital.' Know-ing the 1978 number of bypasses had already been exceeded, and anticipating a rise to 450–500, the UMG undertook 'to keep within the . . . unit budget allocated . . . and . . . ensure that during 1982–83, . . . the remaining function of the Hospital will continue without detriment.' The new undertaking, changing the terms from numbers of operations to budgetary limitation, was accepted.

Meanwhile the new Regional Management Team was formulating its next Strategic Plan. In 1983 Harefield received yet another inves-tigative visit, this time a Regional Cardiothoracic Working Group, and a Transplant Research Group was also to report. Decisions on vital Harefield developments, which already figured in the Regional Capital Programme, were held up. The local press was prompted to theorise that Harefield might be one of 30 hospitals the new Regional Officers were planning to close. 'The effect on morale . . . was . . . most concerning.'

# · 14 ·

# Transplants

CARDIAC transplantation had been tried a few times in Britain but with little success. The body invariably rejected the implanted heart. To allow immunological research to develop, the Government imposed a voluntary moratorium on the procedure. When the time was ripe two men, Terence English at Papworth and Magdi Yacoub at Harefield, once again took up the challenge of 'one of medicine's most controversial operations'.

## The Beginning

The Transplant Advisory Panel of the DHSS had laid down criteria for units undertaking heart transplantation. Each should 'be a centre for advanced cardiac surgery and, preferably, renal transplantation should already be taking place at the same centre.' Harefield had a nephrologist on the staff who was closely concerned with renal transplantation at a London unit but, like the foremost cardiac transplant centres of the time, renal transplantation was not done on site.

'Donor hearts of high quality should be available.' In the moratorium years, contacts had been established with other hospitals and Coroners, a source of donor hearts developed and Harefield had evolved a 'rigid set of requirements'.

'Adequate support services in . . . immunology . . . must be available at all times.' Mr Yacoub had been working with researchers in several laboratories in the vicinity of Harefield. He had also established preliminary immunology facilities, and a gamma camera, in available cubicles not occupied by offices, in the west end of A Ward.

Regarding staffing and other support service criteria, some local resistance and doubt about their adequate provision surfaced. The DHSS had advised 'that heart transplant operations must not be carried out at the expense of other NHS patients'. In 1977 'the general

162

feeling [of the Medical Committee] was that Harefield was not suited for a cardiac transplant programme as . . . everything else would have to be given up to accommodate such a programme.'

But there was no stopping Mr Yacoub, a man determined to use available treatments as soon as possible. There were many people near death in untreatable 'end stage' cardiac disease who now could be reached. The first of these received his new heart at Harefield in January 1980. Even under the stresses of the fight for survival, 'it [was] possible to start a . . . Programme with the existing complement of nursing staff because of internal reorganisation and willing co-operation by all members of the team, the spirit of which has evolved over the years.' The recovery room of the cardiac operating theatre suite was commandeered for nursing the first few post-transplant patients while, even though funds were meagre, the essential 'clean rooms' were being constructed.

'In the first seven months of 1980, 28 patients were considered for . . . transplantation. . . . Three . . . had coronary artery surgery and nine proceeded to transplantation. Seven . . . died before transplantation could be done.' Harefield had become 'a hospital . . . catapaulted into the national and international headlines in recent weeks because of the two successful transplants that have . . . been carried out there.' It was a great blow to lose the third patient, the first woman, but it was not 'likely to shake the resolve of Mr Yacoub and his team'.

## Resources

Cardiac transplantation was very expensive in 1980. The DHSS provided funding only 'in so far as the costs coincide with the normal cost of open heart surgery'. Their examination of transplantation as a valid and successful treatment was only just beginning. No extra support was yet forthcoming to aid the development. As well as having to continue to finance Harefield's existing, expanding work, Hillingdon AHA, after a very difficult time making ends meet in 1979, had a shortfall of £½ million to make up in 1980. Nevertheless the Programme of 16 transplants per year started.

Extra funds were desperately needed. Grants were obtained from various Foundations such as the National Heart Research Fund, and local Funds were also used, including the Cardiac Research Fund built up over the years from donations from grateful patients. But these were nowhere near enough.

The whole of Harefield, excited by the prospects and knowing the difficulties, were eager to help. The League of Friends, enthusiastic staff and patients, and local people of the village got together. Within a month Harefield Heart Transplant Trust (HHTT) was formed and immediately started fund raising. Even so, the future of the Programme looked bleak in the very early days. But the struggles of both Papworth and Harefield to get their adventurous Programmes under way reached the media. The interest of two benefactors was aroused and one provided the final safeguard for Harefield's fledgling Programme, a generous donation of £300,000.

Until their study of the results of the Programmes at the two hospitals was completed, the DHSS was only prepared to make interim payments for the work. But these still did not meet the need. 'Goodwill had been shown for a long time in the Programme, but now there was a limit on the number of personnel available to undertake the work and the strain has shown through in recent times.' Even so the Harefield Programme expanded.

> Due to reduction in costs, it would . . . be possible to . . . increase . . . the number . . . per annum . . . to 36. Mr Yacoub . . . emphasised the need for Harefield to be seen as a centre . . . that could cope with a . . . larger number than had been undertaken so far. . . . It was felt that . . . the workload inflicted upon other support services . . . was . . . having a damaging effect on the general activities of the hospital . . . [but] . . . there was a need to continue. . . . It was evident that, as 26 transplants had . . . been undertaken in the first nine months of the . . . year, the work would progress unabated.

Impressed with the results by 1985, the DHSS decided that cardiac transplantation was a valid treatment. Central funding of the Programmes started, based on the DHSS assessment of hospital costs. But this still remained insufficient for Harefield. The number of transplants being done was steadily rising, more were surviving, and the range of transplants was extending. Though foreign patients had always been charged the full cost, for the ever increasing numbers of others dependence on outside help continued. It was a difficult time for the Transplant Trust. They were 'finding great difficulty in motivating the public to make donations', but they persevered.

## Outside Help

The HHTT had quickly become a Registered Charity with Patrons Sir John Mills, CBE, and Eric Morecambe, OBE. The latter had been a patient in Harefield in 1979. He died in 1984 and his widow became Patron in his stead. Trustees included Dr Riches, by this time senior physician, Mr Yacoub and the Administrators of both Hospital and DHA.

Under the chairmanship of Mr Sid George, owner of Harefield Travel Agency and previously the Friend's Vice-chairman, the Trust had quickly set to work. In the first two months of 1980 they had collected £11,000 and had doubled it a month later. Fund raising continued apace, reaching over £90,000 by mid-August and £250,000 by December. The methods used were, and are, many, varied and innovative. They ranged from the sale of plants with heart shaped leaves, cakes baked in the shape of a heart and 'Have a Heart' T shirts, still being sold in the Friends Pavilion, to Prize Draws organised by the Night Sisters, and media coverage by newspaper reports of events such as the presentation of a heart shaped cheque and exposure on television news and London radio.

The *Daily Express* launched an appeal. In February 1980, comedian 'Eric Morecambe added his name . . . when he heard that . . . Magdi Yacoub needed £60,000 to pay for six operations on six waiting patients. "He's the Omar Sharif of the scalpel . . . an extremely dedicated man. . . . He literally saved my life though you shouldn't hold that against him. He really deserves all the support your readers can give. . . . It doesn't seem a very high price to save someone's life . . . so lets help," ' said Eric, urging 'give them sunshine'. The work at Harefield obtained further gratuitous publicity when BBC Panorama discussed the whole controversial issue in March 1980. Following in October was a *Sunday Times* Magazine devoted to the operation at Harefield, and two years later the BBC filmed a documentary on transplantation there.

Many ex-patients, and organisations now aware of what was going on, entered the fund raising arena. Their continuing effort ranged from a transplant patient celebrating his first year by a sponsored parachute jump, sponsored swims, fell walking and the London Marathon, to the offer of a bullock being kept from March, when it was worth £600, to its sale in December, the proceeds going to the Trust at no cost! One event has become a popular annual occasion, with Mr Yacoub frequently taking part. On 11 October 1981, 800 gathered for the first 'Healthy Heart Run' and £4000 was raised. It is now known locally as 'The Jog'. Organised by physiotherapist Ann Percival, it raised nearly £200,000 in the first eight years.

The accounts of the HHTT were in the charge of a previous Area Treasurer, a person who knew the 'ins and outs' of how to keep Trust money entirely separate from DHA funds. It was to be used only for the benefit of the Transplant Programme. Among many other things over the years, the Trust paid for non-technical staff, who co-ordinated organ availability with donor and recipient operations and dealt with the prodigious amount of paper work, transplant medical officers and technicians, research personnel and facilities, drugs and travelling costs of patients in financial difficulty. They not only converted G Ward to provide 'hotel' beds for ever increasing numbers of out-patients, but also pay the rent of council flats in the village where patients who live some way away can recuperate with their relatives until ready to go home.

## The Patients

Cardiac transplantation is only available for someone who is critically ill in the last stages of heart disease. 'It is the last – the only – chance of life.' He or she is invariably 'barely able to walk upstairs, perhaps long since retired sick from his job, with no prospect but death within months.' For a 37-year-old man 'it was depressing and humiliating to be dependent on [the family] for everything, but I had no choice.' 'Even cleaning the windscreen was too much. I could do it but it left me exhausted.'

How can someone be brought to this desperate plight? In one third of instances it is the muscle of the heart pump itself which becomes diseased – cardiomyopathy. In another 12 per cent the heart fails because of severe untreatable valve disease or complex congenital heart defects. But far and away the commonest cause is ischaemic heart disease. This affects more men than women, and mostly those over 45 years of age. 'The coronary arteries silt up, causing . . . heart attacks and irreparable damage to the heart muscle.' Someone whose normal activities as family man or mother have come to a halt and life become merely an existence until death comes along, will grasp the opportunity given by the offer of a transplant. Often they have been through the stresses of coronary artery bypass grafting. But this time it is different – if they are to live and lead a normal life, someone has to die.

Support of close relatives is very important. Often they find the rapid improvement after surgery hard to take in after their time of travail: 'There was absolutely no chance until this came along. I always hoped against hope it would be a success, but you think it only happens to others'; 'Without this my husband was finished. The marvellous team . . . has kept my husband alive for me'; 'I certainly intend to get a donor's card. . . . If you can give life to other people it is a wonderful thing.' The patient's reactions are equally jubilant:

166

'Its great to be alive'; 'I feel on top of the world'; 'If it had not been for . . . the team I probably would not be alive today, not only older but having had the joy of seeing a grandchild I most probably would not have known.'

But some 'are haunted by a guilty feeling that somehow life has been taken to give them their new heart. It is easier for most . . . to accept if the donor remains unknown to them.' However, their gratitude knows no bounds – 'But for their brave decision I would not be here now. How can you ever express your thanks for a gift like that?'

Cardiac transplantation thus materially affects more than one family, and in totally different ways. In one is the patient who is given a new life and in the other, the one who has lost it. Permission to use the organ has to be obtained of course, but this is rarely refused. The husband of one donor remarked, 'As long as he survives, Mary's death will not have been in vain.' A father whose daughter's heart had been donated, considered that 'transplant surgery is a wonderful thing. If someone can save a life, what better gift can there be?'

*Before . . .*

In the first five years of the Programme, about 450 patients were assessed for transplantation, usually a 'straight swap' but sometimes for the 'piggy back' operation when the new heart is put alongside to augment the patient's own. As techniques progressed so more came, reaching 369 in 1985 alone. Each and every one is put through a series of tests based on certain criteria.

To enter the Programme, untreatable 'end stage' disease must be confirmed, the patient preferably under 60 years of age and 'be psychosocially stable with a reasonable prospect of rehabilitation.' ECG, cardiac catheter, angiogram and ultrasound tests show the amount of active heart muscle and blood pressures in the lungs and heart chambers. The gamma camera shows, by not taking up radioactive isotope, the parts of the muscle which have died. A chest X-ray indicates the size of the organs, exercise tolerance tests give a good indication of the efficiency of the heart's function, and lung function tests, the efficiency of the lungs. Any focus of infection, such as the throat, teeth and urine is sought. Blood is tested for viral hepatitis antigen and, with the permission of the patient, screened for the presence of the HIV virus.

Contra-indications for acceptance include the presence of active infection, blood clots in the lungs, independent irreversible impairment of kidney and/or liver function and irreversible complications of diabetes.

To be accepted into Harefield's Transplant Programme does not mean that the operation follows at once. A heart of suitable size and tissue type has to become available. But the period of waiting, though very difficult, does allow patient and family to become accustomed to the whole idea. For these, when a heart comes along 'Happiness is . . . A New Heart', as one newspaper headline put it.

Most donors have sustained severe irreparable brain damage, usually as a result of a road accident. For the first few cases in the Programme, the donor had to be brought to the recipient, a very complicated exercise and stressful to families and staff. Fortunately a way was soon found to just transport the heart. Properly packed in sterile saline and surrounded by ice, it will 'come back to life' if implanted within four hours of removal. Organ collection is the responsibility of the surgeon wanting them, and time is of the essence.

In the beginning the wait for a heart was sometimes weeks or months. 'We were never sure. We hoped but . . . did not know if it would ever happen.' All too often at first, it never did happen and the waiting patient died. Donor organs were scarce, being obtained usually by personal contacts between medical colleagues. Even now not everyone is fortunate, but the chances of finding a matching heart is much greater. Through computerised Organ Banks and co-ordination of transport to collect organs, a much wider area is covered, extending all over Britain and into Europe. The search is based on compatability of blood groups and size of the available organs. But even then the waiting is not quite over. One more test, taking about two-and-a-half hours to do, is necessary – tissue typing. The cells of the donor's blood must be mixed with the blood serum of the recipient. Only if these cells continue to live happily and are not killed, is it safe to go ahead.

## Change of Heart

Everything usually goes smoothly. The procedure is now a standard routine, performed many times before and not greatly different from any other 'open heart' operation. In fact the operation is simpler than many, and certainly technically easier than the correction of complicated congenital heart defects.

Sleepy from his premedication the patient is anaesthetised and prepared as for any 'open heart' procedure. But this time the anaesthetist takes strict sterile precautions to avoid any chance of introducing infection. When news of the travellers' progress and their estimated time of arrival with the new heart is received, the surgeons start accordingly. The incision is made down the front of the chest. The breast bone is divided and the two halves are prised apart and held in position by a Sellors' retractor. Immediately underneath lies the heart inside its membrane, the pericardium. This has to be moved out of the way. Only when the new heart has arrived is the patient put on the heart/lung machine.

The donor heart is still. It has not beaten since it was removed. It is trimmed to prepare it for its new home. Then the patient's aorta is clamped and the old heart cut out with scissors. For a moment there is a large empty hole in the chest and the ECG trace is a flat line. The left atrium, one of the low pressure collecting chambers, and the main artery, the aorta, are sewn in place first, usually taking about 20 minutes. The aortic clamp is then removed for the new heart to receive cooled, oxygenated blood via its coronary arteries. The transplant is completed by connecting the right atrium and pulmonary artery. While this is being done, the circulating blood is gradually warmed. The new heart responds by starting to stir and the ECG is no longer a straight line.

With all in place the heart is raring to go. Now moving vigorously, its agitation has to be controlled with drugs until the time is right to come off the heart/lung machine. The final manoeuvre is to use the defibrillator. Two metal paddles about 3 inches across, with insulated handles and leads going to a power box, are placed one either side of the heart. A shock of electrical energy is passed between them and through the new heart. In most instances, one shock is enough to transform the irregular movements into a smooth, regular rhythm. It is the moment everyone has been waiting for. A beautiful, normally beating heart is ready to take over from the heart/lung machine. The time of bypass is often under two hours. But there remains meticulous attention to stopping all bleeding. Within an hour or so of arriving in his cubicle, some eight hours after leaving the ward, the patient wakes up to his new life.

## . . . and After

At the beginning of the Programme in 1980, patients were in hospital for up to 4 months, totally isolated after operation. The first two weeks were spent in the recovery room. There they were reverse barrier nursed – a method protecting them from infection. The next 2–4 weeks were spent in a specially ventilated cubicle. The air pressure inside was slightly raised so that, when a door opened, air would flow out of the room instead of into it. Every single thing that came in had to be sterile, and every person that came in masked, gowned and gloved. Having been checked out for absence of infection, suitably attired visitors were now allowed.

During this period the dosage of drugs for essential immuno-suppression, to prevent the patient's immune system rejecting the implanted heart, is stabilised. At first these included anti-thymocytic globulin (ATG) and cortisone, but in 1982 a new drug, cyclosporin A, revolutionised management – and survival. Though the basic rules remained the same, it was not long after this that the patient was able to get out of bed, move about the special room and take exercise on a special fixed bicycle after only a few days.

By 1986 the period of reverse barrier nursing had dropped to about 48 hours. With the intensive phase over, patient care is transferred to the normal cardiac surgical ward where 'strict precautions are no longer necessary, although sensible hygiene is encouraged.' Within a week or 10 days the masked patient is normally out and about in the grounds. Being nursed in a single room on the ward, he may well be ready for discharge in about 18 days.

All patients report back to Harefield on a regular basis, returning to Out-patients with ever decreasing frequency as the chances of rejection recede. For the first month they return weekly, then every two weeks for the next three, monthly for three, then every two months until, after a year, they are checked every six months. Those who live further afield are discharged to one of the flats in the village, so at the beginning they can easily attend Harefield as often as necessary. When tests are only needed monthly, the patient is well and there are nearby facilities for the necessary blood tests, he returns home.

To monitor immuno-supression, blood tests are needed twice a week for the first three months. Cardiac biopsy, 'where a small piece of tissue is removed from the heart and checked for rejection/infection factors,' is done in the X-ray Department once a week for a month and then every two weeks for the next two months. For those with new lungs as well, the pattern is similar except that postural drainage is added to the exercises, and lung function assessment and a simple chest X-ray, an all important way to detect rejection, to the follow up tests.

Transplant patients have to continue taking various drugs for the rest of their lives, particularly those to prevent rejection. They have to watch their diet, weight and temperature. Household, personal

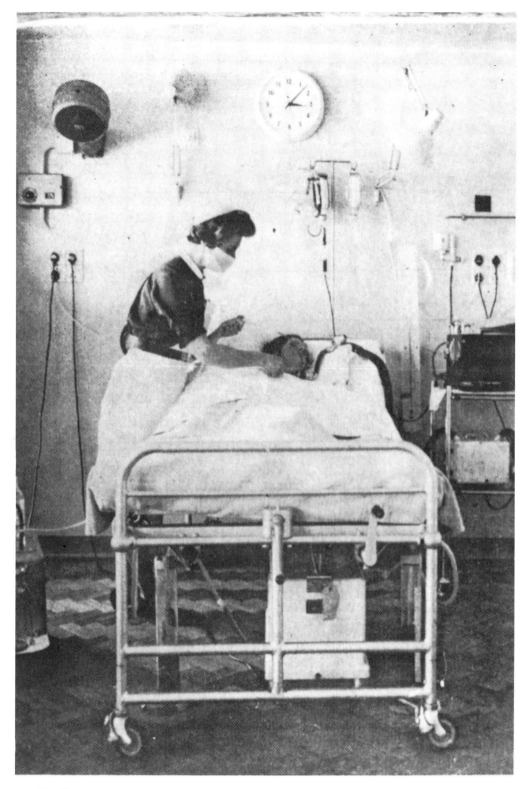

Pl. 61  Sister Tompsett with a patient in the 1964 ITU in the main block at the central end of F Ward.

Pl. 62  The front of the Hospital from the Friends' Pavilion, *c*. 1978.

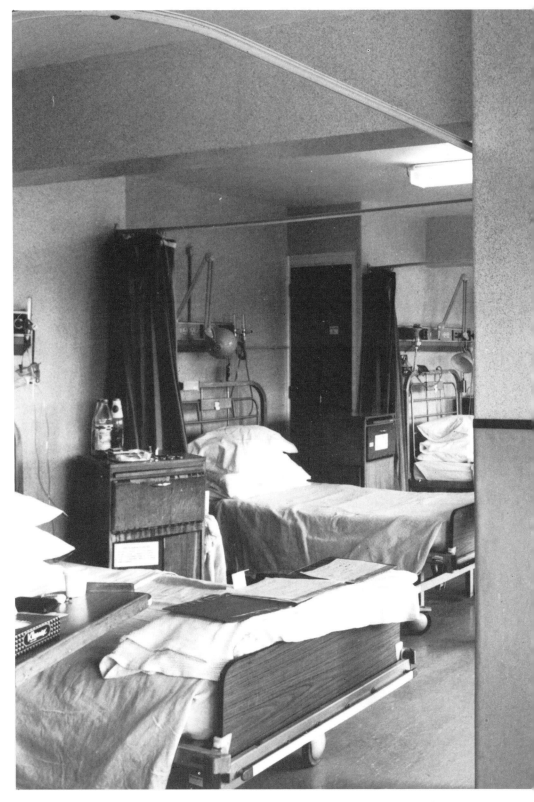

Pl. 63   A main block ward after incorporation of the balcony.

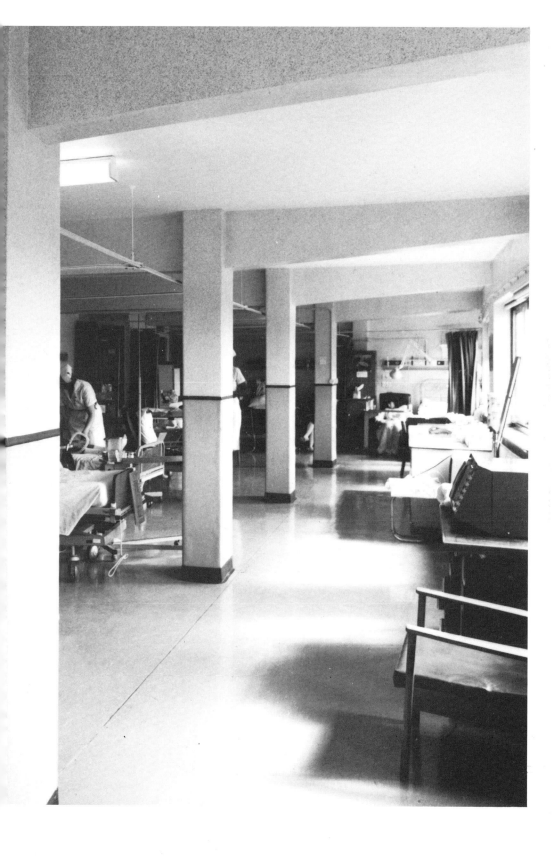

Pl. 64   Aerial view of Harefield Hospital, *c.* 1975.

Pl. 65   The divided dining-room beside the kitchen – half for patients and half for staff.

Pl. 66   The Hospital kitchen beside the dining room.

Pl. 67   The southern aspect of the 1988 custom built ITU.

Pl. 68   View from the main block looking east over the roofs of 1988 buildings. In the foreground is the Eric Morecambe Department of Cardiology. Beyond and to the right is the ITU. The closed corridor joins it to the centre of the Transplant Unit (old E Ward).

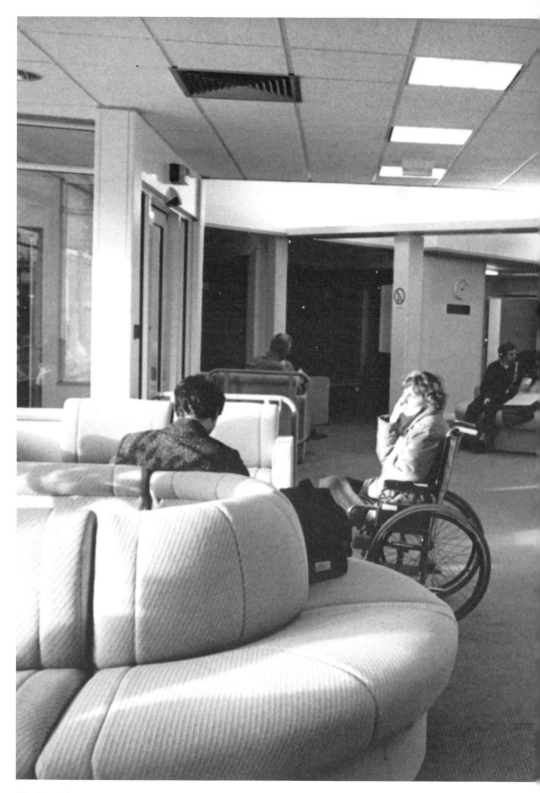

Pl. 69  The reception area of the Eric Morecambe Department of Cardiology and the X-ray Department.

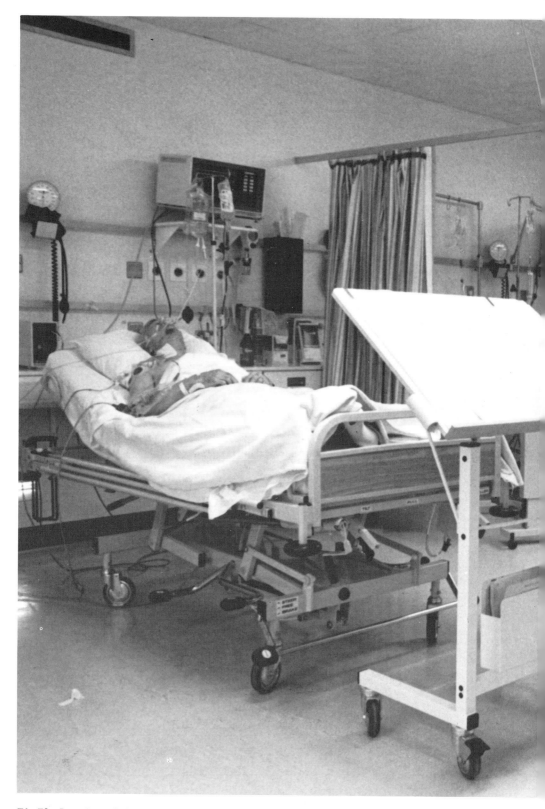

Pl. 70   Interior of the spacious 1988 ITU.

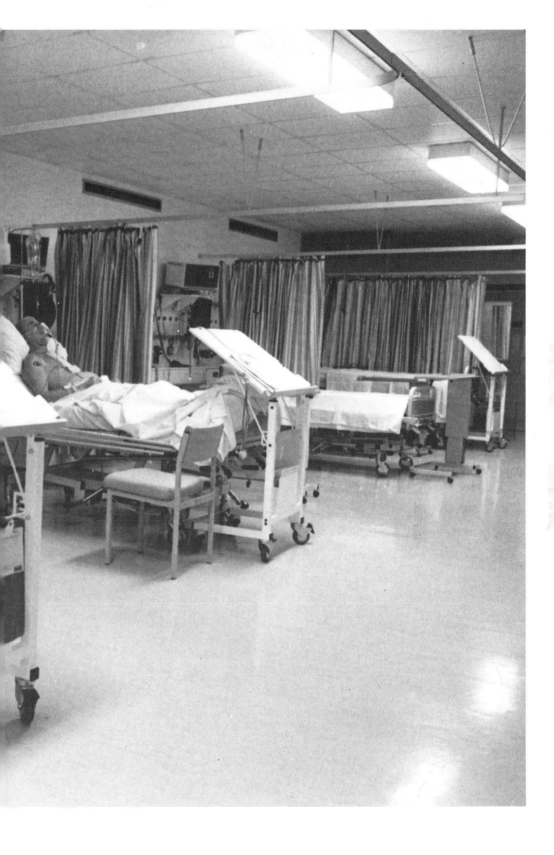

Pl. 71  1989 Pyramidal covered Playdrome next to the eastern wall of the Children's Ward extension.

Pl. 72  1989 Extension of the west end of the Children's Ward (previously PSU). The Special School building is seen on the right.

Pl. 73  The Mansion in 1989.

and dental hygiene, to avoid infections, are also important. They are advised not to keep a bird as a pet as these 'are a well known source of infection; especially parrots and budgerigars.' Otherwise a normal, full life is resumed, with a return to work or school after about three months.

## Support Services

In many and various ways from the beginning of their ordeal, the transplant patient and his relatives are supported. Explanation and counselling is an integral part of treatment. As a start, the patient is given a questionnaire couched in easily understandable terms. The answers, when taken overall, give the helpers a picture of what he feels and thinks about his illness. Information sheets explaining the Programme and covering aspects from selection and transport to survival and life style are provided. Others explain the aftercare and do's and dont's and why, with particular emphasis on the need not to smoke. It is impressed on the patient that 'rejection episodes are *normal* and should be expected, but they can be treated with special drugs' and that 'spouse, parent or close relative . . . is encouraged to participate in looking after you . . . to build up their confidence for . . . discharge home.'

Not only do the nurses provide meticulous patient care, but also they have an extremely important counselling function. Being so close to the patient, they are often the ones to whom he expresses his feelings. Nurses also teach him the importance of his medication and how to take it, and how to take his own pulse, weight and temperature accurately, things so necessary in keeping an eye out for possible later rejection episodes.

The physiotherapist is also involved from the very beginning. Not only does she follow the usual regime for any chest surgical patient, but also she supervises the graduated exercise which keeps new organs up to scratch. She too turns counsellor to patients and relatives alike, teaching them any techniques that may need to be continued at home. At the beginning of the Programme, little was known about physiotherapy for heart, and heart and lung transplants. Walking in the footsteps of Jocelyn Reed and Miss Thacker, Ann Percival led the way in pioneering and developing programmes of physiotherapy for both groups.

With the rising rate of survival, there is a busy Transplant Out-patient Department. In 1986, it combined with a Cardiac Rehabili-tation Programme. The team includes a doctor, nurse, medico-social

171

worker, dietician and physiotherapist. It involves 'exercise testing . . . and providing . . . an exercise prescription.' Patients join three months post-operatively for about eighteen months. 'The aim is to build a patient up to approximately 15–20 miles per week of brisk walking or jogging. . . . Progress is monitored by the return of weekly exercise diaries.'

Medico-social work altered beyond all comparison as the staff became intimately involved with the Programme. They are an integral part of rehabilitation, helping relieve minds if there are financial problems and providing a listening ear. Each week a support group meets for relatives to air their feelings. These families, all under the same basic stresses but with differing reactions, soon become one big family, all sharing the load if things go wrong.

Once the patient goes home there are several support groups, including the BHF and the Coronary Prevention Group. But Harefield has its own club, Harefield Hamsters. Exclusive to the transplant patients, it was formed 'to keep in touch with and support each other, especially wives, and to help raise funds for the HHTT and the Hospital.' The stimulus was an invitation to take part in the British Transplant Olympic Association's Games of 1981, an event in which several Hamsters have participated over the ensuing years. Starting when it did, before the advent of cyclosporin, cortisone was used to help control rejection. 'The name. . . was chosen because . . . the drugs made the men's cheeks look puffed out'!

## Progression

In the first year of the Programme, of 14 transplants only 3 survived, though one lives to this day. The next year the results were not much better. Things really began to improve coincident with the appearance of cyclosporin in 1982, when 20 transplants were done and only 8 died. Cyclosporin also does not inhibit the normal body defences against infection. Used in conjunction with azathioprine (Imuran) and better tissue matching, the incidence of infection or severe rejection fell dramatically.

In 1983 Mr Yacoub took the next pioneering step when he carried out Britain's first heart/lung transplant – at an estimated cost of £25,000. Again it was necessary to bring the heart/lung donor to the recipient initially, but over the next 18 months a portable heart/lung machine, in which to transport the organs, was developed.

The diseases leading to heart/lung transplantation differ from those needing only heart replacement. One is cystic fibrosis, a generalised congenital condition which severely affects the lungs, but the commonest are forms of congenital heart defect which cause blood to circulate through the lungs at high pressure. This results in eventual deterioration of lung function, so that it becomes difficult to take in enough oxygen, and puts great strain on the heart. The patient becomes extremely breathless and ill. The only answer is a new set of organs. Of those afflicted females outnumber males, and half the patients are under the age of 25.

The patients who could be given new hearts were getting ever younger. The next progression came in 1984 with Harefield's first heart transplant in a baby no more than one month old. In these instances, size is all important, the heart often being no bigger than a walnut. Again controversy raged. Would the implanted hearts grow? Follow up was meticulous and it seems they do. After this, came heart and heart/lung transplants on infants and children of all ages.

In April 1986, Harefield was recognised as one of the three Supra-regional Centres for Heart Transplantation in the country. It was also the year that frontiers were advanced a little further when two double lung transplants were tried. Then, in April and May 1987, hearts from live donors were transplanted. Two patients were in the unusual position of only requiring new lungs. 'It was decided to give them full heart and lung transplants – even though there was nothing wrong with their hearts – because lung only transplants have proved much less successful than combined transplants. The operations . . . were both successful and resulted in two ''spare'' healthy hearts.' These were promptly used for two others awaiting heart transplants. This exchange is known as the Domino Procedure. That year too, a triple transplant of heart, lung and liver was carried out at Harefield.

By November 1988 a total of 653 Harefield patients had received new organs: 490 'straight swap' hearts, 151 heart and lungs, 52 Dominoes and 11 lungs. 425 were still alive. Now it could be expected that 80 per cent of those with new hearts would be well after 2 years and at least 70 per cent after five. In those with heart and lungs, the five year figure was nearer 60 per cent. The results in children were marginally better than in adults. But the waiting list remains long, exceeding 250, and the 150 operations planned for 1989 were 'likely to be exceeded because of apparent increase in donor availability, possibly due to favourable publicity and public interest.'

## · 15 ·

# Different and Yet the Same

THE 1980 battle for survival was soon forgotten in the maelstrom of the Transplant Programme, the ever increasing work and media coverage that was coming Harefield's way, the revolutionary changes in NHS administrative structure which occurred yet again, continuing financial problems, and last but not least, concern about the future, not yet secure in the changing times.

### New Moves

Desperate to save money and raise revenue, the DHA had identified 25 acres of the 'north side' as surplus land. Proceeds of sale would be considerable and £50,000 would be saved annually. The Regional Board concurred, allocating £150,000 for the emptying process. The Nurses' Home annexe and School had already gone and the next were the wards. These were gradually moved to B and C Wards in the main block. It was only after a three year battle to get D Ward upgraded, that the last two medical wards could be moved. By 1979 only the two geriatric wards were left in the 'north wards'.

But general surgery and medicine at Harefield were ever diminishing. They were not to occupy wards in the main block for long. Despite strenuous efforts to prevent it, including moves to form a Cardiovascular Unit, the last of the general surgical work, and Mr Bradley, left Harefield for Mount Vernon in 1984. The remaining general medical beds transferred there a year later, leaving only 35 for chest medicine, but making room for the cardiothoracic surgical patients transferred from Colindale Hospital. Harefield was sad to see these much valued general colleagues go, even such a short distance, for what seemed only economic efficiency.

Withdrawal from the 'north' reached its peak in 1984. Supplies moved to Hillingdon Hospital, as did the laundry, to be followed by central and divisional Stores. The Medico-Social Workers went to

G East Ward, as did the District Catering and Domestic Officers. Occupational Health went to the 'south' huts by the Nurses' Home and the sewing room was housed in the Nurses' Home until central-ised with Mount Vernon in 1986.

The plan to put Out-patients from Ward 11 and Medical Records from Ward 1, in the empty laundry had fallen on stony ground when the assessed £150,000 cost was refused by Region. But an offer of a prefabricated Terrapin building free of charge, to which provision of services would be about £40,000, was snapped up. The two Depart-ments moved into their new quarters on the disused bowling green in October 1986. The vacated laundry became the Medical Records and X-ray storeroom.

Moving Pharmacy from Ward 2 was complicated. While waiting for Region to provide a £150,000 custom-built building adjacent to the front door of the Hospital, it had to be moved from one secure place to another. Going first to A Ward dining-room and then to the Sister's sitting-room in the Nurses' Home in 1986, Pharmacy finally came to rest in its new home a year later.

In 1986 the Rehabilitation Unit and geriatric beds from Wards 5 and 6, having been halved in number, were the last to leave the 'north side'. Temporarily housed on G and C West Wards respectively, they too went to Mount Vernon in 1988. Harefield had indeed become the specialist cardiothoracic hospital envisaged by Holmes Sellors some forty years before.

## New Buildings

By 1985 progress in emptying the 'north side' was such that, on the financial potential of the prospective land sale, the Regional Board sanctioned the 'go-ahead' for a £1 million ITU. It was not before time either. With heart operations rising in number, the ceiling manage-able in the existing ITU had been reached in 1984. But the nursing staff struggled on, in conditions which were quite inadequate, to provide this special care to the ever increasing numbers of patients. The ITU development had been part of the Regional Capital Pro-gramme for some years. 'The contract marked the end of much uncertainty . . . dating back to 1979. It is the wish of Members [of the DHA] that a letter of thanks be addressed to the Sportsman's Aid Society, . . . acknowledging their patience and understanding during this time.'

As Harefield's reputation was growing, this large London charity had taken considerable interest. It undertook to finance, whatever the cost, the building of a new Cardiology Department between the X-ray Department and the central end of E Ward, and provide equipment and amenities. The League of Friends were to provide the furniture and fittings. But they needed some sign that Harefield was reasonably secure for the forseeable future. The Region's 'OK' for the ITU to start was the signal required. Building began almost at once.

Having waited for its new, spacious quarters in A Ward dining-room for a year or so, Cardiology moved in to the £¼ million Eric Morecambe Department of Cardiology in 1987. With its automatic door entrance on the theatre corridor, 'the Department . . . is linked to the X-ray Department, with a stylish common reception area. . . . There are patient treatment facilities, as well as laboratories for measurement and reporting of results. . . . The Sportsman's Aid Society asked that the Department be named after the late Eric Morecambe, following approval by his widow. . . . Both . . . have long been friends of Harefield.'

The ITU turf cutting ceremony was performed by the Regional Chairman in May 1986. The building opened

> eighteen months after the building contractors moved in to dig up a huge lawn behind the main . . . block and cardiac theatres. Construction went well and the building was ready on time. The opening . . . was a . . . special moment for the staff at Harefield after a long fight to obtain Regional funding.
>
> The Unit is spacious and well designed, with 16 beds. There are 8 ICU beds, 4 transplant rooms and 4 high dependency beds. There are very adequate staff facilities, relatives' waiting areas and storage rooms. The unit is linked to the Cardiac Theatres and the main ward block by light and airy corridors.

The new Unit, also furnished by the Friends, could safely care for some 750 by-passes a year, including 120 transplants, and any thoracic surgical patient in need of special nursing. But there was a close shave in October 1987. An old Harefield Park tree, which had been preserved between the new ITU and Children's Ward, was blown down in the hurricane. Thankfully it fell conveniently and neatly with no damage to either building.

On 18 February 1988, the Hospital welcomed its fourth British royal visitor, the Duchess of York. In a 90-minute visit she opened both the new Units. On her tour, which included the Transplant Ward (E Ward), the Duchess met two patients who demonstrated the ever advancing transplant techniques. Pedalling on their exercise bicycles, one was a 15-year-old girl who had had a heart/lung transplant 2 months before

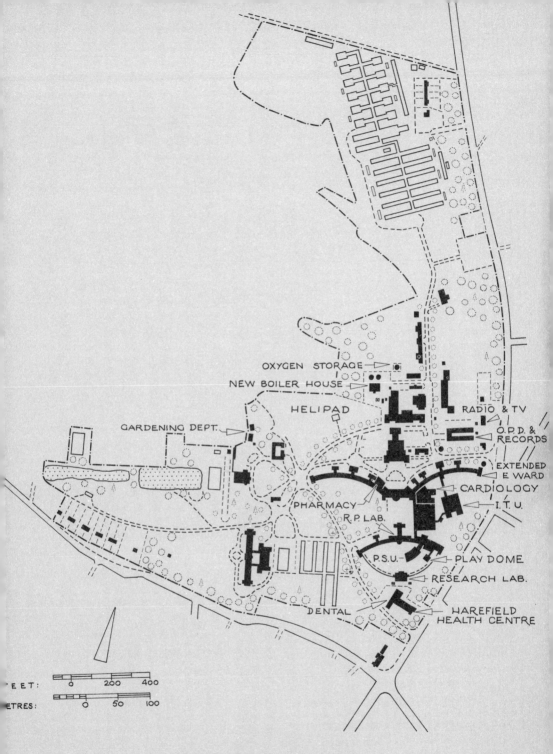

OXYGEN STORAGE

NEW BOILER HOUSE

HELIPAD

GARDENING DEPT.

RADIO & TV

O.P.D. & RECORDS

EXTENDED E WARD

CARDIOLOGY

I.T.U.

PHARMACY

R.P. LAB.

P.S.U.

PLAY DOME

RESEARCH LAB.

DENTAL

HAREFIELD HEALTH CENTRE

FEET:       0    200   400

METRES:     0    50    100

Fig. 10   1988: Harefield Hospital

and the other, a 9-year-old boy who had received her heart, the Domino Procedure. Both were nearly ready to achieve their ambitions, she to go back to school and he to play football!

## Extensions

E Ward, equipped with piped oxygen, was initially developed as the cardiac ward. Then it catered for the early cardiac transplants as well. Three cubicles adjacent to the old ITU were the first ones converted for reverse barrier nursing of these patients. Facilities for the increasing number of transplant out-patients were provided first in the old day room at the east end of the ward. Gradually E Ward became the Transplant Unit. The east end, beyond the corridor at the centre joining it to the new ITU, was extended to the north to provide seven more beds, and expansion to the south incorporated the verandah. The main block end was altered to accommodate Transplant Out-patient and Rehabilitation Services.

At the east end of A Ward too, the first of three planned phases to develop the PSU, extension of the intensive care area, was soon followed by the next which provided improved staff facilities and a better play area. The cost of these alterations, completed by 1984, were met by the PSU Trust Fund, voluntary contributions and local charities. These improvements were a start, but not really enough to meet the ever increasing need. When Harefield received funding as a Supra-regional Transplant Centre, the HHTT was no longer needed to raise money for it. 'It gives us an opportunity to go on to . . . our new project, . . . very much needed, . . . a new block for the children.' Needing about £1 million for the Children's Ward, they launched the 'Give a Child a Chance Appeal' with the Hospital authorities. The Sportsman's Aid Society also decided now to direct its considerable energies in aid of this project.

'Because we have all these children who keep coming back, we are very anxious to have a play area so they think of the hospital as a place which is pleasant and not a frightening place to come back to.' So said Mr Yacoub. 'Our local Mayor, . . . a Harefield man, had undertaken as his yearly Charity, to furnish the play area. . . . Which leaves us [HHTT] the job of equipping, and starting the building for about three years.' It all happened just in time as, after constant pressure, Harefield was recognised as a Supra-regional Centre for Neonatal and Infant Cardiac Surgery in 1987. Now, with appropriate DHSS revenue forthcoming, 'an expansion of workload . . . was envisaged during 1988–89 and beyond.'

The final phase of the Children's Ward extension started on 11 January 1988 when the first turf was turned. Providing six intensive care beds, three transplant rooms, an improved ward area, more room for staff and visitors, and a futuristic Playdrome in the shape of a glass pyramid, the extension was available for use about a year later. The formal opening on 18 July 1989 occasioned Harefield's fifth British royal visitor, The Princess Royal, President of the Save the Children Fund.

## Staff Perspectives

Dr Somerville left Harefield in 1978 and was invested CBE in the Birthday Honours the following year. Helping cardiologists Malcolm Towers and Rosemary Radley-Smith were colleagues from nearby hospitals with honorary contracts, and excellent junior medical staff. In 1984 ex-senior registrar Andrew Mitchell joined them, and three years later Charles Ilsley, another Harefield trainee, replaced Dr Towers.

Also in 1978 Mr C. A. Jackson retired, and John W. Jackson and H. C. Nohl-Oser in 1981. Surgeon Edward R. Townsend arrived the following year, taking considerable interest in oesophageal work. S. W. Fountain replaced me in 1986 and Mr Maiwand came with the Colindale thoracic work. Both had been TSU registrars. Coming in the stead of anaesthetist Dr Leighton was Dr Powrie until 1984, the year that Dr Lewis retired. Then Drs Beechey and Boscoe came and Dr Wright took on the Directorship of the new ITU in 1987. By that time Harefield was carrying out more heart operations than anywhere in Britain, and doing 75 per cent of the Regional thoracic work. A year later Mr Yacoub became the first Professor of Cardiothoracic Surgery of the Cardiothoracic Institute at the Brompton Hospital in London, creating closer ties with this postgraduate establishment.

The Transplant Programme altered the work of many of the staff. The expertise of psychiatrist Dr D. M. Lewis, who had joined the staff in 1975, was invaluable. While he assessed adults for transplantation, their attitude to the concept and their suitability, a research psychologist was appointed in 1986 to review the children. Dentistry, already important in pre-operative elimination of oral infection in cardiac patients, escalated to the extent that more help was needed. In Pathology, bacteriologist Dr Nakla and haematologist Sheila Amin had replaced Dr Nassau and Dr Hamilton. Their work load rose commensurate with cardiac surgery and transplantation but, in addition, theirs was the responsibility to lay down guidelines and to monitor the measures necessary to keep Australia antigen infective hepatitis and later, AIDS, from reaching a very high risk group of patients – and staff.

The success of transplantation was a great stimulus for clinicians of all disciplines to record their experience. Papers appeared ranging from observations on transplant patients by the dentists and oto-laryngologists to aspects of immunological response; the effects of anti-rejection measures and management to histopathological find-ings; and operative results and survival statistics to the control of post-transplantation infections.

The Programme also dramatically changed the work of the heart/ lung perfusion technicians. Many transplants were done at night, the other heart surgery occupying the daytime, and George Wiggins had to have more help. Since his departure in 1984, the number of tech-nicians has risen further and a 'night shift' instituted. His sterilisation method by 'gassing' in ethylene oxide escalated too as, from books to television sets, everything for the transplant rooms has to be sterilised.

Having gone through the difficult period of extreme staff shortage during amalgamation with Mount Vernon, things eased considerably for the physiotherapists. The potential experience offered by com-bined appointments had gradually become apparent. Visitors and students from home and abroad reappeared, staff went on courses at home and abroad, and some became clinical supervisors, them-selves running courses at Harefield. The standard of physiotherapy was restored to its previous high level, and the pioneering spirit returned too. By 1984 Ann Percival was Harefield's Superintendent Physiotherapist with over seven staff. As the 'north wards' closed and general work decreased, a Community Service was established at the Harefield Health Centre. This has become a thriving concern and, of course, they are also much involved with the Cardiac Rehabilitation Programme.

## The Nursing Staff

In the 1970s, nurse establishment at Harefield was still based on the 'partly acute' hospital classification, a throwback to the sanatorium days. No longer did it reflect the work of the Hospital nor was it commensurate with its needs. Correction of this anomaly was well nigh impossible as long as recruitment to the existing establishment level could not even be reached. To fill the many gaps, frequent use had to be made of Nursing Agencies. This was not an ideal recourse because these nurses could come and go almost as they chose and did not have a particular commitment to the Hospital. But quite a few elected to take a drop in 'take home' pay and come onto the staff.

Directives began to appear from the European Economic Community aimed at establishing a common nurse training syllabus by May 1979. The General Nursing Council was 'endeavouring . . . to ensure maintenance of British nursing standards'. But it would once again result in 'a reduced student service in . . . general medicine and general surgery . . . due to . . . increased demands of other studies on their time', and reduced time for night duty. The unhappy Harefield Medical Committee considered 'implementation would lead to a fall in the standard of patient care; the hope that qualified nurses . . . be recruited in place of students was remote as all hospitals would be doing the same; the budget for nurse recruitment must be increased so that at no time would we be held back because we could not afford to employ nurses.'

In 1982 the GNC became the English National Board (ENB) for Nursing, Midwifery & Health Visiting, trained nurses became Registered General Nurses (RGN) instead of SRN and the Cardiothoracic and Theatre Courses became ENB ones. Hillingdon District Central School of Nursing, having met the stringent requirements, was officially recognised in 1984 and the Nursing Process, by which a nurse is responsible for the total care of assigned patients instead of being allocated jobs, had been implemented. Two years later nurse training was altered again with even higher standards. It was a further year before the School, now the Breakspear Nursing Education Division, was recognised once more. And now Project 2000 is in sight with yet further revision of training methods.

'The provinces are over producing nurses, [but] . . . south east England has . . . problems. London Hospitals offer better employment . . . and even nearby Districts offer superior accommodation. Hillingdon . . . has particular problems staffing two "high Tech" hospitals.' Trained nurses were in much demand in places abroad and being offered inviting tax free salaries. But by 1986 the Harefield recruitment position had eased somewhat. Better techniques for advertising, involving television and local London radio, were formulated; conditions for working and living were gradually improved, the Nurses' Home being modernised; in-service training for Enrolled Nurses, pay incentives for good performance, free transport and adequate car parking were provided, and events such as participation in a regular Nurses' Forum, also publicise Harefield's work.

The new ITU did much to help, attracting 45 nurses with its up-to-date facilities. 'The prospect . . . has helped swell recruitment of specialist ITU nurses and there are nearly twice as many in post now than at the start of 1987.' But 'I have the feeling that one of the big hurdles we have got to get over is this regrading of nursing staff. . . . We may lose some blue dresses over it.' The controversial changes were instituted in 1988. 'How much damage is going to be caused between the workforce and management or between [members of] the workforce themselves' has yet to be seen.

## 'Griffiths'

In 1983 the Government accepted the advice contained in their commissioned Griffiths Report. It would revolutionise NHS management, embracing 'devolution of decision making and control to hospital level . . . [with] . . . encouragement for medical staff to be involved.' Once again, 'the timetable is necessarily rather tight to allow us to set further improvements in train by the start of the next financial year'. The DHA saw it to be 'of at least equal significance to the last two reorganisations of 1974 and 1982'. To the UMG 'it was evident decisions . . . had . . . already been made. The medical staff . . . again expressed their reservations about the speed at which the proposals were to be implemented. . . . Groups in the District had not had . . . opportunity to establish themselves properly and this next change would undermine their role.' Indeed, in their existing form, UMGs were about to disappear.

In 1985 'General Management arrived'. The traditional team of District Administrator, Treasurer, Nurse and Medical Officer disappeared. Now the DHA's team comprised a General Manager (DGM) and 'five directors: . . . Finance, Estate Development, Service Planning, Personnel, Quality Review & Consumer Relations.' Each one had 'clear . . . responsibility for a defined managerial function. The new rôles were to . . . ensure that the ability of these senior staff was fully utilised.' Medical advice still came from the District Medical Committee 'which would have a greater rôle'. Also, Heads of Services have been identified. 'A consultant, usually the most senior of a group doing similar jobs, [does] the administration such as sorting out what equipment is required. . . . Administrators then only have to go to one person, but it is up to the Head of that . . . Service to . . . get a concensus.'

Local executive responsibility also altered. Harefield's Administrator of three years, David Thomson, was appointed Unit General Manager (UGM). His UMG comprised the Unit Managers for Personnel, Estates, Finance & Information, the Director of Nursing Services Kerry

Boston, replacing Miss Holbrook and Deputy UGM, Theatre Manager Tara Shaddick, who had followed Miss Demulder, Ward and Outpatient Manager previous NO Michael Allen, the Medical Committee Chairman and one of the surgeons. The changes were again unsettling until belief in Harefield's capabilities was re-established with higher management. For the consultants at Harefield, 'with the contraction in number of beds . . . , there are far fewer of us to take the load of administrative duties . . . and . . . committees. . . . Those of us involved are finding it takes up a great deal of time and energy.'

The District Administrator had said 'there was a tendency for "Griffiths" to be seen as a panacea for all the problems . . . in the NHS – but this was not the case. Basic problems of finance and resources would not disappear with the appointment of a General Manager.' How right he was!

## Persisting Problems

With the new management in 1985, along had come the 'Regional Strategy Towards 1994'. There was still no firm commitment about Harefield's future. Now too, a new Regional Health Authority had to decide which cardiac surgical units could be supported within their cash limits in the long term. Grave concern was again expressed at the 'residual uncertainty about Harefield's future. This undermined staff morale for no definite reason. . . . Region should make an unequivocal statement . . . that there would be no plans to move Harefield during the remainder of the Strategic period.' The medical staff 'deprecated the suggestion that . . . relocation of Harefield may be brought up again the future. This has led to much uncertainty and unhappiness. . . . It would be to the great benefit of all . . . if the Region would . . . state without qualification that it is not intended to move the cardiothoracic unit from Harefield.'

When yet another Option Appraisal Working Group was set up by the Regional Board in 1987, the Harefield defence committee was resurrected. With the Appraisal complete, objection was raised to the repeated separation of cardiac and thoracic services, especially now with heart and heart/lung transplants being done. Nor had paediatric or chest medicine services been mentioned in the Appraisal. In the opinion of the DGM the Regional Board had given an unbalanced view of cardiothoracic surgery, underplaying 'thoracic services . . . compared with cardiac services'. Doubt continued to reign and, though 'the Regional Planning Manager does not plan to move Harefield in the next five to ten years, . . . steps must be taken to fight for the . . . long term future by promoting the Hospital at every opportunity.'

Financial pressures had also continued. With closure of the 'north wards', the Hospital had shrunk to only about 200 beds – and a correspondingly smaller budget. In addition, 'the DHA was having to make reductions from an expanded level of service. . . . Hillingdon was almost unique in its involvement with Regional Specialties' and as far as the DHA 'was concerned large, underfunded pay settlements . . . could well result in . . . redundancies as well as further service reductions.' It was no wonder that Harefield continued to find it extremely difficult to make ends meet.

Lack of money reached another peak in 1987 and Harefield's thoracic medicine service was threatened. Some other source of revenue had to be found. With changed DHSS attitudes, the required amount could be realised if 80 private patients a year had major cardiac or thoracic operations at Harefield in Saturday morning operating sessions. The DGM proved to be a positive man prepared to accept innovative thinking. A plan to convert B East into a Private Ward of 12 beds for this purpose was accepted. 'Contrary to the situation a few years ago, income from private work was now subsidising NHS work.' With 75 per cent occupancy and success in raising revenue, the new UMG was 'delighted that the . . . issue of Thoracic Medicine has been avoided for the time being. . . . It is imperative that . . . this scheme . . . works to avoid the DHA . . . reconsidering, . . . and . . . start to look again at Thoracic Medicine.' Now it was possible to continue with the plan to set up a bronchoscopy suite for the physicians in the thoracic theatres.

In December 1987, the Minister of Health, on the advice of yet another Advisory Group, finally announced national Supra-regional Service funding. Harefield was named not only a Centre for Heart Transplantation but also one for Neonatal and Infant Cardiac Surgery. The costs of Harefield's main workload still had to be paid for out of the relatively meagre District allocation, but there is no doubt that the Supra-regional central funding alleviated some of the problems in these two very expensive areas. Indeed, the 1989–90 allocation was such that the DHSS 'quite clearly sees Harefield as . . . the leading heart transplant centre in the country.' Perhaps now Harefield would be very difficult to move.

*Environs*

With the east end of A Ward accommodating tiny patients, the cubicles of the west house offices and, for a time after being set up in 1982, Biochemistry and Immunology Laboratories. Now one finds the cardiac office and offices for the Transplant Co-ordinator and Research Nurse there. After Cardiology moved to its new abode, the School building was turned into a research building for immunology, biochemistry and pharmacology. Respiratory Physiology had taken over A Ward dining-room. It needed the space in view of its added important role in checking function in transplanted lungs and its participation in the Cardiac Rehabilitation Programme.

In the X-ray Department too, where 'all radiological investigations necessary to a district general hospital as well as a . . . cardiothoracic unit' are still carried out, techniques by which patients may be treated effectively, but more simply, continue to evolve. Apart from their slick and quick insertion of pacemakers, cardiologists may now save someone the traumas of a vein bypass operation by one such method, angioplasty, done under X-ray control. The criteria for accepting cardiac patients has widened and the increased need for this sort of procedure should be met with the planned, Regionally funded, new angiogram suite.

Even the Homograft Laboratory, where heart valves were prepared from collected hearts, is no longer needed. On being moved from the 'north' it was put in G Ward on the top floor of the east wing of the main block. But now many hearts being transplanted still have perfectly good valves. Prepared at the time of their removal in the operating theatre, the numbers obtained meet the need.

Vacant G Ward now provides unstaffed 'hotel beds' for out-patients returning briefly from afar. The Bungalow and Observation Ward are furnished for 56 overseas patients, and relatives as well, also thanks to the League of Friends and HHTT. Many visitors, and relatives who stay, need to park their cars. As time has passed, parking has become much more difficult. Not only is the 'north wards' car park no longer available, but the staff complement has risen to 650 or so. But local visitors can perhaps use the bus instead, as the service has improved. Bus No. 218 joined No. 347 in 1978 and comes right into the Hospital grounds. It has no timetable and can be hailed at any point in its journey to and from Rickmansworth.

Providing everyone with accounts of Hospital news, including social events and the Hospital Appeal, are the Hospital Newsletter 'Focus on Harefield', and Radio Harefield. Now run by some fifteen volunteers, it broadcasts at weekends and Monday and Wednesday evenings. In 1979 a television studio appeared in the old Bowling Club House, previously the Social & Sports Club. Shown through the Hospital cable system are events such as the 'Jog' or the annual Fête captured by camera or on videotape.

Harefield patients have included well-known people from the world of commerce, radio and films. But in recent times, the Hospital itself has acquired a high public profile attracting considerable media interest. To help staff handle the attention of press and television, Media Management training is now provided. But this no longer involves the Hospital telephonists. Local communications were brought into the 'high tech' era in 1988 when a District-wide switchboard was installed at Hillingdon Hospital. Harefield did not greet the innovation enthusiastically. It had greatly valued the personal touch of its own telephonists. It was a time before the now faceless folk who answered the telephone became familiar with who was what, and where, at Harefield. In an effort to fill the gap, the Hospital Reception area was improved and suitable people appointed to man it. But it was not quite the same.

## Impressions

A 'routine admission' to Harefield is greeted in the now spacious entrance hall and waiting area by a smart Receptionist. No longer having to make the long trek to the 'north wards', the patient is directed to one in the main block. There he is met as usual by the Ward Clerk who takes his details, now recorded by the computerised 'Patient Administration System'. He will probably only be in hospital a week or two at the most, and won't have much time to get to know anyone very well.

He finds that Sisters' caps and nurses' aprons have disappeared, and name badges a terrific help, as the Unit Managers do not wear uniform any more. He becomes aware of general busy-ness. 'When you walk down the corridor, everybody is much faster. Everything is moving at a greater pace.' A lot of smartly dressed people go about their tasks in an efficient and informal way. One might be a Domestic Manager in her light grey two piece suit or a Sister of the Occupational Health team in her dark grey worsted. Even 'the ward rounds are different but . . . the same. Its modern, . . . its not the . . . old ward round . . . when we all followed [the consultant]. . . . I loved it but it was very time consuming' says a Sister who remembers. One patient 'had the feeling that a lot of skilled folk knew exactly

185

what they were doing and that they had done it all before, many times. . . . I can only describe my feelings as . . . entering a great big ''get-better sausage machine''.'

For those confined to the wards the method of catering has changed. Plated food is delivered. Prepared in bulk in the kitchen the day before by the Cook-chill method, the meals are heated on the wards in microwave ovens. For everyone else, patients who are up and about and their relatives as well as staff, meals are taken either in the Pavilion or the dining-room, or they use one of the vending machines in the main block.

The Friends' Pavilion, open for 10 hours each week-day and four hours each week-end day, has become a busy place. It even has its own teletext system. Among the many people in there, or sitting outside, may be anxious relatives perhaps awaiting news of a transplant, or one of the patients themselves in a surgical mask. Conversing with them might be a Harefield Hampster, recognisable by the small lapel pin in the shape of a heart. One might easily also have bumped into John Dunne pausing during one of his interviews, or Russell Grant reliving his childhood in a 'Down Your Way' programme, or *Sunday Times* reporters and photographers, or a BBC film crew capturing the story of the transplant team and their patients and relatives.

There is no telling either when the drone of a helicopter will drown out the conversation. A helipad appeared on the old putting green by the Building Department in 1986 with the financial aid of the HHTT. The ability of a helicopter to land and take off in the Hospital grounds has greatly assisted the collection of organs for transplantation from all parts of the country.

# · 16 ·

# From Generation to Generation

HAREFIELD. A word that conjures up many thoughts in the minds of many. In the days of the Domesday Book it meant a tiny hamlet, Herefelle. All over the country today it means 'the place where transplants are done'. To the generations in between it has meant home, happiness or sadness, or the restoration of well-being in one way or another.

Throughout the history of the Hospital, there have been days when the sky above was clear and blue, and others when it was full of cloud and foreboding. But the sun has always reappeared. Like the clouds of swallows which gather on and around the concert hall before migrating to fresh fields, so Harefield Hospital has, from time-to-time, collected itself to take off into the unknown. And no doubt the swallows will gather again.

What has made Harefield Hospital the place it is? 'The Australian soldier felt that at Harefield he was at home – and one of the prerogatives of home is a latchkey.' Though one might have seen unpleasant sights and sounds there resulting from war on the battlefront or in the operating theatre, there were many smiling faces to be found too. It mattered not whether they belonged to those who had survived or those helping them, only that they were there. Thus dawned 'the spirit of Harefield'.

From the days of the Australians, young, a long way from home, hurt and afraid, to those adults and children of the present day with fell diseases, life threatening conditions, and sometimes at death's door, Harefield Hospital has always been a place of hope; a place where people in trouble are welcomed and made to feel at home; an atmosphere most conducive to recovery. The Australians felt Harefield Park a home away from home and were happy to go there, and there is ample evidence that today's patients feel exactly the same.

## The Oldest Legacies

For nearly three centuries the house at Harefield Park has been a home. First a comfortable, nay luxurious, one for many generations of Cookes and Vernons to be happy in and live off the fat of the land. Apart from changes wrought by the first great war and more recent times, 'gentle living' continued there for several generations of doctors. Comforts of the house had been restored for the Sanatorium Medical Superintendent to live in grand style. This rubbed off on the residents. Even less than 30 years ago they lived 'the gentleman's life', Sunday lunch being served with wine and cooked by the Mansion chef. 'We used to call him in to the dining-room to thank him.'

But as time has passed the Mansion, its two flanking buildings and the lakes behind, have needed more and more upkeep. Though the basic fabric of the Mansion remains remarkably good and, unchanged since 1898, the lead roof does not leak, the plumbing leaves much to be desired. To keep up with the advance of modern standards, it is in sore need of preservation or restoration. But resources do not allow for this. Other means are earnestly being sought, including its sale, to turn the Mansion into a happy, busy and flourishing place once again.

The legacy of the Australian 'invasion' of Harefield is an eternal one. In response to a request in 1917 for turf for the graves of the Australians who died at No. 1 Australian Auxiliary Hospital, Capt. A. W. Tarleton RN of Breakspears said:

> I should like very much to take this matter on myself and if the Australian Authorities would permit this small help would undertake that Breakspears will grass the graves and keep them in order. This would be a very little thank-offering in recognition of the help given by the gallant action of Australian soldiers in preserving such peaceful homes from the violence of the enemy. I know my children would faithfully keep the trust, and that, in this old country, means from generation to generation.

Though the Imperial War Graves Commission keeps the graves in order, the trust has been kept. Every year since 1921, a Memorial Service has been held in the Church and in the Cemetery on ANZAC Day, and the children have never failed to place their posies of flowers. 'I remember I nearly always put mine on a stone in memory of Private Farthing.' The 'Act of Memorial' was broadcast by the BBC in its Pacific Service in 1946 and again in 1951 on 'London Calling'. On that occasion the treasured bugle of the ANZAC bugler, who married a local girl but fell later in France, was used to sound Last Post and Reveille. Subsequently the service has been televised in Australia.

A Memorial Chapel was also established in the Church in 1921. Formerly the Breakspear Chapel, it was re-dedicated by the Bishop of London, previously Bishop of Brisbane. There resides a Roll of Honour and the Visitors' Book. In such ways are these brave men remembered.

## Links With the Past

An erstwhile Harefield Junior School pupil, having been part of the ANZAC Day tradition, has since gone to live in Australia. With the co-operation of the South Australia branch of the Returned Services League, she started a new link in 1986. 'There are a number of Harefield people living in Australia who would like . . . to take part in a commemorative service' in Adelaide where the school's Union Jack now resides. 'We hope our reunion . . . will strengthen the bond that our home has with yours.' But the Australian connection is not forgotten at the Hospital. Staff always join the ANZAC Day Service. In rain or shine, they hear the bagpipe Lament played over the nearby grave of Lt-Gen. G. L. Goodlake, VC, of the Coldstream Guards and see the children, many in Brownie or Cub Scout uniform, paying their floral tribute.

An ANZAC Garden was laid out in the Hospital grounds with the help of volunteers in the late 1950s. Through the efforts of the Entertainments Committee, the League of Friends and a landscape architect, it was refurbished in 1967. Bushes and rockeries were laid out amongst the trees beside the near end of the lake behind the Mansion. Provided with seats and a fountain, fed by a man-made stream running under a little stone bridge, it formed a delightful haven in which to contemplate surrounding nature or watch a fisherman, leaning on an old magnolia tree, try his luck. Care was undertaken voluntarily by one of the gardeners. But the lakes quickly became choked with weeds, despite the introduction of water lilies and three ducks expressly to keep them down! Members of the newly formed Government Young Volunteers Force and local Venture Scouts helped clear the weed and trim trees and shrubs to prepare the Garden for the ANZAC Day of 1969.

More recently both money and help for maintenance has been sadly lacking. The Garden is no longer the carefully tended place it used to be. The fountain no longer plays nor does the stream run.

Trees beside the lake have grown bigger of course and the aspect was changed again when one or two of them blew down in the hurricane of 1987.

Charles Billyard-Leake left one enduring legacy, cricket. It has been played at Harefield off and on ever since. The men of the 'Australian Hospital' were naturally enthusiasts, whether wounded or not. Then along came Dr Stokes. He re-established the old pitch, and added a pavilion. With the help of 'the St Mary's contingent' cricket was played almost every week throughout the war, and an annual confrontation continued in the post-war years. Other wartime players were those patients of 'F Ward, virtually a military ward, . . . on the grass area in front of the ward.' Regular matches continued into the 1960s, with Dr Riches and other keen players, and a 'cricket tea' in the Mansion afterwards. In its day, Harefield was 'host to players such as David Shepherd and Trevor Bailey'.

In latter years Hospital matches have become infrequent. There are not so many 'living in' and there seems to be less time too. However the pitch is used regularly by the Harefield Cricket Club and from time-to-time, perhaps twice a year, the Hospital will challenge the District Authority, or they will challenge the local General Practitioners to a match.

## Memories

Evoking various periods of Harefield's past are several, and very different, memorials. A plaque just inside the Hospital gates was officially unveiled in 1962, at a short ceremony attended by Mr T. L. Wakley, marking the centenary of the death of his forebear. The stone recording Wakley's association with Harefield was 'put up by Kenneth Stokes. He was wandering in the gardens of an unoccupied house in Harefield . . . [and] . . . found this stone which was a tombstone to a dog. He had the inscription to Wakley put on the other side. . . . You can still see it on the back if you look carefully. Stokes had a very good sense of humour.'

There is another plaque in the Hospital Chapel. Put up in memory of Dr Stokes by his relatives, it was dedicated on 15 May, also in 1962. The Swimming Pool Fund, to which the village children contributed 10 guineas, resulted in the Hospital's memorial to him, the pool behind the Mansion. Then Dr Houghton's retirement was marked by the addition of changing facilities. Every Nurses' Prizegiving several others are brought to mind: the Herbert Smale Memorial prize for best nurse of the year, the Annie Dewar Memorial Prize for Practical

Nursing, and the Shaw Memorial Prize. The League of Friends will be remembered too. Another of the prizes presented now is one they have endowed for 'consistent performance in theoretical studies and nursing practice'.

The birdbath near the Hospital entrance is another memorial, this time to one who had suffered much in the Second World War. A Polish prisoner-of-war, freed by Russians from a concentration camp in Poland, made his way to France and then to Britain. Speaking no English, he came to Harefield via the local Polish community, and was in Ward 5 for seven years. He expressed his gratitude by bequeathing all his money to the Queen. On his death the birdbath was put in place. For a time there was also a memorial to Paul Chin, financed by the League of Friends. It was later presented to Southampton Hospital.

There are things at the Hospital which no longer exist and live only in the minds of those that remember. The old Australian Chapel, used as such by the first Sanatorium, 'the metal hut on what is now the extension of the Mansion car park', is but a memory as are all the other remnants of the first hospital and the first sanatorium. Also gone are the Mansion courtyard walls and rooms, the farm, kitchen garden and glass houses which, throughout the war and beyond would maintain 'the tradition of decorating the entrance hall of the admin. block with tiers of colourful flowers and plants, such as cinerarias, . . . whenever possible.'

Few now remain in the village who recollect the 'walking wounded Aussies'. But many recall the British 'wounded soldiers around the village in their blue uniforms' and the village involvement with the Hospital during the second great conflict. There are those too who still shudder at the memory of seeing from the road, patients in their sanatorium beds on the verandahs in all weathers. Of more recent memory is the excitement and activity engendered by the Transplant Programme and the gathering of support in Harefield's time of trial.

## Enduring Traditions

Following in the footsteps of the Australians, pioneering Holmes Sellors and Vernon Thompson continued the tradition of advancing with, or even ahead of, the times to encompass treatment of previously untreatable conditions or new or changing disease. But people have always been part of the essence of Harefield's history and of its ambience. From the days when loyalty was shown to

191

country and colleagues by the Australians, to the days of Kenneth Stokes and Beatrice Shaw and the influence of Thomas Holmes Sellors, Harefield staff have always clearly demonstrated their primary commitment – to the patient. Their loyalty to the Hospital where patients are also top priority, has been unshakeable.

Probably the most valuable legacy the Harefield of today ever received was the wartime National Thoracic Service Unit. With today's innovators, the service to patients now extends to all the protean forms of disease of the heart. Though renowned for its treatment of heart disease, what is less well known is that since 1940 Harefield has also treated all types of disease or injury to the lungs and the oesophagus. Such diseases can be life threatening too. The lungs are essential to support life, as is the oesophagus, being the normal passage for food. Some could be severely injured road accident victims. These people are also ill and frightened but, like the heart patients, most leave relieved and grateful that perhaps they too have a better life ahead.

Though patient commitment flourishes, in recent years the advance of medical technology has perhaps altered the emphasis slightly. Those who have mastered the complicated techniques, like Professor Yacoub, have of necessity had to put perfection of their skills high in the scheme of things. If a complicated procedure or operation is done well, the chances are good that the patient will also do well. 'I was able to return to . . . all of the things that meant life was back to a healthy normality. I owe a great debt to all the skilled folk . . . for giving me a second chance to live.'

Of the legacies left for the next generation to build upon to progress and survive, one has been the ability to overcome the problems of inadequate funding. With the development of expensive cardiothoracic surgery, this seems to have become a tradition at Harefield. There have always been people prepared to go to battle on Harefield's behalf, especially in latter years, and these include the many ranks of volunteers. Indeed, without them Harefield would never have achieved what it has, and quite possibly would not be in existence today. 'Harefield has a tradition with regard to the help of volunteers. The League of Friends' Pavilion has always been seen as a vital part of the Hospital's infrastructure.' It is there 'a thank you party . . . is held every Spring . . . taking the form of a buffet super organised by the management team.'

## 'A Happy Ship'

From before the days when 'benevolent Kenneth Stokes, a great wit, raconteur and bon viveur . . . ruled a "happy ship" in a somewhat effortless manner' to the present day, things have not greatly changed. The 'ship' continues to sail on happily, but in different seas. 'Harefield village has changed. It has extended [with] a lot more people coming into it . . . [who] just commute into London to work and don't actually become part of the community as it used to be. It is becoming less and less "the village" and more like an extension of London. Surburbia.' At the hospital 'one can't leave ones door open any more but then I think that's society. . . . But . . . it still has the old feel.'

But changes there are. 'When we all lived in we made our own entertainment . . . We were a sort of family . . . and we all knew each other because we all lived in the place. Its not like that any more. That part of it has gone I think. . . . Now you find the younger people who come in are not quite as friendly. I walk down the corridor and everybody I meet I say "Hello" to whoever they are. . . . I might not know them but most of them answer. There is a change but . . . even when the "old guard" have gone, . . . I don't think Harefield will ever lose that friendliness. . . . It's never going to get too big . . . so big that you lose contact with each other.'

Another view is that 'it probably will go. It's not necessarily because we don't have a Matron any more or a Medical Superintendent any more. With the management structure as it is, if a non-nurse manager takes over areas with nurses and patients, you will get an entirely different environment.' But no matter what, the nursing staff have always 'paid their dues' to the full. They are responsible, and have been ever since the days of Miss Gray and the Sanatorium, for the high standards of care that Harefield's patients receive. By dint of hard work and attitude in the face of many changes and hard times, they have added much to the richness of Harefield's history. Long may this continue. With the provision of modern facilities, may recruitment also continue to improve as it has in recent years.

John Roberts felt 'the atmosphere at Harefield was unique. It was largely due to Stokes. . . . I certainly have happy memories of the place, and everyone who has worked there has.' For 'Uncle Tom', 'Harefield stays as one of the most fascinating times of my career. I have great affection of the place and all its magnificent staff – not all with us now.' Some feel that 'Harefield was like a home to me. . . . I still get a pang when I go down to visit'. Another feels 'Harefield

Hospital . . . is a way of life. . . . I am sure this is true of many other Harefield families. It would be a strange thing if Harefield Hospital were ever to close. . . . People . . . have fought for its existence not purely as a place of work for themselves but because it represented something important in their lives.'

## Transient Traditions

Many, many people have come, worked, and gone from Harefield over the years – of all nationalities from all over the world. Inter-mittent links with Australia have continued by this means. One of the first was ex-ANZAC Tom Maishman, for 20 years a familiar figure on the switchboard. Another was H. D'Arcy Sutherland who returned home to Adelaide after the last war, became President of the Royal Australian College of Surgeons and invested CBE in 1982. Others have included the erstwhile Medical Superintendent of Fremantle Hospital, Western Australia, a surgeon in Brisbane, Queensland and more recently, transplant patients. The present Director of Nursing is also Australian. On telling her family she was coming to Harefield, an older friend promptly dug out a photograph of her father, a patient at the 'Australian Hospital'!

From the very beginning Harefield Hospital has been a home too for many faithful retainers and their families who have lived within the Hospital precincts. Now this long tradition is dying out. As they have retired or when their homes have been sold, they have moved away. The Hospital's long time four-legged residents, the wild cats, have gone too – for good! The effort put into inoculating and neuter-ing them, decreasing their numbers from 73 to 16, was not enough. Their end came in 1986 when the last were shot.

Nor can it be assumed any longer that hospital 'hotel services' will be provided by Hospital staff. These are now put out to tender. Though the Catering staff will remain for a bit longer, the tradition partly died in 1989 when an outside firm won the Domestic contract. The 'In-Service' team has gone for the time being.

But the traditional provision of accommodation, if not a home, for many nurses lives on, with the Health Authority very mindful of the need for modern standards. However, today many staff do not wish to live on the premises. 'Everybody has a car . . . so they live out and commute to work. So you don't get that social life that we had 20-odd years ago.' 'There isn't the family environment there used to be . . . because we have moved into the "high tech" era away from the patients who were here for months and months. . . . The nursing staff as well. Many are moving all the time.'

Work has escalated and attitudes changed. Through the forces of circumstance, and finance too, some traditions have fallen by the wayside. Many social events and much spontaneity seem to have disappeared. Though Christmas activities for the patients are largely unaltered and the wards still decorated, the Carol Service has not been available to them since 1986, even through the Hospital television network. The Pantomime has also died out and no longer do the nurses practice for their Christmas Eve tour of carol singing on the wards. Any such event is now a spontaneous occurrence. The main social occasion is the lighting of the Christmas tree outside the front door. A traditional lunch is available for those who wish, with a free glass of wine. A few official parties are given, the main one usually in the Mansion in the New Year. But seasonal unofficial libations in the Departments continue.


## *Looking Ahead*

'The . . . size of the capital programme would not have been possible without the Authority's . . . policy of making good use of the money . . . from the sale of surplus land. . . . With Regional capital heavily overcommitted, . . . District will increasingly have to rely on land sales to carry out much needed further improvements for patient and staff facilities. . . . The voluntary sector also continues to make an extremely valuable contribution to our programme'. The Harefield Hospital Appeal was launched in 1988.

The overall plan for future development at Harefield is to concentrate residential and social facilities in the 'south' part of the site and develop the 'north'. Sale of the 'north' 25 acres should realise several million pounds. 'There are . . . plans to turn over one part of the Hospital grounds to build the world's first Medipark', described as 'a light industrial estate comprising research and development buildings, owned by companies with involvement in the medical, bio-engineering and pharmaceutical fields.' The site would allow 'researchers to be near the work which is being done – the clinical work. . . . They could be drug companies, or people interested in developing different things [which] will benefit by being just on the doorstep of the clinical facility' and 'their links with ourselves or other local hospitals will help further scientific research'.

'The rebuilding and landscaping of the north of our site will be a major step forward and improve the grounds considerably', though a planned new Hospital entrance may result in one casualty, Cathard.

The Medipark, which 'could be a very, very exciting thing' is also thought of as something which will 'be of great benefit to the Hospital in the long term'. Included in the conditions of sale is the provision of a hostel for some 100 patients returning for follow up, and relatives, replacing the Visitors' Bungalow and the old Observation Ward.

In the 'residential zone', the Nurses' Home improvements and residential building behind the Park Lane houses will help provide the needed 25 per cent increase in staff accommodation. Part of the 'south' near the Home replaced by the wartime huts, could soon be replaced by a Nursing Home for the mentally ill. But there is also the possibility of more radical change. Sale of some 20 acres, including the Mansion the lakes and the Park Lane staff houses, is contemplated, but only if the 'package' includes provision of all the accommodation needed. The thought of the Mansion being restored to its former magnificence, perhaps for use as a Conference Centre, pleases many.

There are plans afoot as well to build a Harefield Heart Research Institute adjacent to the Harefield Health Centre. No land sales proceeds should be involved, the costs being met entirely from research grants and private fund raising. It is also planned to provide a permanent alternative to the prefabricated home of Out-patients and Medical Records. Harking back some 30 years, *déjà vue* for those that remember, the front of the main block may be joined to the concert hall.

## For Future Generations

Though people change, the atmosphere pervading the Hospital does not, even if there have been some 'sticky patches'. Those who experience life at Harefield, where the patient has always come first, are invariably imbued with a great love of the place, even though some would say its increasing busy-ness no longer leaves much spare time to enjoy it.

Hopefully some more of the traditions which have died out will reappear in the future, or new ones start. The annual Summer Ball was resurrected in 1989, the last having been held in 1986. That was a year when, on 7 November, an Open Day was combined with a bonfire, fireworks and a staff social. The Entertainments Committee, for many years active on behalf of the staff, faded out when the stalwarts responsible for it retired. A few of their activities are continued by others: the 'pensioners' are remembered at Christmas by the Unit General Manager and outings are now arranged by the Social Club, but its membership has broadened and includes many not on the

Hospital staff. The Hospital Fête, now called the Fayre and no longer associated with the village, is sometimes 'poorly supported by staff before or on the day'.

From the first hospital, Harefield has had an international reputation. The 'Australian Hospital' became as well known in Great Britain as Australia, and news of its activities soon spread to France and other theatres of war. During the next war, and beyond, Holmes Sellors and Vernon Thompson were achieving international fame for their work in thoracic and cardiac surgery. In addition there was Alexander Fleming and the famous development of penicillin; the wide recognition of Dr Nassau and his work in the laboratory diagnosis of tuberculosis and testing for drug resistance, and of Dr Houghton for his studies on hypnosis in the treatment of asthma.

Now it is Professor Yacoub and his expertise in transplantation and the correction of complex congenital cardiac defects. With the escalation of media coverage of advances in techniques involving this emotive organ, the name of Harefield is more widely known throughout the world than ever before. Combined with the extensive general thoracic work, surely there will be young men or women more than willing to come to this happy place of international renown and be able to ensure its continuance.

From what has gone before, perhaps it is possible to draw a few conclusions. Because the medico-political 'powers-that-be' seem to become jealous from time-to-time – and somewhat covetous of Harefield's achievements – some could say the future for Harefield looked a bit bleak. But Harefield will always fight to survive. This survival instinct, as well as the willing readiness of people to do everything necessary to achieve it, is another of the legacies left for future generations. But in every other way, far more important to patients and staff, the future seems very rosy indeed. Perhaps this dichotomy is a good thing. No one knows what effect new developments in the Region will pressage, or what the next Regional Strategic Plan going beyond 1994 will contain. It will certainly be known that some senior members of the staff will be approaching the age of retirement. Will the medico-politicians renew the attack on Harefield?

## What is the Future?

A centre of great excellence, financial resources have been forthcoming to allow even greater expansion of expertise at Harefield. The advent of a YAG laser allows a wider variety of treatments to be available for a larger spectrum of patients, the extension of F Ward as a second Transplant Ward, and a third cardiac operating theatre at the south corner of the existing ones between the ITU and Children's Ward, will permit more people to be given hope.

In 1989 'the Government White Paper . . . promises the most sweeping reforms in its [the NHS] 40 year history'. Whoever takes up the Harefield cudgels will have to cope with 'Working for Patients'. This should not be too difficult for Harefield because 'underlying every proposal in the White Paper is a simple aim – a Service that puts patients first' and one 'which provides not only clinical excellence but also makes patients feel valued'. But it does mean that, once again, the now smaller number of senior staff are confronted with a great deal of administrative work with medico-political overtones.

Acknowledged is that 'RAWP has . . . achieved its purpose of equalising the resources available . . . but it has its disadvantages. It is highly complex and slow to compensate . . . Regions which take extra patients from elsewhere. District funding is too slow to reflect these flows of patients across administrative boundaries. As for hospitals, they are at present subject to the perverse effects of a system which can penalise success. The Government wants to change all this.' The plan is also intended to 'make the most of the enthusiasm and ability of hospital staff, by setting them free from many of the current constraints.'

It is proposed that some hospitals will become 'self governing' and part of a NHS Hospital Trust within the NHS. Such hospitals 'will earn their revenue from the services they perform, mainly for health authorities. A hospital which is good at its job and attracts increasing numbers of patients will see its income rise.' They 'will be free to determine the pay and conditions of their own staff . . . and they will have freedom (within limits) to borrow money.' Will Harefield 'opt out', or be able to?

And so the future remains somewhat uncertain. But, perhaps as a result of past experience, contingency plans are already being laid. Made big enough, with a reputation big enough and links forged with interests outside the medico-political sphere, Harefield will be difficult to harm. Having lived through the previous great threat, and being aware of the events and problems that have arisen since, I trust the ambience of the place to remain such that everyone concerned, loving Harefield for one reason or another, will join together as closely as we did and confront any common danger. I for one do not believe the 'spirit of Harefield' will ever die.

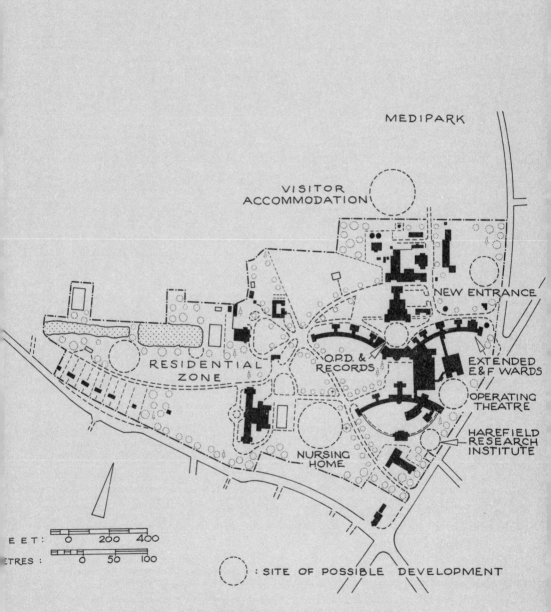

MEDIPARK

VISITOR
ACCOMMODATION

NEW ENTRANCE

RESIDENTIAL
ZONE

O.P.D. &
RECORDS

EXTENDED
E.& F. WARDS

OPERATING
THEATRE

HAREFIELD
RESEARCH
INSTITUTE

NURSING
HOME

E E T :      0      200    400

ETRES :     0      50    100

◯⋯ : SITE OF POSSIBLE DEVELOPMENT

Fig. 11   ? Harefield Hospital in the year 2000

# · Appendix 1 ·
# Owners and Occupiers – Harefield Property

| | |
|---|---|
| John Cooke<br>d. 1711 | 1700 |
| Sir George Cooke<br>b. 1675  d. 1740 | 1700–1740 |
| George Cooke<br>b. 1708  d. 1768<br>(buried at Harefield) | 1740–1768 |
| George John Cooke<br>b. 1736  d. 1785<br>(buried at Harefield) | 1768–1785 |

Penelope Anne    Maria    Edward    Eliza    Kitty

James Thomas
7th Earl
Cardigan

| | |
|---|---|
| Gen. Sir George Cooke, KCB<br>b. 1766  d. 1837<br>(buried at Harefield) | 1785–1837 |
| Maj-Gen. Sir Henry Frederick Cooke<br>b. 1783  d. 1837<br>(buried at Harefield) | 1837–<br><br>Widow 1837–1840 |
| William Frederick Vernon<br>b. 1807  d. 1889 | Owned 1840–1873<br>Occupied 1862–1889 |
| Lessees:<br>William Filke Haines, Esq.<br>Thomas Wakley, MP, HM Coroner<br>William Hitchcock, Deputy Lieutenant<br>of Wiltshire | <br>1840–1845<br>1845–1856<br>1857–1862 |
| Lt-Col. George Augustus Vernon<br>b. 1811  d. 1896 | Occupied 1889–1896 |
| Bertie Wentworth Vernon<br>b. 1846  d. 1916 | Owned 1873–1909 |
| Mr and Mrs Charles Arthur Moresby Billyard-Leake<br>CAMB-L  b. 1860  d. 1932    SLB-L  b. 1859  d. 1923<br>(both buried at Harefield)<br>(No. 1 Australian Auxiliary Hospital) | Occupied 1898–1914<br>Owned 1909–1920<br><br>1915–1920 |
| Middlesex County Council<br>(Harefield County Sanatorium) | 1920–1948 |
| North West Metropolitan Regional Hospital Board<br>Harefield & Northwood Hospital Group<br>(Harefield Hospital) | 1948–1974 |
| North West Thames Regional Hospital Board<br>Hillingdon Health Authority<br>(Harefield Hospital) | 1974–to date |

# · Appendix 2   The Military Cemetery ·

## Australians buried in
## St Mary's Churchyard, Harefield

| | Name | Rank | Number | Died | Age | Regiment |
|---|---|---|---|---|---|---|
| 1 | Wake, Robert Sidney | Pte | 170 | 8.2.16 | 24 | 5th Battalion, AIF-ANZAC |
| 2 | Keeley, George Arthur | Pte | 185 | 17.4.16 | 31 | 2nd Battalion, AIF-ANZAC |
| 3 | Regan, T. | Sgt | — | 2.7.16 | 27 | 8th Light Horse, AIF-ANZAC |
| 4 | Taylor, Arthur John | Pte | | 16.6.16 | 35 | 10th Battalion, AIF-ANZAC |
| 5 | Rowlands, C. R. | Pte | 5 | 20.7.16 | 26 | Regiment No. 323, AAMC-ANZAC |
| 6 | Hitchins, William Thomas | Pte | 1677 | 3.9.16 | 44 | 45th Battalion, AIF |
| 7 | Kennedy, Percy | Pte | 2494 | 15.9.16 | 18 | 23rd Battalion, AIF |
| 8 | Moffat, Mervyn Francis | Pte | 13810 | 10.10.16 | 19 | 1st Aus. Aux. Hosp., AIF-ANZAC |
| 9 | Farthing, Arthur Vincent | Pte | 5685 | 9.11.16 | 19 | 13th Battalion, AIF |
| 10 | Knox, Leslie | Pte | 1562 | 15.11.16 | 21 | 1st Battalion, AIF-ANZAC |
| 11 | Giddins, Percy | Pte | 1742 | 1.1.17 | 21 | 14th Battalion, AIF-ANZAC |
| 12 | Anderson, William Leith | Driver | 1464 | 8.2.17 | 31 | 5th DAC, AIF |
| 13 | Johnston, Andrew David | Pte | 9446 | 10.2.17 | 25 | 1st Aus. Aux. Hosp., AIF-ANZAC |
| 14 | Cookesley, Clifford | Pte | 17 | 28.2.17 | 19 | 11th Battalion, AIF-ANZAC |
| 15 | Graham, Melville Adrian | Pte | 12307 | 9.3.17 | 25 | 10th Field Ambulance, AIF |
| 16 | Mickels, James Henry | Pte | 3560 | 20.3.17 | 32 | 60th Battalion, AIF |
| 17 | Hingst, L. C. | Sapper | — | 26.3.17 | 30 | 1st Pioneer Battalion, AIF |
| 18 | Hayden, John Arthur | Pte | 2163 | 3.4.17 | 37 | 55th Battalion, AIF |
| 19 | Dines, Charles Stewart | L/Cpl | 74 | 4.4.17 | 22 | 36th Battalion, AIF |
| 20 | Tuck, William | Pte | 759 | 18.4.17 | 37 | 41st Battalion, AIF |
| 21 | Bice, John Gilbert | Pte | 2187 | 25.5.17 | 20 | 7th Battalion, AIF |
| 22 | Snadden, Robert Showers | CSM | 1931 | 30.5.17 | 24 | 3rd Pioneer Battalion, AIF |
| 23 | Howlett, J. R. | Driver | 3043 | 2.6.17 | 24 | 5th Field Coy Engineers, AIF |
| 24 | Adkins, Charles | Pte | 5791 | 5.6.17 | 24 | 28th Battalion, AIF |
| 25 | Little, John Henry | Pte | 4727 | 8.6.17 | 34 | 20th Battalion, AIF |
| 26 | Barnes, Keith | Pte | 2820 | 14.6.17 | 22 | 33rd Battalion, AIF |
| 27 | Johnson, John Stobart | Pte | 5118 | 22.6.17 | 24 | 3rd Battalion, AIF |
| 28 | Hall, Charles Samuel | T/Sgt | 2606 | 22.6.17 | 23 | 14th Battalion, AIF |
| 29 | Clover, William Cryllin | ?TPR | 1233 | 23.6.17 | 24 | 2nd ANZAC MR(?) |
| 30 | Koop, Frederick William | Pte | 8046 | 22.6.17 | 25 | 6th Battalion, AIF |
| 31 | Stevens, Charles Edward | Pte | 834 | 26.6.17 | 24 | 7th Battalion, AIF |
| 32 | Smith, Bert | Cpl | 5140 | 19.7.17 | 22 | 19th Battalion, AIF |
| 33 | Hartley, Charles Frederic | Pte | 562 | 24.7.17 | 25 | 18th Battalion, AIF |
| 34 | Power, Leo Joseph | Pte | 2437 | 31.7.17 | 21 | 67th Battalion, AIF |
| 35 | Osborne, William Lyle | Sgt | 932 | 28.8.17 | 23 | 11th FAB, AIF |
| 36 | Menzie, Frederick Bertram | Pte | 6315 | 7.9.17 | 22 | 12th Battalion, AIF |
| 37 | McCarthy, James Desmond | Driver | 18707 | 2.11.17 | 32 | 7th FAB, AIF |
| 38 | Keegan, Roderick James | Pte | 498 | 20.11.17 | 21 | 39th Battalion, AIF |
| 39 | Armstrong, Ernest George | Pte | 1897A | 21.11.17 | 23 | 29th Battalion, AIF |
| 40 | Richards, Albert Stanley | Cpl | 2016 | 1.12.17 | 23 | 48th Battalion, AIF |
| 41 | Bucknall, Guy | 2nd A/M | 527 | 4.12.17 | 22 | 69th Squadron, AFC, AIF |
| 42 | Scott, George Alexander | Pte | 897 | 9.12.17 | 22 | 22nd Battalion, AIF |
| 43 | Duddle, William Colbert | Pte | 781 | 25.12.17 | 25 | 56th Battalion, AIF |

| | | | | | | |
|---|---|---|---|---|---|---|
| 44 | Elliott, Michael | Pte | 4412 | 7.2.18 | 23 | 24th Battalion, AIF |
| 45 | Kempf, T. V. | Pte | 312 | 27.2.18 | 23 | 29th Battalion Aus. Infantry |
| 46 | Dennis, J. W. | Pte | 5813 | 7.3.18 | 46 | 23rd Battalion Aus. Infantry |
| 47 | Hogarth, Joseph | Driver | 1725 | 9.3.18 | 39 | 26th Battalion, AIF-ANZAC |
| 48 | Lakie, Douglas Vowles | Pte | 2944 | 14.3.18 | 19 | 50th Battalion, AIF |
| 49 | Clements, Frederick | Pte | 2612 | 28.3.18 | 29 | 12th Battalion, AIF |
| 50 | Sutherland, W. J. | Pte | 3196 | 23.4.18 | 35 | 4th Aus. Pioneers |
| 51 | Connor, R. | Pte | 3047 | 29.4.18 | 25 | 4th Battalion Aus. Infantry |
| 52 | Hobbs, A. J. | Pte | 1760 | 28.5.18 | 26 | Aus. Machine Gun Corps |
| 53 | Reilly, W. M. | Pte | 4558 | 20.6.18 | 32 | 9th Battalion Aus. Infantry |
| 54 | Grubnow, M. | Pte | 3152 | 23.6.18 | — | 46th Battalion Aus. Infantry |
| 55 | Dickinson, Ruby | Stf/Nse | — | 23.6.18 | 32 | AAN Service |
| 56 | Jones, O. H. | Pte | 8894 | 23.6.18 | 25 | AAMC |
| 57 | Dale, J. J. | Pte | 642 | 27.6.18 | 29 | 39th Battalion Aus. Infantry |
| 58 | Baufoot, J. C. | Pte | 3544 | 30.6.18 | — | 50th Battalion Aus. Infantry |
| 59 | MacKay, H. G. | Pte | 2743 | 25.7.18 | 20 | 21st Battalion Aus. Infantry |
| 60 | Genge, J. W. | Pte | 3647 | 2.8.18 | — | 48th Battalion Aus. Infantry |
| 61 | Kelly, W. | Civilian | — | 9.8.18 | 50 | Aus. Munitions Worker |
| 62 | Walton, C. | Pte | 3004 | 10.8.18 | — | 50th Battalion Aus. Infantry |
| 63 | Copton, W. | Pte | 1440 | 19.8.18 | 26 | 8th Battalion Aus. Infantry |
| 64 | Elliott, E. R. | Pte | 4767 | 9.9.18 | 25 | AAMC |
| 65 | Fletcher, J. D. | Pte | 3393 | 12.9.18 | 42 | 57th Battalion Aus. Infantry |
| 66 | MacDonald, N. | Pte | 3343 | 24.9.18 | 22 | 21st Battalion Aus. Infantry |
| 67 | Luby, R. | Pte | 2939 | 30.9.18 | — | 18th Battalion Aus. Infantry |
| 68 | Teakel, C. | Pte | 2464 | 2.10.18 | 23 | 30th Battalion Aus. Infantry |
| 69 | Anderson, A. A. | Pte | 3440 | 5.10.18 | — | 11th Battalion Aus. Infantry |
| 70 | Manns, T. H. | Civilian | 2152 | 9.10.18 | — | Aus. Munitions Worker |
| 71 | Austin, W. J. | Sgt | 1033 | 11.10.18 | — | AIF, attended GHQ |
| 72 | Bradford, C. E., M.M.&Bar | Sgt | 2730 | 12.10.18 | 22 | 50th Battalion Aus. Infantry |
| 73 | Heron, E. G. | Driver | 1108 | 19.10.18 | 26 | 26th Battalion Aus. Infantry |
| 74 | Thornton, M. W. | Pte | 100 | 20.10.18 | 24 | AMC |
| 75 | Flaherty, P. B. | Driver | 5090 | 24.10.18 | 29 | 13th Aus. Brigade HQ |
| 76 | Kelly, J. P. | Gunner | 5388 | 26.10.18 | 39 | Aus. Field Artillery |
| 77 | Bone, G. W. | Driver | 3012 | 28.10.18 | 30 | Aus. Army Service Corps (MT) |
| 78 | Dynes, T. W., M.M. | Pte | 4679 | 29.10.18 | — | 23rd Battalion Aus. Infantry |
| 79 | Alford, R. H. | A/Bombdr | 8023 | 30.10.18 | 21 | Aus. Field Artillery |
| 80 | Blake, Richard Charles | Pte | 4733 | 2.11.18 | 26 | Aus. Cyclists Corps |
| 81 | Lingley, W. L. | Gunner | 33736 | 5.11.18 | 27 | Aus. Field Artillery |
| 82 | West, C. H. | Sgt | 978 | 6.11.18 | — | 42nd Battalion Aus. Infantry |
| 83 | Abberon, E. | Sapper | 10831 | 6.11.18 | — | Aus. Engineers |
| 84 | Feild, G. W. | Cpl | 787 | 9.11.18 | 34 | Aus. Flying Corps |
| 85 | Ivett, W. J. | Pte | 1864 | 9.11.18 | 30 | Aus. Machine Gun Corps |
| 86 | Naylor, J. | Pte | 4189 | 9.11.18 | 21 | Aus. Cyclist Corps |
| 87 | Robinson, R. | Bombdr | 2896 | 13.11.18 | 23 | Aus. T.M. Battery |
| 88 | Noble, George Franklin | Pte | 4754 | 13.11.18 | — | AAMC |
| 89 | Luff, C. J. | Pte | 2658 | 25.11.18 | — | 4th Aus. Pioneers |
| 90 | Moore, J. T. | Gunner | 5802 | 27.11.18 | 21 | Aus. Field Artillery |
| 91 | Eastham, H. J. | Pte | 3565 | 30.11.18 | — | 2nd Aus. Pioneers |
| 92 | Marshall, F. W. (?S) | Driver | 33307 | 3.12.18 | 22 | Aus. Field Artillery |
| 93 | Sherlaw, H. W. | Pte | 5410 | 9.12.18 | 37 | 20th Battalion Aus. Infantry |
| 94 | Lucas, P. C. | Pte | 2443 | 10.12.18 | 27 | 56th Battalion Aus. Infantry |
| 95 | Rugg, F. | Cpl | 2805 | 11.12.18 | 25 | 56th Battalion Aus. Infantry |
| 96 | Smith, C. | L/Cpl | 9671 | 31.12.18 | 32 | Aus. Engineers |
| 97 | McDonald, J. | Pte | 3398 | 2.1.19 | 33 | 4th Aus. Pioneers |
| 98 | Bassett, L. J. | Pte | 4712 | 10.1.19 | 37 | 32nd Battalion Aus. Infantry |
| 99 | Lange, L. J. E. | Pte | 6602 | 8.4.19 | — | 28th Battalion Aus. Infantry |
| 100 | Touchell, T. D. | Sgnlmn | 343 | 11.4.19 | 19 | Royal Aus. Navy – HMS *Kent* |
| 102 | Bartlett, J. | Sapper | 5428 | 13.4.19 | 39 | Aus. Engineers |
| 103 | Clarke, W. A. | Pte | 6534 | 29.4.19 | — | 18th Battalion Aus. Infantry |
| 104 | Wilkinson, W. | Pte | 4923 | 2.5.19 | 23 | Aus. Imperial Force HQ |
| 105 | Leitch, W. D. | Cpl | 2255 | 4.5.19 | 34 | Aus. Army Ordinance Corps |
| 106 | Dobson, F. | Civilian | 3428 | 8.5.19 | — | Aus. Munitions Worker |
| 107 | Waring, F. C. Mac L. | Cpl | 9339 | 19.5.19 | 27 | Aus. Field Artillery |

| 108 | McCalla, J. T. | Pte | 2625 | 25.5.19 | — | 41st Battalion Aus. Infantry |
| 109 | Clifford, H. W. | Pte | 2626 | 3.6.19 | 40 | 58th Battalion Aus. Infantry |
| 110 | Moore, H. W. G. | Pte | 267 | 26.6.19 | — | 39th Battalion Aus. Infantry |
| 111 | McCullough, R. J. | Gunner | 2203 | 30.12.19 | 25 | Aus. Field Artillery |
| 112 | Knell, E. N. | 2nd/Cpl | 182 | 15.1.20 | 25 | 22nd Battalion Aus. Infantry |
| 113 | Kilby, T. | Pte | 2397 | 12.11.56 | 65 | 60th Battalion Aus. Infantry |
| 114 | Murray, William | L/Cpl | 3419 | 27.12.70 | 71 | 45th Battalion Aus. Infantry |

# · Appendix 3 ·
# Harefield Hospital Administration

MEDICAL ADMINISTRATION

Commanding Officer
  Capt. M. V. Southey, AIF, June 1915–July 1915
  Capt. R. E. Shuter, AIF, July 1915–August 1915
  Major E. Buller-Allen, AIF, September–October 1915
  Lt-Col. W. T. Hayward, AIF, November 1915–August 1917
  Lt-Col. C. Yeatman, AIF, September 1917–December 1918
  J. Warneford, AIF, December 1918–1920 (closure)

Medical Superintendent
  John Roy MacGregor, 1921–40

Medical Director
  Kenneth R. Stokes, 1940–59
  Lionel E. Houghton (Acting), 1959–60

Medical Administrator
  Lionel E. Houghton, 1960–62
  Harry R. C. Riches, 1962–66
  A. J. Moon, 1966–69

Chairman of Harefield Hospital Medical Committee
  John C. Roberts, 1951–54
  Kenneth S. Mullard, FRCS, 1954–55
  Leslie G. Blair, 1955–65
  Vincent C. Snell, FRCS, 1965–68
  John W. Jackson, FRCS, 1968–71
  A. J. Moon, 1971–74
  Harry R. C. Riches, 1974–77
  Malcolm K. Towers, 1977–79
  Harry Westbury, 1979–82
  Tim J. Goodwin, 1982–84
  Ron B. Pridie, 1984–87
  Rosemary Radley-Smith, 1987–to date

Chairman of Medical Advisory Committee
  Dudley M. Baker, 1950–71
  E. Idris Jones, 1971–74
  K. V. Robinson, 1974–77
  Harry R. C. Riches, 1977–80
  Diana Rimmer, 1980–83
  Ann P. Triscott, 1983–86
  Diana Rimmer 1986–to date

## NURSING ADMINISTRATION

Matron
  Miss Ethel Gray, AQANC, May 1915–November 1916
  Miss E. J. Gould, AQANC, November 1916–November 1917
  Miss Ross, AQANC, November 1917–20
  Miss Ferguson, 1921–26
  S. Clarice Woodward, 1926–38
  Beatrice Anne Shaw, 1938–60
  Ann Thornton Monteith, 1960–67
  Edna May Hughes, 1967–70 (Acting)

Senior Nursing Officer
  Betty Froud, 1970–73
  T. Myrtle Holbrook, 1973–82

Director of Nursing Services
  T. Myrtle Holbrook, 1982–87
  Kerry Boston, 1987–to date

Harefield and Mount Vernon Hospitals
Matron
  Grace Schofield, 1967–69

Principal Nursing Officer (General)
  Edna May Hughes, 1970–74

Chief Nursing Officer
  Dorothy A. Hunt, 1969–73
  June V. Richardson, 1973–74
  Edna May Hughes, 1974–78

Divisional Nursing Officer
  Edna May Hughes, 1978–82

## LAY ADMINISTRATION

  G. F. Catenach, Steward, 1921–47
  Alfred Leonard Pearmund, Steward, 1947–49
  John Henry Marks, Chief Clerk, 1922–59
  D. F. Campbell, Deputy Steward, 1938–46
    Administrative Assistant, 1946–49

Frank J. Green, Deputy Steward, 1946–49
  Administrative Assistant, 1949–75

Hospital Secretary
  Vernon H. Green, 1960–62
  Geoffrey F. Owens, 1962–64
  Dennis H. Chandler, 1964–67
  Anthony C. Blee, 1967–70
  Stuart, E. Ingham, 1970–73
  Barry G. Bowles, 1973–75

Unit Administrator (Sector 1977–82)
  Jeremy Millar, 1975–83
  David P. Thomson, 1983–85

General Manager
  David P. Thomson, 1985–89
  John Hunt, 1989–to date


HAREFIELD & NORTHWOOD GROUP MANAGEMENT COMMITTEE

Chairman
  Fred Messer, MP, JP, 1948–49
  Mrs Ena Daniels, 1949–64
  L. G. Ponsford, 1964–66
  A. Staveley Gough, FRCS, 1966–74

Members appointed by Board 1948:
  Dr W. Arklay Steel
  Col. G. Beach
  Dr H. E. A. Boldero (Sir Harold)
  Sir Christopher G. A. Cowan
  County Ald. L. M. Graves
  Dr Lionel E. Houghton
  Viscount Knollys
  Viscountess Knollys
  Lady Moran
  Miss E. Sands
  T. J. O'Sullivan
  Mr Vincent E. Vincent
  Dr H. W. C. Vines
  Dr W. Roy Ward
  County Ald. Mrs S. E. H. Williams
  Prof. B. W. Windeyer (Sir Brian)

Group Secretary
  Frank A. Watson, 1948–65
  Leonard Whitney, 1965–68

S. Argyrou (Acting), 1968
Dennis Felstead, 1968–73
William J. Tucker (Acting), 1973–74

## HILLINGDON AREA HEALTH AUTHORITY, 1974

Chairman
  E. E. Hughes, 1974–77
  Alderman Ken A. Gigg, 1977–82
Alderman J. G. Bartlett
J. W. P. Bradley, Esq, BM, BCh, FRCS
V. Callender, Esq, FSVA, Vice-Chairman       Appointed by
Professor K. R. Dumbell, MD       Regional Health
G. L. Fordyce, Esq, FDS, RCS       Authority
J. Haigh, Esq, JP
J. C. Lewis, Esq, OBE, JP, FOCS
Miss D. J. Markham, SRN, SCM, RMT, HV, DN
Mrs M. Plouviez, MA MTech
Dr Ruth D. Price-Williams, MB, ChB
Councillor Mrs B. D. Bell
Alderman K. A. Gigg       Appointed by
Councillor A. J. Potts       Local Authority
Councillor J. Row

## AREA MANAGEMENT TEAM

Administrator
  Ian N. Smith, 1974–79
  J. David Blythe, 1979–82

Treasurer
  David S. M. Purser, 1973–82
  Stanley Griffiths, 1980–82

Nursing Officer
  Joyce Byatt, 1974–81

Medical Officer
  Catherine E. Holman, 1974–79
  Peter W. Briggs, 1979–82

General Practitioner
  Ruth D. Price-Williams

Consultant
  Kenneth V. Robinson

*Appendix 3*

## HILLINGDON DISTRICT HEALTH AUTHORITY 1982

Chairman
    A. C. Barrett, 1982–86
    David W. Swarbrick, 1986–to date
Mrs J. Bowen
Mr R. J. Cooper
Dr J. M. English
Professor J. F. Fowler           Appointed by
Mr E. Harris                    Regional Health
Mr W. F. Hollis, BDS           Authority
Professor G. Jackson
Mr W. MacDougall, SRN
Mrs M. Plouviez, MA, MTech
Mr I. C. Taylor
Mr J. P. Thompson
Dr Ann P. Triscott, FFARCS
Councillor S. N. Ali Khan
Councillor Mrs E. G. Boff
Councillor Dr D. W. Payne      Appointed by
Councillor J. A. Woolf         Local Authority
CHC Observer – Mrs R. J. Kverndal


## DISTRICT MANAGEMENT TEAM

Administrator
  J. David Blythe, 1982–84
  Michael Bellamy, 1984–85

Area Treasurer – S. E. Anderson, 1982–85
Nursing Officer – Mrs M. P. (Iona) William, 1981–86
Medical Officer – Paul A. Kitchener, 1982–85
Consultant – Diana M. D. Rimmer
General Practitioner – B. K. Rogers


## HILLINGDON DISTRICT MANAGEMENT BOARD 1985

General Manager – Michael Bellamy
Director of Finance and Computing – Steve Lynch
Director of Planning & Information – Dino Oddi
Director of Estate Development – John Mills
Director of Personnel – Mrs Julie Kennedy
Director of Nurse Education and Nursing Adviser –
  Mrs Sheila Roy, 1986–88
  Sheila Jack, 1988–89
Director of Nurse Education – Mrs Jean Powell, 1989–to date

Nursing Advisers – The Directors of Nursing Services, 1989–to date
District Medical Officer – Dr Paul Kitchener 1985–87
Unit General Managers – Phillip Brown, Hillingdon Hospital
                      – David Costain, Mount Vernon Hospital
                      – John Hunt, Harefield Hospital
                      – Sue Mowatt, Community & Primary Care
Clinical Co-ordinator – Dr Diane M. D. Rimmer, 1985–88

# · Glossary ·

**adhesions, pleural** – Abnormal union of the surface of lung to the inner surface of the rib cage.

**adhesion section** – Surgical cutting or division of pleural adhesions to allow the lung to collapse

**anastamosis** – The establishment by surgical means of a communication between two blood vessels or other hollow anatomical structures

**angiogram** – see cardiac catheterisation

**angioplasty** – The stretching of a narrowed artery by the manipulation of a little balloon into it, under local anaesthesia and X-ray control, and stretching it by blowing up the balloon with saline

**aspiration** – Act of sucking up or sucking in; method of clearing fluid or secretions

**atrial septal defect** – A hole in the wall between the right and left atria of the heart. The first chamber (right) receives blood from the veins of the body, and the second (left) the veins of the lungs

**BCG** – Bacillus Calmette-Guerin, a vaccine used for immunization against tuberculosis. Prepared from a strain of tubercle bacillus attenuated by extended culture

**bactericide** – A chemical agent that destroys bacteria

**bacteriology** – The science and study of bacteria

**Balkan beam** – An overhead frame supported by uprights fixed to bedposts: used to suspend immobilised, splinted fractured limbs and to apply continuous traction by weights and pulleys

**biopsy** – The excision of tissue during life, to establish a diagnosis by means of microscopic examination of the excised piece

**Blalock operation** – A palliative operation to relieve congenital obstruction of the pulmonary artery. The subclavian artery is anastamosed to the side of one of the pulmonary arteries, thus permitting more blood to reach the lungs

**blood culture medium** – A substance containing blood used for the cultivation of bacteria

**bronchial, bronchus** – Appertaining to, or one of, the primary branches of the trachea

**bronchiectasis** – Dilatation of the bronchi due to an inflammatory or degenerative process; usually associated with chronic suppuration

**bronchogram** – Radiograph of the bronchial tree made after the injection of a radio-opaque substance

209

**bronchopleural fistula** – An abnormal track communicating between a bronchus and the pleural cavity

**bronchoscope** – Instrument for the visual examination of the interior of the bronchi

**bronchospirometry** – The determination of various aspects of the functional capacity of a single lung

**bypass, cardiopulmonary** – Circulation of the blood outside the body, excluding the heart and lungs. Synonymous with extracorporeal circulation and the use of the heart/lung machine

**bypass, coronary artery** – The surgical insertion of vein or artery conduit, anastamosed above and below a block, to allow blood to flow around obstructions in the coronary arteries

**bypass, heart/lung** – The procedure whereby apparatus temporarily replaces the heart and lungs, maintaining circulation of oxygenated blood while the heart is operated upon

**cardiac catheterisation** – The procedure in which a fine tube is passed, under X-ray control via a vein, into the heart allowing pressures in the chambers to be measured and blood samples taken. Angiography comprises injection of a radio-opaque substance permitting visualisation of the chambers and coronary arteries

**catgut** – Surgical suture material prepared from sheeps' intestine

**coarctation** – Congenital narrowing in the aorta

**collapse therapy** – The treatment of lung disease by deliberately causing collapse of the affected lung

**constrictive pericarditis** – The adhesion, thickening and contraction of the two layers of pericardium resulting from tuberculosis. It can result in impairment of heart action by constriction

**consumption** – An old term for tuberculosis

**diaphragm** – The musculo-tendinous partition separating thorax from abdomen and chief muscle of respiration

**empyema** – The presence of pus in a cavity or space, such as the pleural cavity

**endobronchial** – Within a bronchus

**exudate** – The material that has passed through walls of blood vessels into adjacent tissues or spaces as a result of inflammation

**Fallot's Tetralogy** – A congenital heart malformation described by Etienne Louis Arthur Fallot comprising a right-sided aorta, right ventricular hypertrophy, ventricular septal defect and pulmonary stenosis.

**fibrin** – The fibrous protein formed by the interaction of thrombin and fibrinogen, in the network of which blood corpuscles are enmeshed in the clotting of shed blood

**flow meter** – A device for measuring the rate of flow of expired air

**gastric lavage** – The irrigation or washing out of the stomach

**gentian violet** – An aniline dye and powerful antiseptic

**haemothorax** – An accumulation of blood in the pleural cavity

**hiatus (or hiatal) hernia** – A hernia, usually of the stomach, upwards into the chest through the hole, or hiatus, in the diaphragm through which the oesophagus normally passes

**homograft** – A graft of tissue taken from an individual of the same species

**hypertrophy** – An increase in size of an organ, independent of natural growth

**hypothermia** – Subnormal body temperature

**inert** – A substance which causes no reaction from the tissues of the body is said to be inert

**intrathoracic** – Within the thorax or chest

**isoniazid** – Anti-tuberculous drug

**lateral** – At, or pertaining to, the side; situated on either side of the median vertical plane

**ligature** – A cord or thread for tying vessels

**ligation** – The act of tying or binding

**lobe** – An anatomical portion of the lung

**lobectomy** – Excision of a lobe of the lung

**locum** – Short for locum tenens. A doctor who temporarily acts as a substitute for another

**manometer** – An instrument for measuring the pressure of liquids or gases

**media room** – Room where the medium on which bacteria are grown is prepared, and cultivation of bacteria carried out

**mediastinoscopy** – A method of visual examination of the central part of the chest, the mediastinum, through a small incision in the base of the neck, and the means whereby small pieces of tissue may be obtained for biopsy.

**meningococcal meningitis** – Inflammation of the membranes surrounding the brain and spinal cord caused by the bacterium Neisseria meningitidis

**mitral stenosis** – Disease of the mitral valve of the heart causing obstruction to the flow of blood from the left atrium into the left ventricle

**Monaldi drainage** – A method of draining pulmonary cavities in advanced tuberculosis, to facilitate closure by natural processes. Negative pressure is maintained within the cavity by means of a catheter passing through the chest wall.

**monitor** – n. An oscilloscope recorder, usually of the electrical output of the heart. A visual ECG
    – v. To watch or check a person or thing

**morbid anatomy** – The anatomical study of disease or diseased parts of the body. An old term for pathological anatomy.

**myocardial infarction** – Synonymous with the colloquial 'heart attack' or coronary thrombosis. The result of occlusion of a coronary artery. The death of tissue due to complete interference with its blood supply.

**neurology** – The study of the anatomy, physiology and pathology of the nervous system

**obstructive emphysema** – The coalescence of groups of the air sacs of the lungs resulting from obstruction of either the major or smaller bronchi

**occupational therapy** – The teaching of trades and arts as a means of rehabilitation of patients
**oesophagectomy** – Surgical resection of the oesophagus
**oesophagus** – The gullet; the canal extending from the pharynx to the stomach
**ophthalmologist** – One skilled in the field of diseases of the eye
**organisms** – Bacteriology: pathogenic bacilli
**otolaryngologist** – One skilled in the field of diseases of ear, nose and throat
**PAS** – Para-aminosalicylic acid. An anti-tuberculous drug
**patent ductus arteriosus** – Connection between pulmonary artery and aorta which persists after birth
**penicillin** – A bactericide produced from Penicillium notatum, a fungus
**perfusion** – The introduction of fluids into a part or all of the body by injection into the supplying arterial blood vessels
**pericardium** – The closed membranous sac enveloping the heart
**phrenic** – Pertaining to the diaphragm
**plombage** – The extrapleural compression of a tuberculous pulmonary cavity by the surgical insertion of a plastic material. A form of collapse therapy
**pneumonectomy** – Excision of an entire lung
**pneumonitis** – Inflammation of lung tissue as opposed to bronchi
**pneumoperitoneum** – The injection of air or gas into the peritoneal cavity (abdomen)
**pneumothorax, artificial** – The introduction of air into the pleural cavity through a needle to produce collapse and immobility of the lung, with obliteration of tuberculous cavities
**pneumothorax, extrapleural** – The introduction of air into the space formed by stripping the outer pleural layer from the chest wall
**pneumothorax, spontaneous** – Air in the pleural cavity occurring from causes other than its introduction from without
**postural drainage** – Removal of bronchial secretions by placing the patient head downwards
**radio-opaque** – Material which shows up on X-ray
**resection** – The surgical cutting out and removal of part or all of an organ
**screening** – The radiological examination of the lungs in motion using fluoroscopic apparatus without taking an X-ray
**secondment** – The temporary transfer of people to another department
**sleeve resection** – The removal of a length of bronchus, with or without a lobe of lung, and rejoining the cut ends
**streptomycin** – A water-soluble antibiotic obtained from Streptomyces griseus
**stricture** – A narrowing of a tube such as the bronchus, following inflammation and scarring of its wall
**sulphanilimide** – A chemical which exerts a potent antibacterial effect

**sulphonamide** – One of a group of antibacterial compounds derived from sulphanilimide

**suppuration** – The formation of pus

**TAB** – Typhoid-paratyphoid A & B vaccine

**tannic acid** – A water-soluble styptic and astringent used as a local dressing for burns

**tension cavity** – A cavity in lung tissue caused by tuberculosis, in which pressure is greater than atmospheric with consequent stretching of the walls of the cavity

**thoracic** – Appertaining to the thorax, or chest cavity

**thoracoplasty** – A surgical method of permanently collapsing a tuberculous cavity in the lung. Part of the chest wall is mobilised by removal of ribs, wholly or in part, so decreasing the size of the thoracic cavity and consequent collapse of the section of lung containing the cavity

**thoracoscopy** – Examination of the pleural cavity in the presence of pneumothorax, using a lighted tubular instrument designed for insertion between the ribs

**thoracotomy** – Surgical incision of the chest wall

**tuberculosis** – An infectious disease caused by the Mycobacterium tuberculosis, commonly called the tubercle bacillus

**vaccine** – A substance prepared from dead or attenuated organisms used for preventative innoculation

**valvotomy** – Surgical incision of a valve of the heart

**ventricle** – The muscular chambers of the heart which pump blood either to the body (left) or the lungs (right)

**vital capacity** – The volume of air that can be expelled by the most forcible expiration after deepest inspiration

# · Index ·

215

216

217

221